W9-BZD-016

Environmental Leadership in Developing Countries

Environmental Leadership in Developing Countries

Transnational Relations and Biodiversity Policy in Costa Rica and Bolivia

Paul F. Steinberg

The MIT Press
Cambridge, Massachusetts
London, England

©2001 Massachusetts Institute of Technology

All rights reserved. No part of this book may be reproduced in any form by any electronic or mechanical means (including photocopying, recording, or information storage and retrieval) without permission in writing from the publisher.

This book was set in Sabon by Graphic Composition, Inc.
Printed and bound in the United States of America.

Library of Congress Cataloging-in-Publication Data

Steinberg, Paul F.
  Environmental leadership in developing countries: transnational relations and biodiversity policy in Costa Rica and Bolivia / Paul F. Steinberg.
    p.   cm. — (American and comparative environmental policy)
  Includes bibliographical references and index (p.).
  ISBN 0-262-19465-1 (hc.: alk. paper)—ISBN 0-262-69266-X (pbk.: alk. paper)
  1. Biological diversity conservation—Government policy—Costa Rica. 2. Biological diversity conservation—Government policy—Bolivia. 3. Environmental policy—Costa Rica. 4. Environmental policy—Bolivia. I. Title. II. Series.

QH77.C8 S74   2001
333.95'16'0097286—dc21

                                                              2001030658

10 9 8 7 6 5 4 3 2

To Jennifer,
teacher, traveler, artist, advocate

Contents

Series Foreword

At the outset of the twenty-first century it is apparent that developing countries are facing enormous challenges and obstacles in their quest to simultaneously promote economic development and to conserve natural resources and control pollution. Most analysts assume that developing countries cannot achieve both goals on their own and argue that wealthy nations must help poor nations reduce their debt, increase their standard of living, and improve their environmental quality. Recent debt forgiveness initiatives by certain developed nations and lending institutions will undoubtedly help to decrease the pressure on developing nations to plunder their natural resources as quickly as possible. Analysts also argue that technology transfer and the export of scientific expertise and equipment by rich countries can help developing nations manage their natural resources affordably and effectively.

At the same time, elites in poor countries must crack down on corruption, redistribute land, and adopt conservation and pollution control measures if they hope to develop and maintain sustainable communities. At some point, short-term goals must give way to long-term planning to protect the natural environment and achieve intergenerational equity. Otherwise, the future prosperity and environmental health of developing nations will be imperiled.

Latin American nations face all of these dilemmas. These nations contain an abundance of biodiversity and natural resources. Yet, most of Latin America continues to experience difficult economic conditions and widespread poverty. Rapid population growth and poor land distribution, among other factors, are leading to a rapid loss of biodiversity and a decline in valuable natural resources. Perhaps nowhere else on the planet are the stakes higher and the need for environmental protection greater than in Latin America. This is one reason why a growing number of researchers are traveling to and investigating the conditions and policies of nations in this region. Such studies can help shed light on the precise nature of the problems that these countries face and determine which policy approaches work or do not work there and why.

In this book Paul Steinberg challenges the prevailing assumption that developing countries are too busy addressing the demands of poverty alleviation and development to give serious consideration to environmental protection. His book examines how Costa Rica and Bolivia, both of which contain considerable biodiversity and natural resources, have emerged as leaders in tropical conservation. While previous studies have focused primarily on international collaboration or on community resource management, his research explores the dynamics of national policy reform in the South. He draws on the theoretical literature in comparative politics and public policy to help explain the evolution of environmental policy in Costa Rica and Bolivia.

In addition, Steinberg closely examines transnational environmental advocacy and the causal mechanisms through which nongovernmental actors achieve (or fail to achieve) their objectives. His book not only has important implications for environmental policymaking in other developing nations but provides insights on how to enhance the effectiveness of international environmental regimes. This ambitious and provocative book is sure to generate a great deal of discussion and debate about the future role of developing nations in global environmental politics.

Steinberg's work illustrates the kind of books published in the MIT Press series in American and Comparative Environmental Policy, which encourages books that examine a broad range of environmental policy issues. We are particularly interested in volumes that incorporate interdisciplinary research and focus on the linkages between public policy and environmental problems and issues both within the United States and in cross-national settings. We anticipate that future contributions will analyze the policy dimensions of relationships between humans and the environment from either an empirical or theoretical perspective. At a time when environmental policies are increasingly seen as controversial and new approaches are being implemented widely, the series seeks to assess policy successes and failures, evaluate new institutional arrangements and policy tools, and clarify new directions for environmental politics and policy. These volumes are written for a wide audience that includes academics, policy-makers, environmental scientists and professionals, business and labor leaders, environmental activists, and students concerned with environmental issues. We hope that these books contribute to public understanding of the most important environmental problems, issues, and policies that society now faces and with which it must deal well into the twenty-first century.

Sheldon Kamieniecki, University of Southern California
Michael E. Kraft, University of Wisconsin-Green Bay
American and Comparative Environmental Policy Series Editors

Acknowledgments

Among the many people who provided support for this research, several deserve special mention. Daniel Press's tireless advocacy for policy research based on the study of actual outcomes—rather than outputs—nourished a productive skepticism that I carried with me to the field and made the achievements documented in this book all the more impressive for having passed this tougher test. Dan Doak and Sonia Alvarez first introduced me to the literatures of conservation biology and comparative politics, respectively, which helped me to situate my findings in the larger context of political and ecological change in Latin America. Robert Keohane offered insightful critiques of the methods and concepts of each chapter. For a scholar of his magnitude to devote such energy to the work of a relative newcomer attests to both his commitment to the profession of political science and to his personal generosity. Others to whom I owe special thanks for intellectual guidance include Thomas Rochon, William Clark, Ronald Mitchell, Paul Sabatier, and Robert Asher.

At the outset of the project, Raymond Dasmann, Thaddeus Trzyna, Kenton Miller, Richard Rice, Meg Symington, and Jeffrey McNeely filled my rolodex with important contacts in the environmental policy communities of Costa Rica and Bolivia. During the project's final stages, comments from Miranda Schreurs, Toddi Steelman, and three anonymous reviewers at MIT Press strengthened the quality and coherency of the resulting manuscript. This work has also benefited enormously from feedback provided by seminar participants at Duke University, the Monterey Institute for International Studies, the University of Colorado at Boulder, Yale, U.C. Berkeley, U.C. Irvine, U.C. Santa Cruz, the University of Maryland, and the University of Southern California.

My hosts at the University of Costa Rica, Carlos Quesada and Daniel Masís, helped make my stay enriching and hassle free. Carlos Quesada's connections to Costa Rican policy circles opened countless doors during my field research. Daniel Masís taught me to appreciate the subtleties of Costa Rican politics, and was a gracious host throughout. I owe an enormous debt to the many Costa Ricans who took the time to share their insights on the politics of environmental policymaking in their country. Though the full list of interview participants is too long to detail here, I would especially like to thank Carlos Manuel Rodríguez, Pedro León, José María Rodríguez, and Robert Wells.

In Bolivia, Kathy Mihotek arranged for my affiliation with Gabriel René Moreno Autonomous University. Robert Albiol of the World Wildlife Fund provided crucial in-country logistical support; our open-ended conversations on South American politics were a source of great enjoyment. Timothy Killeen of the Natural History Museum in Santa Cruz de la Sierra helped me to refine my case studies during the early stages of my research, sharing his unique perspective as one of the few foreigners who has stayed with Bolivian conservation efforts over the long haul. The Kempff family in Santa Cruz de la Sierra generously made available the collected private letters of environmental pioneer Noel Kempff, providing a rare window on Bolivian environmentalism in the early 1960s. My greatest debt is to the dozens of Bolivians who spent so many hours imparting their thoughts and experiences during interviews. Especially generous in this regard were Mario Baudoin, Alexandra Sánchez de Lozada, Arturo Moscoso, Antonio Andaluz, and Juan Pablo Arce. Were it not for the efforts of these and other environmental advocates cited throughout this study, there would be no pattern of institutional accomplishments in need of explanation.

Behind every tidy content analysis graph in the pages to follow is a story of Latin American research assistants hauling heavy newspaper archive tomes to photocopy centers, negotiating with bureaucrats and business-people on my behalf, and spending hundreds of hours reading and analyzing environmental news stories. Thanks go to Costa Rican research assistants Patricia Barrantes, Silvia Bonilla, Milena Gutiérrez, Sileny Mata, José Alberto Ortíz, Raymi Padilla, and Evelyn Villarreal; Bolivian research assistants Rosario Bustillos, Geovana Carreño, Roberto Vargas, and Beatriz Parra; and to Edgar Becerra in the United States. The maps displayed in this book were produced by Kelly Woo.

A project of this scale would not have been possible without the generous financial support provided by the National Science Foundation, the MacArthur Foundation, the U.C. Institute on Global Conflict and Cooperation, the Hewlett Foundation, the Switzer Environmental Foundation, and the Organization of American States. Richard and Alice Garcia provided me with both a house and a home during the transition periods before and after foreign travel. Additional support was provided by the faculty, staff, and especially the doctoral students of the Environmental Studies Department at U.C. Santa Cruz. There is no clearer proof of the value of an interdisciplinary, policy-oriented graduate program than the high-caliber students I had the pleasure to interact with during my time in Santa Cruz.

Although Jennifer Quintana is nowhere cited in the text, she has been my most indispensable intellectual resource throughout the course of this research. Jennifer and I shared the experience of research and travel together in Costa Rica and Bolivia, where she worked as a public health educator and women's rights advocate. She helped me at every stage of the project, from planning and logistics to the newspaper content analysis, where her exacting standards of quality control kept me and my research assistants on our toes. It is to Jennifer, my wife, that I dedicate this study.

I

Global Concern, National Authority

1

Introduction: Bilateral Activism in Global Environmental Politics

Speaking before Costa Rica's Legislative Assembly in 1969, congressman Guardia Hurrero bemoaned his country's lackluster response to tropical deforestation. "Ours is the only country in Latin America without forestry legislation," he complained (Hurrero 1969). At the time there was virtually no interest in conservation on the part of Costa Rica's government or civil society. The few who took up the environmental banner faced "nearly total indifference to the problem of environmental degradation," in the words of one longtime activist (Boza 1993: 240). Twenty-five years later Costa Rica's national park system was widely considered to be one of the best in the world. Costa Rica had a strong environmental regulatory agency, had pioneered concepts like ecotourism and biodiversity prospecting,[1] was home to hundreds of citizens' environmental groups, and was led by a president who made sustainable development the conceptual underpinning of his entire administration.

The Bolivian conservation scene in the late 1960s was similarly bleak, consisting of a few scientists working in isolation and with little effect. The sense of hopelessness was reflected in a letter written in 1968 by Bolivian naturalist Noel Kempff to an American colleague, María Buchinger. "The truth is, Doctora María, that in this world the economic interests of certain sectors are stronger than all the solid reasoning of the conservationists; the struggle is a considerable one, especially in an environment in which we are basically misunderstood" (Kempff 1968). By the time Bolivia hosted the Summit on Sustainable Development in the Americas in 1996, however, that country had implemented a series of conservation policy innovations including the world's first debt-for-nature swap,[2] the world's largest forest-based climate change mitigation project, and a national environmental endowment that served as an exemplar for other nations in the region. Bolivians designed an ambitious protected areas system administered by nonprofit organizations and indigenous groups, established an effective, high-profile biodiversity conservation agency, passed important laws for environmental protection and forestry sector reform, led the international campaign to protect mahogany, and had active environmental organizations in every major city.

What forces brought about these dramatic changes in countries often considered too poor to care about global environmental problems, and what have been the relative roles of international and domestic actors in this process? This two-part question is the central concern of this book. It arises from two salient characteristics of global environmental problems such as biodiversity loss. First, these problems are by definition global, affecting many people in many countries around the world. Bolivia's national parks benefit not only Bolivians but people everywhere who might benefit from a medicinal compound, a scenic vista, or the knowledge that pink river dolphins have a home. The second distinguishing feature of global environmental problems is that they occur in a political setting characterized by the absence of world government and the dominance of the principle of national sovereignty (Young 1994; Roseneau and Czempiel 1992). Although the interests are supranational, the political authority to act on these problems rests squarely with national governments. Of particular importance are the governments of developing countries, where most of the world's biological diversity resides and where national policy can have a profound impact on environmental outcomes (Ascher 1999; Binswanger 1985; Repetto and Gillis 1988; Bedoya and Klein 1993). International players have a stake, but not a say, in environmental policy reform in developing countries.

Using this context as a point of departure, this book explores the dynamics of environmental policymaking in two countries over four decades with the hope of providing a window into fundamental issues concerning the role of developing countries in global environmental politics. The book is designed to meet two needs—one theoretical, the other applied. First, I draw on insights from comparative politics and public policy theory to better understand the nature of global environmental politics—a subject of increasing interest to social scientists and more commonly approached from the perspective of international relations. Second, I hope that readers concerned with practical problems of tropical conservation and sustainable development will come away with an enhanced view of the domestic political processes bearing on natural resource management. Scholars and practitioners alike have long operated under the assumption, widely held but seldom examined, that developing countries are too preoccupied with the challenges of poverty and development to give serious consideration to environmental protection. This book explodes this myth, offering instead an analysis of decades-long efforts by environmental advocates and policy entrepreneurs working to protect biological diversity in Central and South America. It is my hope that a more nuanced portrayal of environmental politics in developing countries can inform current efforts to enhance the effectiveness of global environmental treaties and can help us understand the macrocontext shaping the success or failure of local projects.

Costa Rica and Bolivia possess some of the richest concentrations of biological diversity to be found anywhere in the world, and the process by which they emerged as leaders in tropical conservation is a worthy topic in itself. But the goal of this study is a more ambitious one. My aim is to take a close look at two societies with temporal variability in policy outcomes, and to explain these changes in terms general enough to pique the interest of readers with expertise in other parts of the world. At present, environmental policymaking in developing countries is rarely studied and poorly understood. Social science research on global environmental problems has clustered at two levels of analysis—international cooperation[3] and local resources management[4]—leaving a gap where one would hope to find studies exploring the dynamics of national policy reform in the South. The burgeoning literature on transnational environmental advocacy (see, for example, Wapner 1996; Keck and Sikkink 1998; Haas 1992) has taught us a great deal about the motivations and activities of nongovernmental actors operating across borders, but has paid less attention to the causal mechanisms through which transnational actors achieve (or fall short of) their goals.[5] Moreover, works in this area have largely overlooked the role of environmental advocates in developing countries, focusing instead on the activities of highly visible multinational groups operating out of the United States and Europe. The results provide little guidance for understanding domestic-international linkages in the South, where most of the world's people, land, and species are found.

Research on the effectiveness of international environmental agreements has also emphasized outcomes in Northern industrialized countries. Recent attempts to move beyond these limitations (Weiss and
Jacobson 1998; Schreurs and Economy 1997) have provided valuable
country-specific insights, but have yet to produce an analytic approach
that might facilitate meaningful cross-national comparisons. A theoretical
framework is needed to provide a focal point for cumulative research and
to help practitioners interpret their experiences in light of recurrent patterns of political behavior.

Costa Rica and Bolivia offer several advantages for such an undertaking. Although they share in common a dramatic rise in state and social
concern for environmental protection, they have differed in the timing and
nature of these changes, providing an opportunity for comparative inquiry. The choice of Costa Rica and Bolivia is also designed to take
advantage of a most-different-systems approach (Przeworski and Teune
1970; Meckstroth 1975). Maximizing variance on a suite of political and
social variables, my hope is to increase the potential applicability of these
findings to a wide range of countries. Relative to the rest of the developing
world, Costa Rica has a relatively high per capita income (though it represents the middle range within Latin America), while Bolivia is among the
poorest countries in the Western Hemisphere, with income levels more
typical of African societies. Costa Rica has high levels of adult literacy,
while Bolivia's are relatively low. Bolivia is a culturally and linguistically diverse society, with an estimated 60 percent of its population of indigenous
origin. Many Bolivians speak Spanish as a second language after pre-Incan
languages such as Aymara, Quechua, and Guaraní. Costa Rica, by contrast, has only 1 percent indigenous peoples and is a self-consciously westernized society. With respect to political stability, Costa Rica is considered
the most stable democracy in Latin America, while Bolivia is among the
least politically stable, having experienced well over 100 changes of government since independence (see Booth 1989; Klein 1992).

To better understand the sources of effective environmental policy and
institutions in these countries, I undertook a year of field research, inter-
viewing dozens of environmental activists, agency leaders, elected officials, field biologists, park directors, indigenous rights campaigners,
legislative aides, and other key players, who together provided a wealth of
"insider information" on the politics of environmental policymaking over

the past thirty-five years. By conducting extensive in-country research, I have taken an unconventional approach to the question of whether global environmental concerns have affected domestic policy outcomes. Students of international organization tend to select an institution of particular interest, such as a multilateral treaty or U.N. agency, and characterize its impact in target countries (see Haas, Keohane, and Levy 1993; Bernauer 1995; Victor, Raustiala, and Skolnikoff 1998). My approach instead views international influences from the inside out. I first identify what have historically been the most important instances of biodiversity policy reform in these countries. I then analyze the relative contributions that domestic and international players have made to these outcomes, with the expectation that for either group the answer might be "none whatsoever."

Spheres of Influence Over Domestic Policy

The theoretical framework emerging from this research is based on two observations. First, there has been an enormous foreign influence on domestic environmental movements and conservation policy in Costa Rica and Bolivia. The major environmental groups in these countries receive most of their funding from abroad, and international funds rarely constitute less than a third of the budget for government conservation agencies. Their wildlife biologists and resource managers also maintain close ties with foreign scientific institutions, relying directly on international technical resources and expertise. The second observation, however, is that when one probes beneath the surface to see who have been the political catalysts for conservation—who started the environmental groups, who created the regulatory agencies, who convinced the politicians, who led the protests— the foreign influence suddenly disappears, or at least recedes far into the background. Moreover, the political knowledge, skills, and contacts needed to win these struggles require a long-term, in-country presence that few foreign advocates or international organizations possess.

In a context of global concern and national political authority, the resources brought to bear on environmental policy in developing countries are of two types: those closely associated with a given domestic political system, and those whose essential productive dynamic resides beyond that society's borders. Accordingly, we may think of two spheres of influence affecting environmental policy in developing countries: an international

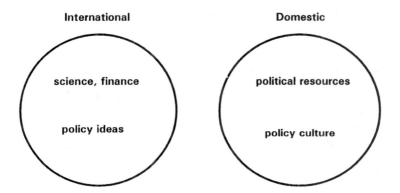

International   Domestic

science, finance   political resources

policy ideas   policy culture

Figure 1.1
Spheres of influence over domestic policy.

sphere and a domestic sphere (figure 1.1). Those with access to the resources of the international sphere affect national policy primarily by deploying financial and scientific resources, while those with access to the
resources of the domestic sphere impact national policy with their extensive political resources. These political resources include personal political
contacts, an intricate knowledge of bureaucratic power structures, and a
long-term, in-country presence needed to take advantage of fleeting windows of opportunity, to acquire domestic political savvy, and to ensure
long-term program success.

The resources of the international and domestic spheres of influence
may be further broken down into institutional and ideational resources.
The resources described above are of the institutional variety, with science,
finance, and political know-how applied to the creation and strengthening
of institutions such as national parks and regulatory agencies. But policy
is also a function of ideas which imbue these institutions with a direction
and purpose. Using Schattschneider's (1960) conception of institutions as
the "mobilization of bias," we may think of ideational resources as those
affecting the bias, while institutional resources are those applied toward
the mobilization of this bias.

The international sphere has long served as a wellspring of policy
ideas—norms, evaluations, and prescriptions relevant to the business of
governance. In every country, policy reformers routinely draw on the insights and experiences of policy initiatives abroad. Especially in develop-

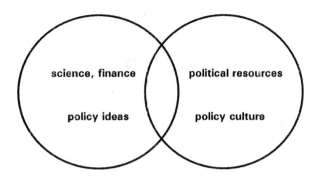

Figure 1.2
Bilateral activism.

ing countries where, as Grindle and Thomas (1991: 49) aptly put it, "[i]nformation is limited, needs are great, resources are scarce, and responsibilities are extensive," policymakers look beyond their borders for new ideas about health care, military strategy, economic organization, social security, education, and environmental regulation. Accordingly, in the course of policy agenda setting and institutional design, individuals with broad exposure to international policy ideas are in great demand.

These international ideas interact in specific ways with a nation's domestic norms and understandings. This interaction is mediated by actors operating within that nation's borders—in the domestic sphere—who can press the case at home and shape international ideas into something that fits domestic realities. These actors can influence environmental policy by fostering a supportive environmental *policy culture*—a concept I use to characterize the level and type of public attention accorded a policy issue area in a particular society.

Importantly, the major players in environmental policymaking in Costa Rica and Bolivia have always been individuals who operate simultaneously in both spheres of influence—possessing both close ties to domestic politics and a broad exposure to international resources and ideas. This group, which includes such key figures as Pedro León, Alvaro Ugalde, Daniel Janzen, Mario Baudoin, and Arturo Moscoso, I describe as *bilateral activists* to emphasize their entrepreneurial role and the unique combination of resources they dispatch to promote desired policy outcomes (figure 1.2). Sometimes these are expatriate scientists who have spent decades in a particular developing country, acquiring domestic resources in the process.

More often they are nationals with a propensity to operate in international circles. Bilateral activists are at ease in two worlds. Cosmopolitans in the truest sense of the word, they are typically fluent in two or more languages and interact frequently with international donors and prominent foreign scientists. Compared to their fellow citizens, they are not only more likely to encounter foreign ideas by virtue of their travels, but they are more apt to embrace them as a function of their worldly outlook (see Hannerz 1990).

At the same time, bilateral activists are well known in (and know well) their home country. They can write a foreign grant application with the same ease that they might lead students to march on congress. From their offices in universities, environmental organizations, or government agencies, they are likely to have the Rockefeller Foundation on one phone line and a presidential advisor on the other. Bilateral activists, however, are not mere "go-betweens" or guns for hire. They are self-described environmentalists, making normative claims for ecology and seeking out the foreign and domestic resources needed to advance their cause.[6]

Throughout this book I will use the term *activist* in its broadest sense to denote reformers within government as well as nongovernmental advocates pressing for policy change. This broad usage is necessary because bilateral activists typically alternate between these roles over the course of their decades-long involvement. In common with most policy entrepreneurs in developing countries, bilateral activists are typically educated urban professionals. This may explain why their pivotal role has been overlooked in the literature on environmental politics in developing countries, which has given preferential coverage to rural resource conflicts and zero-sum interactions between state authorities and social actors (see Peluso 1992; Gadgil and Guha 1995; Blaikie 1985). Although class conflict and irreconcilable differences of interest may help to explain why many policy initiatives fail, they have little to say about why things sometimes go right. The findings reported in this book support the view that government can exercise discretion, leadership, and creativity, in addition to its better known traits of corruption, foot-dragging, and cronyism. To understand the origins of successful policy reforms requires that we take a closer look at the complex internal workings of "the state," at the evolution of policies and institutions over time, and at the resources and resourcefulness of the actors leading these efforts.

To lay the conceptual groundwork for subsequent chapters, in what follows I describe the domestic and international spheres of influence in more detail. In developing my arguments I draw on empirical evidence from four decades of policy reforms in Costa Rica and Bolivia. There is good reason to believe, however, that the spheres of influence framework can help to describe the political dynamics of conservation policymaking in a broad range of developing countries. This follows from the fact that the distinguishing characteristics of the two spheres are the result of institutional and historical constraints common across developing countries. Northern finance and scientific expertise will be cherished in developing countries as long as there are asymmetries in the international division of labor and in the relative economic power of nations. Likewise, domestic political expertise is very difficult for foreigners to acquire. It requires a long-term, in-country presence, and domestic laws and norms often inhibit direct political access by foreigners. Both categories of resources are necessary for the development of effective domestic environmental regulatory structures in developing countries. Yet it is precisely because the end of colonialism in Asia, Africa, and Latin America brought significant political independence without a corresponding redress of economic disparity that these resources reside in separate spheres of influence. In sum, the different capabilities of actors operating in one or another sphere are the result of structural constraints common across developing countries.

With its emphasis on the methods used to overcome barriers to reform, the spheres of influence framework cannot provide an exhaustive explanation for cross-national variation in policy outcomes, because the barriers themselves—entrenched timber lobbies, corruption, and civil strife, to name a few—vary in their nature and intensity across countries and over time. However, I maintain that on matters of global concern, environmental policy reform in developing countries cannot be understood without reference to the actors, resources, and processes highlighted by this analytic framework—that, to my mind, is justification enough to devote a book to its elaboration.[7]

Institutional Resources of International Origin

Few analysts would disagree with the proposition that there exists an inverse relationship between the location of biological diversity and the concentration of financial and scientific resources needed for its conservation. Following a pattern known as the latitudinal diversity gradient, the greatest species concentrations in the world are found in those countries located in the tropics (Wilson 1992). As a result of the historical trajectory of capitalist development and the legacy of colonialism, global centers of capital and technology are concentrated in the Northern industrialized countries. For as long as this situation holds true, there will exist powerful incentives for concerned Northern publics to transfer money and scientific expertise to developing countries for the purpose of slowing global extinction rates.[8] I will argue later that the flow of resources and expertise is much more reciprocal than this widely recognized observation allows. But to understand the dynamics of conservation policymaking in the South, we must begin with an appreciation of the crucial role played by international science and finance.

Financial Transfers

With few exceptions, donors from industrialized countries can protect many more species per dollar by contributing to protected areas in the tropics than they can by purchasing habitat at home. Environmentalists have long found this logic irresistible. In the early 1960s the World League Against Vivisection and for the Protection of Animals coordinated the first international fundraising campaign for Costa Rican rainforests, boasting to potential donors, "It can be had at the ridiculously low price of $10 an acre. . . ." Two decades later, in a fundraising appeal published in The New York Times, conservation scientists courted donors with the same argument. With "a diversity of animals and plants known only from the site," they argued, "at the price of $4 an acre, the venture may well be the conservation bargain of the century" (quoted in Wallace 1992: 7, 166). More recently, recognizing that even conservation-oriented developing countries often lack the resources needed for effective environmental management, new international institutions have been created to facilitate a flow of hundreds of millions of dollars in environmental aid from North to South (see Keohane and Levy 1996).

Indeed, it is difficult to find a major conservation policy initiative of the past thirty-five years in either country that did not receive significant support from overseas. Dozens of private, governmental, and nonprofit donors are the lifeblood of Costa Rica's National Biodiversity Institute.

Revenues from nature-oriented tourism, estimated at $336 million in 1991 (Boza 1993), have been essential to the survival of the country's national park system, while the vast majority of funds for Bolivia's protected areas come from overseas aid. In the executive branch, the biodiversity policymaking arm of Costa Rica's environment ministry is funded by the MacArthur Foundation, while Bolivia's biodiversity conservation agency is supported primarily by the Dutch government. Within the legislature, foreign donors have provided the financial backing for national dialogues leading to legal reforms in forestry, wildlife management, and biodiversity conservation. At the local level, environmental planning in Bolivia is supported by the Germans, and urban air pollution abatement in Costa Rica is supported by the Swiss.

From the perspective of an environmental policy entrepreneur in a developing country, however, the breach between the theoretical possibility of foreign financial support and its timely application in specific settings is a wide one. To access such resources requires a particular set of skills and a familiarity with the appropriate routines and social networks. Grant applications generally must be written in the language of the donor organization, which makes individuals with foreign language skills particularly sought after. The formats, catch phrases, and accounting standards must conform to donor expectations. Personal relations with private philanthropists or influential individuals in granting agencies can make all the difference, and these relations are more easily established among individuals sharing common points of cultural reference. This fact gives bicultural individuals a distinct advantage. There is a game to play and its most adept competitors have had considerable international exposure.[9]

Scientific Resources

Environmental policy is an issue area rife with scientific uncertainties, which accords an important role to scientists in environmental policy debates (Haas 1990, 1992). This is especially true of biodiversity conservation, which is a technically intensive activity precisely because of the diversity of natural systems involved.[10] Apparently simple questions concerning the appropriate boundaries of protected areas or sustainable levels of hunting and harvesting require a great deal of information. Researchers often draw on the practical knowledge (*metis* in James Scott's formulation) of local resource users, synthesizing this information and relating it to the cumulative insights gained from similar studies around the world (see Scott 1998; Sponsel, Headland, and Bailey 1996). But in natural systems subjected to the myriad pressures of modern development, local knowledge is not enough. For better or worse, the importance of the technology of conservation grows in proportion to the impact of technologies of development.

In developing countries, foreign-trained scientists play a central role in managing these uncertainties, conducting species surveys, teaching university courses in ecology and wildlife management, and designing park management plans. This is true both because the relevant scientific expertise is concentrated in industrialized countries and because science is an inherently transnational enterprise, and has been so since the emergence of scientific communities in the seventeenth century (Crane 1971). Most developing countries lack doctoral programs in the biological sciences, and the bulk of their ecologists are trained in Europe and the United States. Moreover, the demand for foreign scientific information does not decrease with the development of domestic scientific capacity. On the contrary, it increases as a growing body of domestic researchers seek the best available information worldwide. As a result, scientific expertise takes its place alongside finance as a resource characteristic of the international sphere of influence. Individuals with access to this resource are especially valuable to decision makers, and their credibility in policymaking circles is enhanced by their reputation as technical experts.

Given the extent of foreign involvement, it is tempting to jump to the conclusion that these countries are essentially being coerced by foreign interests. The reality, however, is far more complex. In the 1970s a succession of Costa Rican administrations provided most of the funding to create their now-famous national park system. It was only after these protected areas were established that foreign aid and nature tourism dollars began to pour in. Likewise, Bolivia's most important protected area, Noel Kempff Mercado National Park, was initially supported by a grant of several hundred thousand dollars from the regional government in Santa Cruz de la Sierra. Only later did it receive assistance from The Nature Conservancy and U.S.-sponsored climate change mitigation projects. Moreover, as the historical narratives of chapters 3 and 4 make clear, these efforts have been accompanied by high levels of social support, volunteerism, and personal sacrifices that cannot credibly be reduced to a quest for foreign aid. With this proviso in mind, it is important to grasp the extent to which cross-border relations have affected domestic policy processes: International resources have had a pervasive influence on nearly every conservation policy initiative undertaken in Costa Rica and Bolivia over the past four decades.

Institutional Resources of the Domestic Sphere

That international science and finance have been important to domestic conservation efforts in developing countries is widely appreciated. However, an entirely different category of resources—*domestic political resources*—has been equally important yet entirely overlooked in academic analyses of global environmental problems. The lower visibility of political resources stems from the reality that politics is often a shady business. The back room deals and Byzantine channels of political influence that determine whether conservation initiatives sink or swim are not polite topics of conversation in the project reports of donor agencies and environmental organizations. By contrast, the visibility and legitimacy of international financial resources are apparent in the menu of organizational logos decorating printed accounts of environmental projects in developing countries, and the importance of international resources figures prominently in the causal stories told therein.

The U.S. Agency for International Development rightly boasts in its widely distributed materials that Bolivia's Gran Chaco National Park— the world's largest protected tropical dry forest—was created with the help of American foreign aid. The untold story is how the park owes its success in part to bilateral activist Alexandra Sánchez de Lozada, who convinced her father—the Bolivian president—to back the proposal. The foreign journalists who flocked to Central America in the early 1990s to report on Costa Rica's National Biodiversity Institute (INBio) presented a similar causal story, reporting that INBio resulted from the intellectual leadership of prominent international scientists and the financial initiative of the MacArthur Foundation. One does not read about how INBio director and bilateral activist Rodrigo Gámez secured political backing for the proposal through his family connections to President Oscar Arias:

It happened that President Arias was an old friend of mine . . . because we came from the same town, Heredia. My father had been involved in politics in many ways, and during the Figueres administration he'd been Minister of Education when Arias was Minister of Planning. So there was an old familial, political, and local relationship. . . . I didn't want to go through the minister, but to have a direct relationship with the president. This opened many doors. . . . (quoted in Wallace 1992: 155)

Access

As the above examples suggest, one of the most important types of political resources dispatched by policy reformers in developing countries is extensive personal contacts with individuals in positions of influence. Although connections to presidents provide the most dramatic examples, these contacts need not be with heads of state. In all but the most centralized political systems, there exist numerous loci of political influence. The fate of environmental policies is determined in newspaper rooms, governing bodies of national banks, village councils, legislative committees, party headquarters, police stations, agricultural cooperatives, and teachers' unions. Accordingly, individuals with numerous social contacts have the greatest such resources at their disposal. Whereas a Greenpeace program director or European Community consultant may arrive in a developing country with a few dozen names and numbers, long-term residents possess thick webs of social relations, to use Alvarez's term (1998), which they mobilize to win allies and punish adversaries. Geertz's description of Morocco is appropriate here:

Morocco, once one looks beyond its absolutistic self-presentation, is (and always has been) less a monopole despotism than an irregular field of micro-polities, small, smaller, and smaller yet . . . reaching into its narrowest and most intimate social corners: families, neighborhoods, markets, tribes. Immediate, one-on-one, bargained out dependency relations between personal acquaintances, what is sometimes called patronage, sometimes clientage, and by the Moroccans *sedq* (which means at once "loyalty," "trustworthiness," "friendship," and "truth"), lie at the base of things. What larger connectivities are achieved are brought about by establishing similar relations, similarly immediate, over broader and broader ranges of action. (Geertz 1995: 27)

Reciprocal favors and interpersonal bonds of trust are of particular importance in countries where institutions are weak, where they act as a surrogate method for resolving collective action problems. When put to public-minded uses, such resources are described in the literature with terms like social capital or village reciprocity (Putnam 1993; Edwards and Foley 1998; Portes 1998; Scott 1976). In less public-spirited contexts, they are the social technology underpinning political cronyism and good-old-boys networks. Whether used for good or ill, these political resources rely on repeated face-to-face contact, and are accordingly a place-based domestic resource.

Political Expertise

Long-term studies have gained currency in the policy sciences precisely because the success or failure of major policy initiatives unfolds over a period of decades (Baumgartner and Jones 1993; Sabatier 1989). As with personal contacts, other types of political resources are available only to those who spend a great deal of time in a particular developing country. This is true of knowledge concerning bureaucratic power structures: knowledge of where the power is and how to use it. This information constitutes the "mental maps" that policy entrepreneurs carry in their heads detailing likely sources of support and opposition to reform (Grindle and Thomas 1991). Policy reformers in India must navigate the taluks and zillas, Mexicans the party bosses and judicial politics, Liberians the village chiefs, rice growers' unions, and mystics. They know both the formal organizational structures and the unwritten hierarchies and power configurations underlying them. A passage from a recent analysis of Bolivian politics conveys the complexity of these power structures:

In the complex world of Bolivian party politics, it is one thing to win an electoral plurality, an entirely different thing to be chosen president, and yet another thing to govern. This reality was captured in a joke circulating in the aftermath of the 1989 elections. Gonzalo Sánchez de Lozada at the head of the MNR won a plurality, only to see Paz Zamora emerge as president in a coalition where true power was reputed to be in the hands of [former dictator] Bánzer, leader of his new right-wing Acción Democrática y Nacionalista (ADN). As the joke has it, before the election the three candidates visited the Virgen de Urkupiña, who offered them one wish each. Sánchez de Lozada wished to win the elections; Paz Zamora, to be president; and Bánzer, to run the country. The generous Virgin granted all three wishes. (Gamarra and Malloy 1995: 413)

Political learning—transferring lessons from one policy arena to the next—is another political resource available only to those with long-term domestic involvement. Within government, the accumulated wisdom from past efforts at policy reform—"thinking in time"—can provide crucial guidance for the architects of new policy initiatives (Neustadt and May 1986). The institutional successes noted at the beginning of this chapter are the product of many hard-learned lessons from previous failures. Among nongovernmental advocates, learning takes place in the course of venue shopping as reformers try their luck in the courts, on the radio, in the schools, and inside and outside the state apparatus. Political expertise also includes a knowledge of political culture—of "the way politics is done around here." Political culture is manifest in the cult of consultation in Costa Rica and the sacredness of decentralization and indigenous rights in Bolivia. Those with long-term exposure to the domestic sphere of influence draw on appropriate forms of rhetoric, cultural innuendoes, a shared sense of history, and numerous other bits of wisdom concerning political tactics and the rules of engagement.

Domestic political resources are resources in the sense described by Dahl (1961: 226), as "anything that can be used to sway the specific choices or the strategies of another individual." They are political because they are applied by actors struggling to control some aspect of the institutions of governance. Importantly, they are domestic because they not only require a long-term, in-country presence, but there also exist strong legal and normative barriers against foreign intervention in domestic political affairs. Foreign environmental consultants and activists are quick to emphasize that they carefully avoid domestic politics altogether or proceed in that arena with extreme caution. This may strike the reader as counterintuitive, given the history of foreign intervention in developing countries. But it is precisely because of the impunity with which foreigners have impinged on national sovereignty in areas like structural adjustment programs, military support for anticommunist forces, and the war on drugs, that environmentalists are both unwilling and unable to engage in political arm-twisting in the realm of conservation.[11]

If international scientific resources are crucial for the management of ecological uncertainties, these domestic resources are a hedge against political uncertainties regarding the place and timing of opportunities for reform. The creation and implementation of conservation policies takes place in numerous arenas, at different levels of government, and through the course of several administrations. It is impossible to know in advance the full range of decision makers, powerbrokers, and veto points one will encounter. When a relatively unknown figure emerges from political obscurity to assume a position of authority in a conservation agency, bilateral activists draw on their webs of personal connections to gain an audience, present a viewpoint, or offer their services as consultants. When after a long period of stagnation or stalemate a person of influence suddenly and unexpectedly proclaims "something must be done," bilateral activists are on the ground, with plans in hand, enabling them to take advantage of fleeting windows of opportunity.

Ideational Resources of the International Sphere

The international sphere has for centuries been a rich source of ideas on the purpose and means of government. Long before it became fashionable to speak of globalism and the global village, rebels, reformers, and reactionaries eagerly exchanged ideas across borders to advance similar ends. Aristotle, one of the earliest practitioners of comparative politics, surrounded himself with the written constitutions of far off lands in an effort to distill wisdom in the art of governance. Before the *Communist Manifesto* was studied by resistance movements on every continent, Marx and Engels wrote of the remarkable degree to which ideas are exchanged across borders in a modern capitalist economy:

In place of the old local and national seclusion and self-sufficiency, we have intercourse in every direction, universal inter-dependence of nations. And as in material, so also in intellectual production. The intellectual creations of individual nations become common property. National one-sidedness and narrow mindedness become more and more impossible, and from the numerous national and local literatures, there arises a world literature. (Marx and Engels 1978: 476–477)

In Latin America, just as the call for revolution spread like wildfire across the Spanish colonies at the dawn of the nineteenth century, the region has experienced contemporaneous policy experimentation in everything from social security to import substitution industrialization to military tactics (see Jackson 1993; Borzutzky 1993; Hall 1989). Sometimes the exchange of policy ideas is facilitated by government institutions like the Pan American Health Organization or the Organization of American States. In other instances, nongovernmental organizations (NGOs) catalyze the cross-national diffusion of policy ideas as when practitioners of liberation theology pressed for social reforms throughout Latin America following the Second Conference of Latin American Bishops in 1968 (Sigmund 1994; Della Cava 1989).

Policy ideas are conceptual constructs pertinent to government action in a particular issue area. They include (but are by no means limited to) norms, evaluations of the state of affairs, and remedial prescriptions.[12] Normative positions are spread across borders with evangelical urgency by principled issue networks advancing causes like women's rights or the abolition of child labor (Keck and Sikkink 1998). Evaluative ideas are particularly susceptible to the practice of comparison as leaders and publics look overseas for metrics and mirrors of national performance. "A policy problem," Charles Anderson reminds us, "is a political condition that does not meet some standard" (Anderson 1978: 19). The emergence of a new policy problem may therefore result from a perceived worsening of political conditions or by raising the standards—often in light of foreign experience—by which long-standing domestic conditions are judged.

Prescriptive policy ideas respond to the question, central to politics and policy, of "what shall we do?" The international sphere is filled with well-articulated responses to national questions as yet unposed. As Kingdon (1984) has demonstrated in the American context, policymaking rarely proceeds in linear fashion from the formulation of questions to the search for solutions. There are instead numerous preexisting solutions favored by partisan advocates seeking to tie their preferred answer to whatever question comes along. Solar energy, for example, has been offered as a solution to problems ranging from national security to democratization to global warming. In this respect the international sphere of influence—literally, the world of ideas—is a source of thousands of well-developed policy responses waiting for a question. Not surprisingly, this pool of ideas is most readily accessible to individuals who have the benefit of considerable international exposure. In a period of widespread but uneven environmental concern around the globe, the first members of a society to advocate a consciously articulated environmental agenda are typically individuals with a cosmopolitan orientation who have been immersed in dialogue with environmental thinkers abroad.[13]

In chapter 6, I provide evidence for the "neighbor effect"—the tendency for countries to look to their immediate neighbors as sources of policy ideas. Activists in Argentina closely follow political developments in Paraguay, policymakers in Togo learn from their counterparts in Nigeria, and exchanges between reform-minded Malays and Indonesians are commonplace. But policy reformers in developing countries also look to faraway lands for models of success and failure. Though some analysts claim that developing countries have little to learn from rich countries (Rose 1993), this is plainly at odds with the historical record. Just as Chilean secular reformers in the nineteenth century were influenced by the revolution of 1848 in France, India's forest policies were modeled after the German example (Rajan 1998), and Che Guevara studied the guerrilla tactics popularized by Spaniards resisting Napoleon's advance in the previous century (Loveman and Davies 1985). Hirschman (1981) has argued that the propensity of poor nations to borrow policy ideas from abroad is a reflection of their dependency. But even the most autonomous nations routinely gather information on the experiences of others. Before we equate borrowing with dependency, we should bear in mind that Latin American intellectuals elaborated dependency theory partly in response to the shortcomings of Western writings on imperialism, which portrayed developing countries as passive recipients of foreign influences. In practice, modes of borrowing range from intelligent tinkering with the ideas and experiences of others to uncritical parroting of foreign institutions.

A detailed analysis of the impact of foreign environmental policy ideas on contemporary conservation policymaking in Costa Rica and Bolivia is the subject of chapter 6. Suffice it to say here that this influence has been pervasive and long-standing. In addressing the normative, evaluative, and prescriptive questions of environmental management, policy reformers have felt little need to confine themselves to ideas of national origin. During congressional testimony surrounding Costa Rica's Forestry Law of 1969, speakers cited the experiences of dozens of foreign nations, drawing lessons from nature tourism in Eastern Africa, forestry practices in Venezuela and Mexico, and environmental advocacy in the United States and Western Europe. In turn, Costa Rica and Bolivia have served as exemplars for other developing nations interested in learning from their experiences with innovations such as participatory park management, pharmaceutical uses of rainforest products, national environmental funds, debt-for-nature swaps, and user fees for ecosystem services.

Ideational Resources of the Domestic Sphere

The mere existence of a deep well of international policy ideas does not preordain the timing and degree of their acceptance in specific national

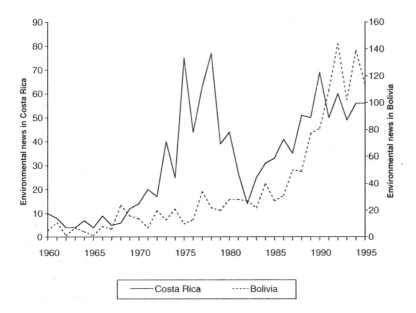

Figure 1.3
Environmental news in Costa Rica and Bolivia. Source. La Nación in Costa Rica and Presencia in Bolivia. See methodological appendix for details. Note. The two newspapers differ in size, therefore intercountry comparisons are based on the timing of changes rather than absolute numbers of articles.

settings. This is apparent in figure 1.3, which shows that environmental protection was not seriously discussed in Bolivia until a full decade after its appearance as an issue of public concern in Costa Rica. Based on a content analysis of over 3,000 environmental news stories (see chapter 6 and the methodological appendix for details), this result is widely corroborated in interviews with long-term observers of environmental politics in these countries. This is the simplest result of the content analysis, and it is perhaps the most important for it poses the question: Why did an active popular interest in environmental issues—what I term an environmental policy culture—arise a full decade earlier in Costa Rica?

I will argue in subsequent chapters that bilateral activists are responsible for the variation observed here. Inspired by environmental movements around the world and deeply embedded in domestic debates, bilateral activists recognized early on the importance of garnering widespread public support for their policy initiatives. They not only worked to buttonhole politicians and experiment with institutional designs but they also spread the word by creating university programs, organizing seminars, and leading discussion groups. They worked with members of the media, and inspired others to create radio and television shows broadcasting the merits of environmental thinking, for the *concientización* of the public at large. The lack of an environmental policy culture in Bolivia in the early 1970s is directly attributable to the absence of a well-developed community of bilateral activists in the country at this time. This begs the question of the origins of bilateral activism, which will be taken up in chapter 6.

While the international sphere of influence provides the raw material for domestic policy ideas, these ideas are *translated* domestically to match national circumstances. The political salience of policy ideas is affected by their perceived "fit" with existing national institutions and understandings (Goldstein 1993; Sikkink 1991). The process is a dynamic one, in which political opponents argue that an international policy idea like environmental protection (or feminism or socialism or free market capitalism) is an absurd foreign import that bears no relation to domestic realities, while partisans argue that it is entirely consonant with national traditions and needs. Translation occurs as domestic advocates package the idea to appeal to important political constituencies and to plug into legitimizing national discourses (Snow and Benford 1988). International policy ideas are also stretched and molded as domestic regulatory agencies and social organizations devote preexisting organizational resources (and their attendant biases) to the cause (see Dalton 1994; McCarthy and Zald 1977; McCarthy 1997: 244–247). Moreover, each country has its own particular environmental and social conditions, and different countries may embrace a policy issue in different historical periods, thereby affecting the content of the policy idea. Translation also results from the fact that many intellectuals and activists in the South, delighting in innovation and sensitive to cultural imperialism from abroad, simply desire to make the idea their own.

Two extremes characterize the translation process. At one extreme, inadequate translation may lead to a careless adoption of ideas from abroad, as occurred in the 1960s when the Bolivian government copied verbatim Venezuelan hunting season regulations despite the fact that the seasons are reversed across the equator. At the other extreme, an international policy idea may undergo so much adaptation that the original idea literally gets lost in the translation (see Steinberg 1998b). Bilateral activists occupy an interesting position in this regard. All else equal, they are more likely than actors who operate purely in the international sphere to ensure that at least some translation occurs, and they are more likely than their compatriots to ensure that the crux of the original idea is not lost. Conversely, they may be more likely to push inappropriate ideas than would actors operating purely in the domestic sphere and more likely than purely international players to let the original idea go. Only by pursuing a compromise between the two extremes, however, can they simultaneously meet the needs stemming from each side of their dual identities. They are the only ones held accountable by both international and domestic communities, in a face-to-face, "what are you doing?" kind of way. To the extent that their effectiveness depends on legitimacy in both spheres, bilateral activists face incentives to stake out a middle ground.

Studying Policy Change

In medical research, the first step in identifying the causal agent of disease is to select sick patients and attempt to isolate the cause of the observed effects; this enables subsequent studies to test for the effects of the posited causal agent in other patients. Geologists wishing to understand the nature of volcanoes do well to study those actively erupting; using this data, they can then make predictions concerning the volcanoes' dormant cousins. In like manner, to understand the uncharted territory of environmental policy reform in developing countries, I have deliberately selected countries with "successful" policy outcomes in an attempt to delineate the forces at play. The sources of variation on these successes are threefold: the change in Costa Rica from the 1960s (a time of scant political interest in environmental themes) to the 1970s; the variance between Costa Rica and Bolivia in the 1970s, during which time only the former witnessed significant environmental policy reforms; and the subsequent temporal change within Bolivia, which saw the rise of an active environmental policy culture and institutional reforms in the late-1980s.

To understand the dynamics underlying these changes, I employ a triangulation approach, combining quantitative and qualitative methods appropriate to the task at hand.[14] To generate insights into mechanisms of political influence, I conducted several dozen semistructured interviews, using a technique that we might term "revealing inertia." This method takes advantage of the fact that there is a certain amount of inertia in any significant social undertaking—meetings are missed, funds are misappropriated, leaders are distracted—and considerable directed energy is needed to overcome this inertia and usher initiatives toward a desired end point. Inertia includes the "clearance points" discussed by Pressman and Wildavsky (1973), Grindle and Thomas's (1991) "slippage," and Hirschman's (1970) "slack." Yet interview subjects may recount an event as if it arose as part of the natural and inevitable progression of events. With the revealing inertia technique, the researcher imagines potential barriers and sources of inertia common to efforts at policy reform and poses these as questions: "The senate has many pressing matters, so how did your bill get to the front of the queue?" "Alliances among environmental groups can be difficult to maintain—how did it work?" "Why did the city council listen to your proposal, when there is an active forest lobby in this town?" "Budgets are so stretched, how did you get the Ministry of Agriculture to provide funds for the new park guards?" From the nature of the response it is usually obvious whether one has revealed or merely invented a source of inertia. Revealing inertia allows the researcher to learn more about the barriers themselves and to learn about the mechanisms whereby difficulties are overcome.

Historical materials were gathered by searching through numerous government and private archives, seeking materials—letters, news clips, government reports, written testimony—that could provide a glimpse into modes of influence. I was the first researcher to study the private archives of Bolivian environmental pioneer Noel Kempff, who maintained a thorough record of his written correspondences dating back to the early 1960s, now maintained by his family. Qualitative research was complemented with a quantitative analysis of environmental news stories appearing in these countries' major daily newspapers from 1960 to 1995. Eleven research assistants, organized into four teams, collected and analyzed over 3,000 news articles. Absent longitudinal public opinion data, this is the most complete data set available for tracing changes over time in the attention given environmental issues in any developing country.

Chapter Overview

The organization of this study is as follows. In the first half of the book I describe in more detail the phenomenon to be explained—the historical emergence of Costa Rica and Bolivia as leaders in biodiversity policy. In chapter 2, I take a critical look at one of the most widely held assumptions concerning the role of developing countries in international environmental policy: that developing nations are too poor to care about environmental protection absent foreign financial inducements. This perspective emanates from several distinct sources, which I label "theories of environmental privilege." This assumption is so widely held, and so completely at odds with my findings, that I felt it necessary to address it systematically in its own chapter. I argue that there is little reason or evidence to support the view that developing nations are predisposed to consider environmental protection a luxury.

It is one thing to argue that environmental movements and policy reform can arise in poor countries and quite another to show that they do. The historical narratives in chapters 3 and 4 should leave the reader with no doubt that important changes have taken place over the past four decades in the level of social and government commitment to biodiversity conservation in Costa Rica and Bolivia. This sets the stage for subsequent chapters that provide an explanation for how these changes came about. Chapters 5 and 6 detail the institutional and ideational components of the spheres of influence framework. Chapter 5 explores the process of institutional reform: how these countries have managed to establish conservation agencies, regulatory structures, and national parks that operate reasonably well despite the enormous odds facing policy reformers in poor countries. This chapter demonstrates that despite their lower profile, domestic political resources have been indispensable assets in efforts at institution building, easily rivaling in importance the more widely recognized assets of international science and finance. A focus on political resources also renders the contributions of domestic environmentalists in developing countries more visible, which I have found necessary not for fairness so much as accuracy. In Chapter 6 I elaborate on the concept of policy culture, which provides an entrée for studying the cross-border movement of environmental ideas and the relationship between changing social perceptions and institutional reform. In Chapter 7, I consider the implications of these findings for social science research on global environmental problems and make some tentative suggestions for how they might be used to improve the effectiveness of international environmental institutions.

2

Environmental Privilege Revisited

Nature appreciation is a "full stomach" phenomenon, that is confined to the rich, urban, and sophisticated. A society must become technological, urban, and crowded before a need for wild nature makes economic and intellectual sense.
—Roderick Nash, *Wilderness and the American Mind*, 1967[1]

Costa Rica firmly and emphatically rejects the point of view that preservation of the natural environment is a preoccupation of privileged nations, and a benefit that poor nations and developing nations cannot enjoy.
—Costa Rican President Daniel Oduber, 1976[2]

There is a great deal of popular mythology surrounding tropical conservation. One of these myths is that rainforests deserve the lion's share of attention, when in fact tropical dry forests possess some of the highest concentrations of biological diversity found anywhere in the world (Bullock, Mooney and Medina 1995). A second popular myth, and the focus of this chapter, is the idea that developing countries are somehow "too poor to care" about environmental protection. It is worth examining this idea in detail for two reasons. First, it is a notion so commonly encountered in writings on sustainable development, and so completely at odds with contemporary reality in Costa Rica and Bolivia, that the researcher arriving in these countries is immediately faced with an empirical anomaly. The journalist David Wallace, after some months in Costa Rica, struggled to reconcile this received wisdom with the fact of Costa Rican environmentalism: "For a third world country to be more prowilderness and biocentric in conservation policy than a first world nation might seem strange to North Americans and Europeans. . . . Where does the Costa Rican attitude come from, in the absence of two centuries of Costa Rican Audubons, Thoreaus, and Muirs?" (Wallace 1992: 126; see also Broad and Cavanagh 1993: 58–59).

Rubber tappers

There is a second and more pressing reason to critically examine the evidence underlying this idea. Over the past three decades international environmental policymaking has been predicated on the assumption that developing countries are too poor to embrace environmental concerns absent financial inducements. Accordingly, policy prescriptions have emphasized North to South resource transfers (Keohane and Levy 1996; Wells 1994; Steinberg 1998b). If this assumption is mistaken, we may be overlooking a variety of other roles international institutions can play to promote sustainable development in the tropics.

The received wisdom about environmental ethics in developing countries is reflected in several literatures, which I place together under the rubric "theories of environmental privilege." These are diverse in origin and some are not theories so much as oft-repeated assumptions. But they share in common the idea that environmentalism is the province of rich people and rich countries. In the following sections, I first describe these theories of environmental privilege, then take a closer look at their logical and empirical underpinnings. There is no reason to believe that environmentalism will inevitably arise in any society.[3] But I will argue that there is no reason to assume that developing countries are less likely than their Northern counterparts to have active environmental movements and domestic constituencies clamoring for effective environmental policies.

Theories of Environmental Privilege

The everyday conversations that a researcher has with friends, family, or a stranger at a bus stop can serve as valuable (if unscientific) sources of information about popular notions concerning environmental protection. In the course of such conversations in the United States, it has been my experience that even those who claim to know little about ecology and development do know enough to say, "It seems to me that in poor countries they're not thinking about conserving rainforests, but about where to find their next meal. Besides, we destroyed our forests while building our country—who are we to tell them what to do?" What this popular perception misses is that Costa Ricans were fighting for biodiversity conservation—establishing a world-class park system with domestic funds—long before tourists in wealthy countries took an interest in tropical rainforests. In fact it was Nicaraguans—Costa Rica's poorer neighbors—who comprised the largest group of foreign ecotourists visiting Costa Rican parks prior to the

Sandinista uprising (Boza 1993). Likewise, Bolivian environmentalists like Noel Kempff and Percy Baptista were writing letters and lobbying politicians decades before groups like The Nature Conservancy and World Wildlife Fund made a serious commitment to conservation in that part of the world.

The popular perception that some countries are "too poor to be green"[4] has been nourished by pronouncements from developing country negotiators at high-profile international meetings. As a bargaining strategy to attract overseas aid, these officials claim that protection of the natural environment is a low priority, a luxury their countries cannot afford without financial assistance. "The environment cannot be improved in conditions of poverty," announced Indian Prime Minister Indira Gandhi at the Stockholm conference in 1972 (quoted in Dias and Begg 1994: 284). Economic and social development, she argued, are necessary conditions for improvements in environmental quality. Industrialized countries must contribute to the former if they wish to see the latter. Yet in the years to come, Prime Minister Gandhi was an outspoken advocate of environmental policy in India, spearheading efforts at legal reform and institutional strengthening (Dwivedi and Khator 1995). Clearly, she believed that conservation should be a priority even in poor countries, contrary to her assertions in international fora.

Similarly, when speaking before international audiences in 1997, Costa Rican Environment Minister René Castro warned that developing countries would not implement their conservation commitments under the Convention on Biological Diversity unless they were paid to do so: "All of the efforts that all delegations have been putting in this present Conference of Parties (COP) and the former ones, as well as efforts made at the national level," he argued, "become a futile and theoretical exercise if our developed country partners in the Convention do not provide the new and additional resources . . ." (Nijar 1998).

This leaves the impression that leaders and publics of developing countries care about short-term economic welfare first and foremost, and that environmental conservation will only be promoted to the extent that it promotes this higher goal. Negotiators from developing countries cemented this impression by successfully inserting a clause in article 20 of the convention stating that "economic and social development and eradication of poverty are the first and overriding priorities of the developing country parties" (UNEP 1992). What Minister Castro's statement hides is the fact that, at home, he frequently confronted powerful economic interests and sacrificed short-term income opportunities for the sake of environmental protection.[5] His pronouncement also belies the fact that 91 percent of Costa Ricans surveyed say they would be willing to pay more for water or electricity if the additional money were devoted to biodiversity conservation (Holl, Daily, and Erlich 1995). Because the international press corps devotes considerably more attention to international summits than to domestic actions in developing countries, Northern publics receive a biased impression from the news media that environmental protection is not a major concern in the developing world.

How can we understand the apparent contradiction between the international proclamations and domestic actions of these officials? The most satisfactory answer comes from negotiation theory, which demonstrates that when negotiators reveal their true interests they risk a loss of bargaining power (Lax and Sebenius 1986). Specifically, if negotiators from developing countries underscore the growing demand for environmental protection on the part of their citizenry, they weaken their position. Why should donors provide financial incentives to countries that already consider environmental protection a priority? This question lies at the heart of the incremental cost approach used by the Global Environment Facility (GEF), the world's largest source of overseas aid for biodiversity conservation. The GEF funds only those initiatives that are thought unlikely to attract domestic support in developing countries, giving these countries a powerful incentive to downplay their enthusiasm for conservation (The World Bank 1992a, 1992b). It is no wonder that even officials who are staunch environmental advocates in their home countries argue in international forums that their countries cannot afford to make conservation a priority without foreign aid, technology transfer, debt relief, and improved terms of trade.

Popular accounts of environmental privilege have their counterparts in academia. Inglehart's work on postmaterial values is the best known (and best supported) body of theory suggesting that poor countries might have lower levels of environmental concern. Using data from the Eurobarometer surveys, Inglehart finds that affluent societies have a higher proportion of postmaterialists—people who are more preoccupied with personal freedom, self-expression, and the quality of life than with basic concerns of physical and economic security. If postmaterial values are more compatible with environmental ethics, and if affluent societies have more postmaterialists in their ranks, we might expect greater support for environmental protection in wealthy countries (Inglehart 1990; Abramson and Inglehart 1995; see also Guha and Martínez-Alier 1998: xi–xv).

Whereas Inglehart's claim is based on a close reading of the empirical evidence, other literatures have adopted environmental privilege as an article of faith. According to Robert Ayres, the idea that developing countries are too poor to care about the environment,

. . . is taken seriously by economists because it has an interpretation that fits economic theory, viz. that as people get richer, they will value the environment more and protect it better. This is *probably* true, for instance, if one compares the attitudes of Northern Europeans with Southern Europeans, or upper middle-class Americans vis-à-vis lower middle-class Americans. (Ayres 1995: 97, emphasis added)

In fact it is not true, according to the public opinion data reviewed below. Data notwithstanding, environmental privilege has been offered as an explanation for the Environmental Kuznets Curve—the finding that economic development is accompanied by an initial rise and then a decline in the levels of certain pollutants. According to Arrow and colleagues,

One explanation of this finding is that people in poor countries cannot afford to emphasize amenities over material well-being. Consequently, in the earlier stages of economic development, increased pollution is regarded as an acceptable side effect of economic growth. However, when a country has attained a sufficiently high standard of living, people give greater attention to environmental amenities. This leads to environmental legislation, new institutions for the protection of the environment, and so forth. (Arrow et al. 1995: 92)

These authors conclude, however, that the Environmental Kuznets Curve only holds for a few pollutants, does not apply to resource stocks such as soil, forests, and ecosystems, and is on the whole an erroneous oversimplification of the relationship between economic development and environmental protection. Similar conclusions were reached by contributors to special issues on the Environmental Kuznets Curve published by *Ecological Economics* and *Environment and Development Economics* (Rothman and Bruyn 1998; Barbier 1997).

Another theory of environmental privilege maintains that Southern support for environmental initiatives, where it occurs, is little more than a coerced response to the carrots and sticks offered by the industrialized

North. In this view, Northern support for environmental protection in the South amounts to "green imperialism," the latest instance of powerful Northern actors flexing their muscles to promote policy reforms at odds with the interests of developing countries. There is ample historical precedent for this assertion. Conservation was imposed coercively by colonial regimes in Africa and Asia (Beinart 1989; Rajan 1998) and colonial-era management philosophies continue to shape conservation policy in some countries (Peluso 1992). But the "imperialist" label has also been applied, in more cavalier fashion, to characterize the central tendency of contemporary international environmental activism and policymaking. This reaction began in the 1960s when environmentalists, the U.N. Food and Agriculture Organization, and Robert McNamara of the World Bank first sounded the alarm on population growth. Their rhetoric stirred deep-seated fears among leaders and publics in developing countries, who saw in these warnings a conspiracy to limit their numbers and influence. "What do the proposals of Malthus's disciples amount to," wrote Eduardo Galeano, "if not a proposal to kill tomorrow's beggars before they are born?" (Galeano 1989/1971: 7). Accusations of green imperialism are reflected today in academic and popular titles such as "The New Imperialism: World Population and the Cairo Conference," "Ecology and the New Colonialism," "Environmental Protection or Imperialism," and "Environmental Imperialism: GATT and Greenery."[6] What matters for the present discussion is not the purity of Northern motives, but the idea that environmentalism is an outside idea that has been imposed on developing countries, against their will and contrary to their true interests and desires.

The notion that developing countries are too poor to care about the environment has even found its way into more careful works on comparative public policy and international organization. "Questions of environmental quality are unlikely to receive careful hearing amid the overwhelming problems of poverty," argues Desai (1998: 3). According to Keohane (1996: 3, 10), "It is futile to demand of poor countries that they give sufficient priority to environmental degradation . . . The asymmetrical levels of concern inherent in international aid for the environment mean that relations between funders and recipients are not harmonious: their priorities differ."

Environmental Privilege: A Logical and Empirical Critique

Are the priorities of North and South fundamentally at odds on the environment? Are poor people and poor countries too preoccupied with material security, their governments too concerned about economic development, to make the environment a major concern? The argument is compelling, intuitive and widely believed. In this section I show that it is also mistaken, logically flawed, and at odds with the evidence. The argument proceeds as follows. First, I adopt the assumption that poor individuals care less about the environment than the well-to-do, and show that even with this assumption, we should expect many developing countries to aggressively pursue environmental policies. Next I relax this assumption, reviewing public opinion data on environmental attitudes and willingness to pay for environmental quality. These data consistently show that citizens in poor countries express support for environmental protection equal to that of their counterparts in wealthy countries. I then consider why these results should come as little surprise, given the diverse collection of issues that comprise the environment, the material element of these purportedly postmaterial concerns, and the many nonmaterial concerns of materially deprived peoples.

Individual Concerns, Collective Outcomes, and Problems of Aggregation

Let us assume for the moment that wealthy individuals care more about environmental protection than do poor individuals. To conclude on this basis that developing countries are less likely to embrace environmental protection is to draw an unsupported inference about the relationship between individual and group (in this case, national) characteristics. To evaluate the relationship between wealth and the environment posited by theories of environmental privilege, we must first distinguish between poor individuals and individuals in poor nations. Next we must clarify our assumptions about the relationship between individual concerns and collective changes in public policy and environmental quality.

To appreciate the importance of distinguishing between poor people and poor nations, we need only consider that there are greater numbers of affluent people in Brazil than in Switzerland—if we may define affluence as possessing a house, nice clothes, an expensive automobile, and an abundance of food. The reader may protest that the *proportion* of affluent people is higher in Switzerland, and this is certainly the case. If policy change is the result of voter behavior and if wealthy people are more likely to cast a green vote, then we might expect Switzerland to pursue environmental policy with more enthusiasm than Brazil. In most societies, however, policy change results from the efforts of small, highly committed groups of individuals as often as it does from mass voting (see Grindle and Thomas 1991; Sabatier 1991: 148–149). This alternative and equally plausible model of the relation between individual concerns and collective outcomes predicts environmental policy reform in countries which achieve a sizable *absolute* number of affluent people. One thousand committed environmental activists (less than one-hundredth of 1 percent of the wealthiest 10 percent of Brazil's population) can establish offices in all of the country's major cities, achieve a division of labor among researchers, educators, grassroots activists, journalists, and lobbyists, and constitute themselves as a force to be reckoned with. Thus even if we adopt the assumption that personal wealth is a prerequisite for environmental concern, there is good reason to believe that environmental movements and policy change can occur in poor countries. And we must resist the temptation to dismiss movements comprised of a small elite as less authentic than their counterparts in industrialized countries, since this is entirely congruous with the historical origins of environmental concern in the United States, where "conservation was never more an elitist conspiracy than at its birth," according to historian Stephen Fox (1981: 110).

Roderick Nash (1967) concludes his influential book *Wilderness and the American Mind* with a chapter entitled "The International Perspective," in which he argues that wilderness preservation is the intellectual preserve of rich countries. He begins with a quote from Tanzanian President Julius Nyerere, who in 1961 characterized wildlife appreciation as a curious foreign obsession: "I am personally not very interested in animals. I do not want to spend my holidays watching crocodiles. Nevertheless, I am entirely in favor of their survival. I believe that after diamonds and sisal, wild animals will provide Tanganyika with its greatest source of income. Thousands of Americans and Europeans have the strange urge to see these animals" (Nash 1967: 342).

Table 2.1
U.S. population characteristics during the 1870s national parks movement compared to those of developing countries today

	Percent population in urban areas	High school education (% of eligible age group)	National wealth (GNP per capita)	Life expectancy
United States	26 (1870)	2 (graduated, 1870)	$2565 (1869–78)	47 years (1900)
Developing countries (average)	41 (1999)	63 (enrolled, 1997)	$1240 (1999)	65 years (1995)

Source. World Bank 1997, 2000; U.S. Department of Commerce 1975. Note. "Developing countries" = low and middle-income countries, as defined by the World Bank. U.S. GNP/capita is the average of 1869 to 1878 decade, expressed in 1991 dollars. Life expectancy data for U.S. as a whole prior to 1900 not available. (For Massachusetts, life expectancy in 1878–1882 was 41.7 for men, 43.5 for women.)

What is noteworthy about Nash's choice of quotes is that Julius Nyerere was at the time a wealthy man, much richer than the average American visitor to Yosemite National Park. Although Nash characterizes conservation as a "full stomach" concern, he is in fact referring to levels of national industrial development rather than personal wealth. Specifically, he claims that those who value wilderness are those who lack it—because they live in developed, urban societies. The problem with this argument as a basis for theories of environmental privilege is that today most people in Latin America, the Middle East, and North Africa live in urban areas.[7] In fact, as table 2.1 shows, when the national parks movement got underway in the United States in the 1870s, that country was less urbanized, its people less educated and with a lower life expectancy than citizens of the average developing country today. This should be borne in mind by Northern critics who may be tempted to dismiss national parks movements in developing countries as unlikely, ungenuine, or inconsistent with national priorities.

Another logical flaw common to theories of environmental privilege is to impute individual motives from observed collective outcomes.[8] Supporters of the Environmental Kuznets Curve theory observe some

differences in pollution levels between rich and poor countries and take
this as evidence for cross-national differences in individual preferences for
environmental amenities.[9] One of the major contributions of social science
research over the past quarter century, however, has been to demonstrate
the many reasons why collective outcomes often fail to reflect the preferences of the individuals comprising the collectivity (Olson 1965; Ostrom
1990). Institutional designs, access to information, and free rider problems
are among the many factors that place a wedge between individual preferences and collective actions.

Beyond questions of aggregation, the relation between action and preferences at either the individual or group level must be handled with care.
Inferring preferences from actions would lead us to conclude that low-
income people care less about air pollution and more about water conservation than do the wealthy, because in the United States the poor drive
older, more polluting vehicles and use less water per capita in drought-
prone areas. What we need are measures of environmental concern that
are independent of the outcomes this concern is said to produce. Such
measures are the focus of the next section.

A Look at the Evidence

The above arguments hold constant the assumption that wealthier individuals are more likely to care about the environment than poor individuals. Here I relax this assumption, with a review of public opinion data on
the subject. Three major public opinion surveys have examined cross-
national differences in support for environmental protection. The 1992
Health of the Planet survey, coordinated by the George H. Gallup International Institute, interviewed over 29,000 citizens in twenty-four countries to measure levels of environmental concern (Dunlap, Gallup, and
Gallup 1993). Survey questions explored topics such as the perceived seriousness of environmental problems, support for environmental protection
measures, willingness to pay higher prices to protect the environment, and
trade-offs between environmental quality and economic growth. Before respondents were informed of the survey's environmental focus,[10] they were
asked, "What do you think is the most important problem facing our
nation today?" The results, plotted against gross national product per
capita in figure 2.1, show no relationship between environmental concern

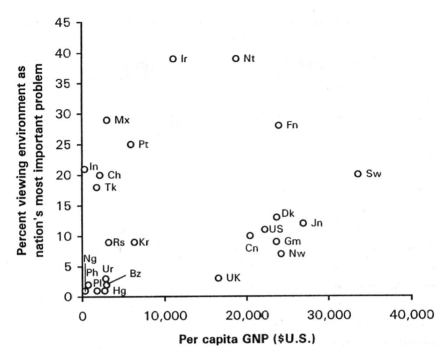

Figure 2.1
Affluence and environmental concern. Source. Dunlap et al. 1993; World Bank 1993. Note. p < 0.34, R-squared = 0.04. In response to the question: "What do you think is the most important problem facing our nation today?" Bz = Brazil, Ch = Chile, Cn = Canada, Dn = Denmark, Fn = Finland, Gm = W.Germany, Hg = Hungary, In = India, Ir = Ireland, Jn = Japan, Kr = South Korea, Mx = Mexico, Ng = Nigeria, Nt = Netherlands, Nw = Norway, Ph = Philippines, Pl = Poland, Pt = Portugal, Rs = Russia, Sw = Switzerland, Tk = Turkey, UK = Great Britain, Ur = Uruguay, US = United States.

and the level of economic development (p < 0.34, r = 0.2). In fact, the survey found that people in poor countries express greater concern about environmental problems than those of industrialized countries in eight of eleven measures.

In table 2.2, we see that respondents in low- to middle-income countries express at least as much concern for national environmental problems as do respondents in affluent countries. This result is robust at different scales of concern (local, national, global) and across a range of environmental issues. Of particular relevance to the present study are the results in table 2.3 on species extinction. People in developing countries express greater

Table 2.2
Perceived importance of environmental problems

View environmental issues as "very serious" national problem		Willing to slow economic growth for environmental protection	
W. Germany	67	Denmark	77
S. Korea	67	W. Germany	73
Poland	66	Finland	72
Mexico	66	Norway	72
Switzerland	63	Mexico	71
Russia	62	Brazil	71
Turkey	61	Canada	67
Chile	56	Ireland	65
Canada	53	Uruguay	64
Hungary	52	Chile	64
United States	51	S. Korea	63
Portugal	51	Switzerland	62
India	51	Philippines	59
Brazil	50	United States	58
Nigeria	45	Netherlands	58
Uruguay	44	Poland	58
Japan	42	Japan	57
Norway	40	Great Britain	56
Philippines	37	Russia	56
Great Britain	36	Portugal	53
Ireland	32	Hungary	53
Netherlands	27	India	43
Denmark	26	Turkey	43
Finland	21	Nigeria	30

Source. Dunlap, et al. 1993. Note. The left column shows responses to the following question: "I'm going to read a list of issues and problems currently facing many countries. For each one, please tell me how serious a problem you consider it to be in our nation—very serious, somewhat serious, not very serious, or not at all serious?" The percentage of respondents indicating "very serious" is shown. The right column is based on the question: "With which of these statements about the environment and the economy do you most agree? Protecting the environment should be given priority, even at the risk of slowing down economic growth, or economic growth should be given priority, even if the environment suffers to some extent." The percentage of respondents choosing environmental protection over growth is shown.

Table 2.3
Perceived seriousness of air pollution and species loss in the world

Percent who say "very serious"			
Air pollution		Species loss	
Uruguay	78	Mexico	81
Portugal	78	Poland	76
Mexico	77	Uruguay	76
Poland	77	Brazil	74
Chile	73	Chile	72
Turkey	72	W. Germany	69
Russia	71	Portugal	68
Brazil	70	Denmark	62
Norway	69	Switzerland	61
India	65	Russia	61
Ireland	63	Turkey	61
Switzerland	62	Norway	61
W. Germany	61	Great Britain	60
Denmark	61	Canada	57
Canada	61	Ireland	55
United States	60	United States	50
Finland	58	India	48
S. Korea	55	Finland	48
Hungary	54	Hungary	47
Great Britain	52	Philippines	45
Philippines	49	Netherlands	45
Nigeria	43	Japan	37
Japan	43	Nigeria	34
Netherlands	30	S. Korea	33

Source. Dunlap, et al. 1993. Note. The exact question was: "Now let's talk about the world as a whole. Here is a list of environmental issues that may be affecting the world as a whole. As I read each one, please tell me how serious a problem you personally believe it to be in the world—very serious, somewhat serious, not very serious, or not serious at all—or you don't know enough about it to judge?" Results listed in the table are the percentage of respondents who identified "air pollution and smog" or "loss of animal and plant species" as "very serious."

concern, on average, than do people in industrialized countries about the worldwide loss of plant and animal species. The only instance in the Health of the Planet survey where citizens of rich countries express greater environmental concern is in their willingness to pay higher prices and to trade off economic growth for environmental protection. In nine out of twelve poorer countries, however, a majority of respondents said they would be willing to slow down economic growth for the sake of environmental protection (table 2.2). The median percentage of citizens in developing countries willing to make this tradeoff (58.5 percent) is similar to that of the United States, Japan, and Great Britain. Looking at the results as a whole, survey project director Riley Dunlap and Angela Mertig conclude, "the preponderance of evidence contradicts the widespread view that citizens of poor nations are less environmentally concerned than are their counterparts in wealthy nations" (Dunlap and Mertig 1995: 134).

A second cross-national survey, conducted by Louis Harris and Associates in 1988 and 1989 for the United Nations Environment Programme, takes a closer look at the relationship between national wealth and willingness to pay for environmental protection. The results are shown in table 2.4. Brechin and Kempton (1994) report no statistically significant correlation between national wealth and citizens' willingness to pay higher taxes for environmental protection ($r = 0.21$, $p < 0.44$). Furthermore, respondents in poorer countries are more willing to pay with time—to volunteer two hours per week to improve environmental protection—than are people in rich countries ($r = -0.78$, $p < 0.0009$).

A third cross-national comparison is provided by the World Values Survey, conducted in seventeen low- to middle-income countries and eighteen industrialized countries. This survey finds wealth to be *negatively* correlated with environmental concern in four of seven measures. On willingness to pay for environmental protection, Kidd and Lee (1997: 8) report that the results "clearly show that more people in the poorer countries consistently indicate they would be more willing to give part of their income to prevent environmental pollution or to pay higher taxes to prevent environmental pollution than would people in the wealthier countries." In the poorer countries, 78.5 percent of respondents say they would be willing to devote part of their income to prevent pollution compared with 70.8 percent in affluent countries.

Table 2.4
Willingness to pay higher taxes and volunteer time for environmental protection

Pay taxes		Volunteer time	
Kenya	94	Kenya	98
United States	81	Nigeria	95
Nigeria	80	Mexico	91
Mexico	80	India	89
India	78	Brazil	87
China	78	Zimbabwe	85
Norway	78	Senegal	85
Senegal	72	Jamaica	85
Zimbabwe	70	Hungary	84
Saudi Arabia	63	China	83
W. Germany	62	Argentina	77
Hungary	60	Norway	76
Japan	60	Saudi Arabia	70
Brazil	59	W. Germany	62
Jamaica	56	Japan	44
Argentina	48	United States	not avail.

Source. Louis Harris and Associates, as reported in Table 6 of Brechin and Kempton 1994. Note. In many developing countries, the sample only included urban residents. Volunteer time = two hours per week.

With public opinion polls consistently refuting the posited relationship between wealth and environmental concern, what then becomes of Inglehart's postmaterial thesis? *Social Science Quarterly* devoted a special issue to this question.[11] The consensus that emerged from this debate is that people holding postmaterialist values do express greater than average concern for environmental protection, but postmaterialism only explains a small portion of the total variation in individual and national support for the environment. Postmaterialists comprise a small proportion of the citizenry in industrialized (39 percent) and developing countries (22 percent) alike, leading Brechin and Kempton (1997: 19, 20) to ask: "If only 22 percent of low- to middle-income country citizens are postmaterialist, why do 62 percent of their citizens score high on the environmental index? The larger question . . . is, How does one explain that citizens of poor countries—materialists and postmaterialists alike—are environmentally concerned? . . . [O]ther phenomena besides postmaterialism must be driving global environmentalism."

Paul Abramson, who coauthored a recent book on postmaterialism with Inglehart, concedes the point that many (as yet unspecified) factors other than postmaterialism apparently influence levels of environmental support (Abramson 1997).

The survey results reviewed thus far tested correlations between aggregate national wealth (as opposed to personal wealth) and public opinion. In a review of the nonmarket valuation literature, McConnell (1997) concludes that the evidence for a positive relation between personal income and demand for environmental quality is mixed at best. Two such studies are available for Costa Rica. Holl and colleagues (1995) report a *negative* correlation between wealth and concern over national and global environmental problems among residents in San José. Echeverría and colleagues (1995) conducted a contingent valuation survey at Costa Rica's Monteverde Cloud Forest Preserve and found that Costa Ricans express a greater willingness-to-pay for protection of the preserve than do foreign tourists (mostly from the United States), both in absolute terms and as a proportion of personal income.[12]

Additional data on the relationship between personal income and environmental concern are available from the United States. In a review of the environmental sociology literature, Buttel concludes:

The results from surveys of the general public thus provide little support for the widespread view that environmental concern is an 'elitist' issue that may be inconsistent with the interests of the less affluent segments of society . . . The elitism charge . . . is often based on evidence of the above-average socioeconomic status of environmental *activists*—such as members of the Sierra Club—rather than on evidence of the correlates of environmental concern among the general public. . . . Mohai (1985) has demonstrated that the link between socioeconomic status and environmental activism is primarily due to the link between socioeconomic status and general political activism. (Buttel 1987: 474, emphasis in original. See also Hirsch and Warren 1998: 4.)

A final piece of evidence suggesting that theories of environmental privilege underestimate the potential for ecological concerns in developing countries is found in the environmental movements that have arisen throughout Africa, Asia, and Latin America in recent years (see Broad and Cavanagh 1993; Lee and So 1999; Hirsch and Warren 1998; Keck 1995; Dankelman and Davidson 1988; Peritore 1999; Fisher 1993; Darlington

1998; Collinson 1996). In an insightful collection of essays, Guha and Martínez-Alier (1998) have attempted to characterize some of the ideologies and practices of these diverse movements. The sheer number of environmental groups in developing countries today provides a startling rebuke to theories of environmental privilege. In 1990 the African NGOs Environment Network counted 530 member organizations in 45 countries. The Indonesian Environmental Forum had over 500 member organizations in 1992, while Bangladesh has more than 10,000 NGOs working on environment-related topics (Tolba et al. 1992; Riker 1992; WRI 1993, all cited in Princen and Finger 1994). Pesticide Action Network International has approximately 600 affiliates advocating alternatives to biocides in over 40 developing countries (Moore 1998). By my count, Costa Rica has roughly 245 citizens' environmental groups—a higher per capita number than exists in the self-consciously environmentalist state of California.[13]

The Many Faces of Environmentalism

Theories of environmental privilege rely on errors of aggregation, tautological inferences that take outcomes as proxies for preferences, and questionable models of the relation between public opinion and policy change. They are at odds with public opinion data and are contradicted by the fact of environmental movements in developing countries. But if environmental concern in poor countries is counterintuitive, it is only because the intuition itself is paper thin. On closer examination, these results should come as little surprise. The most obvious reason why societies with a high percentage of materialists (per Inglehart's definition) might see widespread environmental concern is that environmental protection is often a matter of personal security and material well-being. The World Health Organization estimates that 25 million people—3 percent of all agricultural workers—in developing countries suffer acute pesticide poisoning every year (Jeyaratnam 1990). Similarly the prevention of soil erosion is not a luxury ticket, but a matter of physical survival. The same is true of water quality—as the journalist Alfonso Gumucio-Dagrón (1992: 7) put it, "¿Hay algo más cercano a la conservación del medio ambiente que el agua?" ("What could be more central to environmental conservation than water?") Environmentalism is not strictly a postmaterial concern.

But even the nonmaterial shades of environmental concern—the aesthetic, spiritual element of protecting "Mother Earth," or "Pacha Mama" as it is known by the Aymara people in the Bolivian highlands—should not be assumed a preoccupation of the wealthy. I find most peculiar the idea that the poor are too preoccupied with material concerns to value aesthetic and spiritual qualities, given the breadth and depth of religious conviction in low-income communities around the world. North Africans are not too poor to care about Islam, nor Latin Americans about Catholicism, Tibetans about Buddhism. People believe in spirits, gods, demons, and deities not merely because they hope fidelity will bring material prosperity, but because this gives meaning and a deeper significance to their lives. If the poor devote so much time and energy to religious worship, why should they be considered too preoccupied with survival to appreciate moral and spiritual arguments for protecting nature? To do so requires the absurd proposition that the world can be divided into a hierarchy of conceptual abilities corresponding to wealth, a sort of environmental noblesse oblige. Nor is there any reason to believe that materially deprived people are too poor to value the beauty of a stunning landscape or a blue morpho butterfly. Why would we expect societies whose people so enthusiastically embrace art, beauty, and abstraction—Peruvian textile designers, Jamaican songwriters, Nigerian mask carvers, and those who pay to enjoy their craft—to be somehow too poor to appreciate the beauty of nature?

Environmental activists around the world draw on an enormous stock of cultural symbols, curiosities, pleasures, and familiarities when making the case for conservation. They are able to do this because in every society the natural world has long been a source of metaphors representing both good and bad—beauty and terror, bounty and depravation, life and death. In traditional Mayan lore, forests are associated with beauty and tranquility as well as danger and chaos (Simonian 1995); the seventeenth century paintings of South American artist Melchor Pérez Holguín are adorned with brilliant wildflowers as well as fearsome serpents. Contemporary activists attempting to spread environmental awareness are not inventing nature appreciation from scratch. They are, rather, accentuating the positive—the familiar beauty of colorful feathers and flowers, the neotenous appeal of a lion club—and reshaping the intuitive, like the idea that one should not squander resources at the expense of one's grandchildren. Although the precise content of environmentalism will vary from one

• Author separates "society" + "natural world"

place to the next, self-identified environmental advocates generally share a concern for protecting their person and their natural surroundings and recognizing the link between the two. In this context the many faces of environmentalism present a distinct political advantage, as environmental movements can appeal to numerous potential constituencies while providing a coherent ideological basis for coalition-building and sustained collective action, both domestically and across borders.

I must reemphasize the point I raised at the beginning of this chapter, that in no society is social support for environmental policy inevitable. The thrust of the arguments presented here is simply that politically significant levels of environmental concern are as likely in poor countries as they are in rich countries. To argue that environmental movements and associated policy changes *can* occur in poor countries, as I have here, is an entirely different project from explaining why and how they *do* occur. That will be the task of chapters 5 and 6. But first let us put some flesh on the story, by reviewing the fascinating history of social activism and policy reform in Costa Rica and Bolivia, the subject of the following two chapters.

— Distinguish policy support from environmental concern

II
Historical Perspectives

Costa Rica

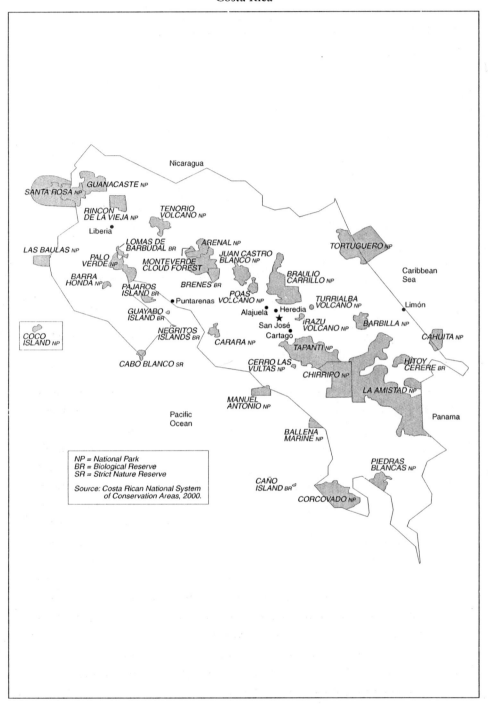

Nicaragua

SANTA ROSA NP

GUANACASTE NP

RINCON DE LA VIEJA NP

TENORIO VOLCANO NP

Liberia

LAS BAULAS NP

LOMAS DE BARBUDAL BR

ARENAL NP

TORTUGUERO NP

Caribbean Sea

PALO VERDE NP

JUAN CASTRO BLANCO NP

MONTEVERDE CLOUD FOREST

BARRA HONDA NP

BRENES BR

BRAULIO CARRILLO NP

PAJAROS ISLAND BR

POAS VOLCANO NP

TURRIALBA VOLCANO NP

Limón

COCO ISLAND NP

GUAYABO ISLAND BR

Puntarenas

Alajuela

★ Heredia

San José

IRAZU VOLCANO NP

BARBILLA NP

CAHUITA NP

NEGRITOS ISLANDS BR

Cartago

CARARA NP

TAPANTI NP

CABO BLANCO SR

CERRO LAS VULTAS NP

CHIRRIPO NP

HITOY CERERE BR

LA AMISTAD NP

MANUEL ANTONIO NP

Pacific Ocean

BALLENA MARINE NP

Panama

PIEDRAS BLANCAS NP

NP = National Park
BR = Biological Reserve
SR = Strict Nature Reserve

Source: Costa Rican National System
        of Conservation Areas, 2000.

CAÑO ISLAND BR

CORCOVADO NP

3

Environmental Leadership: The Costa Rican Example

Mientras febril el hombre se consume
en los horrores de feroz matanza,
por el éter azul . . . tu copa avanza,
saturada de paz, trino y perfume. . . .

Cuál es tu nombre? . . . Roble, Eucalipto,
Cedro, Secoya, Olivo- . . . Poco importa!
El hombre sin escrúpulos te corta,
sea en Costa Rica, en Ecuador o Egipto!

—Gonzalo Castro, *Canto al Arbol,* 1940[1]

While man consumes himself, feverish,
in the horrors of the slaughter,
your crown rises through the blue ether,
saturated in peace, trill and perfume. . . .

By what name are you known?
Oak, Eucalyptus,
Cedar, Sequoia, Olive- . . . No matter!
Unscrupulous man cuts you down,
whether in Costa Rica, Egypt or Ecuador!

When Gonzalo Castro wrote *Canto al Arbol,* contrasting the violence of world war with the natural beauty of Costa Rica, he had little idea that a half century later the international community would mobilize not for war, but for nature—a history in which his homeland would figure prominently. There are many possible ways to relate Costa Rica's environmental history, from the perspective of villages or viceroys, highlighting conflicts or cooperation. This chapter draws attention to events of particular importance for understanding the central subject of this study: how a small, relatively poor Central American country like Costa Rica emerged as a leader in tropical conservation, and the relative roles played by foreign and domestic actors in this process. The emphasis is on the origins of effective public policies, though the insights provided by this approach may also shed light on the concerns of those approaching tropical conservation from different theoretical angles or geographic scales.[2]

The political and biological landscapes intermesh to provide the backdrop for conservation policymaking in Costa Rica.[3] Famous for a long-standing commitment to social welfare, Costa Rica boasts of health and education statistics far surpassing those of wealthier countries like Mexico or Brazil. This is due in part to the abolition of the military by the modern republic's founders in 1948, which freed up funds for social investment. Costa Ricans have also been fortunate to avoid the more egregious forms of U.S. intervention that have taken a toll on their Central American neighbors. Biologically, Costa Rica is a superpower. It is home to approximately half a million species, representing about 4 percent of total world terrestrial biodiversity (Gámez 1993). Roughly the size of West Virginia, Costa Rica has more bird species than are found in the whole of the United States. The legislature is unicameral, with proportional representation, dominated by the social democratic Liberation party and the conservative Social Christian party. The ecosystems are varied, ranging from tropical dry forests in the northwest, to the Andean-like Páramo of the Talamanca mountains and the lowland evergreen rainforests of Corcovado. The executive branch is more dominant than in industrial democracies, but restrained by Latin American standards. Jaguars, vampire bats, anteaters, and armadillos count among its mammalian diversity. Predominantly Catholic, the country has an independent press, a fairly strong union tradition, and a penchant for civil organizing. Its floristic landscape includes approximately 8,000 species of higher plants, while its export economy is dominated by just three—sugarcane, coffee, and bananas—in addition to cattle. To the untrained eye, Costa Rica's jungles appear an undifferentiated mass of green; in reality, these are the result of thousands of complex ecological relationships. To the casual spectator, Costa Rican politics appear peaceful, predictable and provincial, belying complex networks of social relations wherein powerful actors may exert subtle but determinative influences over the course of events.

In chapter 1 we saw that global environmental problems unfold in a political setting characterized by worldwide concern and national-level political authority. This is evident in the history of biodiversity policymaking in Costa Rica, which has been shaped by a remarkable degree of cross-border collaboration yet also attests to the crucial importance of domestic political resources, which have been indispensable in efforts to translate global concerns into functioning institutions. Three additional themes characterize the history recounted in this chapter.

The first theme is the evolving relationship between a small core of bilateral activists—reformers who meld international and domestic resources to promote policy change—and a growing social movement, with the early environmental pioneers eventually finding themselves in the midst of a broad and multifaceted civic debate. Second, it is a history shaped by Costa Ricans' ambiguous relationship to foreigners and foreign centers of power and wealth, with both faces of this ambiguity influencing the course of events. Foreign resources and ideas have been invited by the cosmopolitan orientation of Costa Ricans, while their sensitivity to foreign domination has profoundly affected who participates and how, with the effect that most bilateral activists are worldly Costa Ricans rather than acculturated foreigners. Third, the history unfolds as a dialogue between state and society—between government institutions and social mobilization, political leadership and civic demands.

The Early Conservation Vision

Slash-and-burn agriculture "destroys humus, which gives land its most precious quality," warned Secretary of State Enrique Jiménez in 1913 (quoted in Wallace 1992: 11). As the secretary of development some years later, Jiménez ordered his subordinates to put an end to the practice once and for all. "With the law in hand, stop this burning of residuals for annual plantings, so that we can protect our valuable woodlands and waterways, prevent droughts and avoid the conflagrations that are ruining our lands . . ." (quoted in Fournier 1991: 37). Numerous proclamations of this nature were issued in Costa Rica in the nineteenth and early twentieth centuries, as was the case throughout Latin America. In 1888 the government of Bernardo Soto reiterated a decree from 1846 forbidding deforestation near the waterways surrounding Barba Volcano, to protect the water supplies of Heredia and Alajuela provinces. Policies to regulate the use of wildlife included the 1881 ban on dynamite fishing, and a series of measures passed between 1900 and 1906 that included a proposal to protect Caribbean turtle hatcheries from stray dogs. The national legislature proposed a forest conservation law in 1906, and passed the Fire Law in 1909 to regulate swidden agriculture. Clearly some political leaders felt compelled to act, if only by exhortation, to protect their country's natural resources from what they viewed as unsustainable (what Latin Americans often call *irracional*) methods of exploitation.

The history described in this chapter is not, however, a history of congressional mandates and presidential decrees. It is a tale of hard-won battles, fought over a period of decades, to create institutions that work—agencies to regulate natural resource use, parks to protect species (and, more recently, to meet the needs of local communities), and foundations to promote innovative conservation techniques. By this measure, contemporary conservation policies represent a qualitative break with the past. Prior to the 1970s, enforcement of national policy was so sporadic, its impact so limited, and its supportive coalition so marginal, that today's conservation policies and institutions must be viewed as more than the latest upwelling of an age-old current. With this caveat in mind, a review of conservation efforts in the first half of the twentieth century provides the context and contrarelief necessary to understand the origin and significance of today's environmental policies.

Agronomy and the State

For much of the twentieth century, environmental concern in Costa Rica was confined to a small and outspoken group of agronomists whose arguments for forest and soil conservation carried all the conviction, but little of the impact, of the contemporary movement. From 1926 to 1940 the National Agricultural College served as the hub of environmental concern in the country. In 1939 Rafael Chavarría, who directed the college during much of this period, denounced environmental destruction in terms that many would recognize in national headlines a half century later:

> As a result of certain misguided practices, we find ourselves in a grave and disheartening situation, which future generations will suffer keenly. We are the unfortunate inheritants of our elders' lack of understanding and foresight; but now we are aware of the harm these practices produce, and have no justification to imitate them. I am referring to the excessive, senseless, devastating felling of the forests, the burning of the soils, and the destruction of our fauna. (Fournier 1991: 42)

When President Rafael Calderón established the University of Costa Rica in 1940, the National Agricultural College was transferred to the university, becoming its Agronomy Department, and with it traveled the national locus of conservation concern. In an article entitled "Alert!" published in 1949, agronomist Carlos Luís Valle called on all Costa Ricans to take up the conservation mantle: "the capitalist, the physician, the lawyer, the pharmacist, the priest, the teacher, the shopkeeper, the laborer, the field hand—the pillars of our society—must confront the challenge of producing and accumulating riches *through strict and vigilant measures for the conservation of natural resources*" (Valle 1949: 433, emphasis in origi-

Figure 3.1
"The Imprudence of Mr. Prudencio." (appearing in *Suelo Tico*, 1950)

nal). Tapping into images of war still fresh in the memory of Costa Ricans, he wrote "The world wars . . . of the future will be motivated by the desire to satisfy hunger, and there will be little that the United Nations or any other organization fighting for world peace will be able to do" (Valle 1949: 433).

The agronomists' warnings were a cry in the wilderness at a time when the major thrust of national agrarian policy was to boost production and provide land to those who wished to work it. Government policies directly encouraged deforestation, requiring settlers to "improve" wild areas as a precondition for ownership and providing credit to convert forests to pasture and cropland (Nygren 1995: 204). Government complicity notwithstanding, the agricultural experts, many of whom were on the government payroll, attributed deforestation to the "unpatriotic" short-sightedness of the private sector and the alleged backwardness of rural peoples—deforestation "by commerce or by ignorance" (Valle 1949: 436). This sentiment was reflected in a cartoon series, "The Imprudence of Mr. Prudencio," appearing in *Suelo Tico* (Costa Rican Soil), the official gazette of the Ministry of Agriculture and Industry (figure 3.1). While the agronomists' diagnosis was questionable, their commitment was unmistakable. "If we hope to continue our existence," wrote Valle (1949: 436), "we must realize that the land is the common heritage of humanity, and its owners merely trustees."

That concern over deforestation held some cache among intellectual reformers during this period is reflected in the newsletter of the Center for the Study of National Problems, the think tank that would lay the intellectual foundation for the social democratic revolution establishing the modern Costa Rican state in 1948. In 1943 the center published an article by Luís Villalobos entitled "Deforestation: A Problem We Must Solve."

Villalobos criticized the "illusion that these resources are inexhaustible," and he argued for government measures to stop "the intensive and unmanaged felling of trees, which is converting many areas into veritable deserts and compromising the future self-sufficiency of the country in timber." "The mere passage of laws is not enough," he wrote, presaging contemporary criticisms of "paper parks" in developing countries that provide protection in name only. New government agencies, staffed by agronomists, were needed to "attenuate the insane manner in which our forests are being exploited, which is producing incalculable losses that are already notable and will be more so in the coming years, when climatic disruptions, sterile soils, and wood shortages remind us of the lack of foresight that existed for the resolution of this problem" (Villalobos 1943: 8, 9).

Reaching Across Borders

Transnational relations among Costa Rican and foreign scientists intensified during the postwar era, facilitating the exchange of ideas and information on conservation and the science of ecology. This was part of a broader historical trend toward cross-border collaborative ventures in the Western Hemisphere during and after World War II (see Corrales and Feinberg 1999). The trend was driven by American concerns about collective security in the region during the war, but spilled over into a wide range of transnational activities largely sponsored by the Pan American Union and its successor, the Organization of American States. These included a series of inter-American conferences on health education (1943), economic and financial planning (1942), maritime commerce (1940), astrophysics (1942), and copyright law (1946), and the creation of the Inter-American Commission of Women and the Inter-American Cultural Council.

It was in this context that the Inter-American Institute of Agricultural Sciences was established in Turrialba, Costa Rica, in 1942. The institute soon became an important center for networking among Costa Rican and foreign scientists. In the following decades it would provide an institutional home for prominent foreign researchers like the American Leslie Holdridge, who trained a generation of Costa Rican ecologists, and his compatriot Kenton Miller, a pivotal figure who taught conservation planning and park management at the institute in the 1960s. This and similar institutions would also serve in later years as a wellspring for bilateral activism, exposing Costa Ricans to foreign ideas and to international networks of science and finance.

In the absence of a significant nongovernmental environmental movement during the postwar years, transnational relations among conservationists in the Americas were facilitated by state-sponsored events. Of particular importance was a decision by delegates to the Third Inter-American Conference on Agriculture in 1945 to organize a hemispheric conference devoted exclusively to conservation. The resulting Inter-American Conference on the Conservation of Renewable Resources was held in Denver, Colorado, in September 1948, and it is a remarkable early example of transnational environmental activism. William Vogt, perhaps the most influential conservation advocate of his day, served as secretary general for the meeting, which was attended by delegates from throughout the Americas. Participants presented papers on conservation research and advocacy, covering such topics as "A World Approach to Nature Protection," "Wildlife in a Developing Hemisphere," "The Ecological Approach to Conservation Programs," and "International Cooperation and the Private Citizen." Cuban scientists complained of an "insufficient love of nature" in their country (Moreno and Fernández 1948), Americans shared experiences from soil conservation districts and national parks, and Peruvian delegates wrote on "The Indigenous American Race in Its Relation to the Soil." "The effort we are making to entrench in the consciousness of men the need for defense and conservation of natural resources," said Venezuelan Agriculture Minister Ricardo Montilla, "goes beyond the simple individual interests of each country and projects itself toward human solidarity, endangered as is humanity itself, by the perspective . . . of those countries indifferent to the interests that bring us together here" (Montilla 1948: 9). A special panel on renewable resources and international relations, chaired by Eduardo Mejía of Columbia, recommended that "International credit institutions, such as the Export-Import Bank, should obtain the approval of ecologists and conservationists on specific proposals for resource development," foreshadowing controversies surrounding World Bank loans a half century later (Mejía et al. 1948: 162–164).

The importance of transnational relations to Costa Rica's fledgling conservation community was evident in the pages of *Suelo Tico,* which contain environmental polemics by Mexican agricultural scientists, excerpts from American soil conservation pamphlets, and frequent references to the writings of foreign conservationists like Vogt who in 1946 published *The Population of Costa Rica and Its Natural Resources*. In an article entitled "The Growing Interest Abroad in Soil Conservation," the chief of the U.S. Soil Conservation Service, Hugh Bennett, described his agency's influence on agricultural policy and practice throughout Latin America. Alumni of its conservation training programs went on to become leaders of agricultural conservation agencies in El Salvador, Guatemala, Columbia, Peru, Mexico, Chile, Argentina, Venezuela, and Brazil (Bennett 1949).

Costa Rica's small band of conservationists participated in many of the international environmental meetings of this era, while pressing their case at home. José Torres, a Costa Rican participant at the Denver conference, prepared a report on the state of Costa Rica's environment for consideration at the first meeting of the International Union for the Conservation of Nature (IUCN). In 1950 the Ministry of Agriculture and Industry sponsored the first Natural Resources Conservation Week, with the goal of inspiring reflection among "every Costa Rican man, woman and child, in the countryside and in the cities, on how to live in harmony with Nature, to create a propitious climate for conservation planning, in which the citizen . . . will understand that this patriotic work is not merely an obligation for the organs of the state, but a responsibility shared by all."[4] In 1952 Rogelio Coto wrote the Universal Declaration of the Rights of Nature and the Responsibilities of Man, which he presented at the third general assembly of IUCN in Caracas, Venezuela, asserting that humanity must "know and make known the unquestionable relation between the state of our resources and the welfare of man" (Coto ca. 1952: 276).

If the relation between nature and man was apparent, that between conservationists and politicians was more open to question. The Agriculture Secretariat established in the 1940s (which later became the Ministry of Agriculture and Industry) was led by political appointees who rarely consulted the agronomists comprising their technical staff. These conservation-minded experts, in turn, were hesitant to become directly involved in the formulation of policy, according to an editorial published by the Center for the Study of National Problems. A scientific panel commissioned by the Secretariat to study the impacts of Pan American Highway construction on the oak forests south of San José did see its recommendations incorporated into law in 1945, with the declaration of a 2 kilometer buffer zone on each side of the highway. The law was never implemented, however, and agronomists later complained that the Secretariat ignored their offers to draft a Forestry Code that would have transformed the 1945 law into a general policy for protection of the nation's forests.[5]

In other instances, the influence of these technically oriented conservationists on national policy was quite direct, as when agronomist Alvaro Rojas, a graduate of the National Agricultural College, was elected to the Legislative Assembly, where he introduced the Soil and Water Conservation Law of 1953. But on the whole, for the first half of the twentieth century, Costa Rican conservationists worked on the margins of political power. The priorities of those years were state-building, agricultural development, and the search for economic self-sufficiency. While conservationists spoke of future generations and sustained yield production, the forests were being cleared for pasture and produce, and the population increased nearly threefold.[6]

Ecology Ascendant

Costa Rican conservation in the first half of the twentieth century was marked not only by its weak influence in political circles but by its exclusive emphasis on sustained resource use. The agronomists who dominated the early conservation discourse denounced deforestation as the scourge of sustained timber yields, agricultural productivity, local climate, and water provision. Its effect on intact ecosystems, and the diversity of flora and fauna they shelter, was not a major concern. To those concerned merely with long-term production, deforestation was reprehensible but could ultimately be remedied by reforesting denuded areas. In the 1960s this view came to be challenged by individuals trained in ecology and wildlife biology, who were more preoccupied with the long-term survival of wild species. This new generation of conservation advocates shared earlier concerns about deforestation. Because destruction of natural forest cover results in an irreversible loss of species, however, they promoted parks rather than reforestation as the appropriate policy response.

The growing concern in Costa Rica for what is now called biological diversity was promoted by the confluence of two trends. The first was Costa Rica's investments in the biological sciences. A biology department was established at the University of Costa Rica in the late 1950s with an emphasis on zoology and ecosystem ecology, and in 1970 the National Museum was revitalized as a center for research (Gómez and Savage 1983). The university produced a cadre of Costa Rican biologists who in 1968 formed a professional association, the Colegio de Biólogos, which would be an important player in environmental policy debates in the years to come. The ascendance of ecology in public debates and state policy was not the result of professional biologists replacing agronomists in positions of influence (per Haas 1992). Rather, the biologists' teachings on the diversity of life, and on park management to protect that diversity, won adherents among actors in a wide range of professions, including molecular biology, agronomy, and law, some of whom would emerge as leaders of Costa Rica's environmental movement.

Costa Rican investments in the biological sciences promoted, and were in turn bolstered by, a second trend—the arrival in the 1960s of a wave of foreign scientists with professional training in theoretical ecology and personal commitments to wildlife conservation. In 1959 Archie Carr, the world's foremost expert on sea turtles, established the Caribbean Conservation Corporation, for the study and preservation of turtles of the Caribbean coast. In 1962 three Americans affiliated with the Inter-American Institute of Agricultural Sciences founded the Tropical Science Center, a private organization that would serve as another important meeting place for foreign and domestic conservation advocates. Most important of all, the Organization for Tropical Studies, a major consortium of American research universities, was established in Costa Rica in 1963, making it the destination of choice for foreign ecologists. Costa Rica provided a propitious environment for tropical research because of its extraordinary biological diversity, investments in public education, and stable democracy—an important consideration for long-term field studies, as American researchers discovered when Fidel Castro appropriated Harvard University's Atkins Gardens in Cuba.

The Forestry Law of 1969

The tension between the new ecological perspective and the reforestation mentality of the earlier generation of conservationists is apparent in the debates surrounding the Forestry Law of 1969. Costa Rican environmentalists consider this legislation to be a watershed that facilitated the creation of their now-famous national park system. But a reading of legislative testimony reveals that parks and wildlife were only minor considerations in the Forestry Law. The intent of the legislation was unmistakably conservationist, but it was of the reforestation genre, emphasizing plantations, harvesting techniques, cut permits and incentives for reforestation. The law was drafted by a commission led by Alvaro Rojas, the agronomist-turned-politician who had introduced the Soil and Water Conservation Law of 1953. The brain power of the commission came from graduates of the Inter-American Institute of Agricultural Sciences, such as Arnoldo Madriz, Mario López, and Luís Fournier, who had been discussing the idea of a forestry law since the 1940s (Fournier 1997). The new generation of ecologically oriented scientists were nowhere represented on the commission.

Although the bulk of the law's text was dedicated to traditional forestry concerns, "We were aware of the importance of parks," recalled Fournier (1997), because the American Kenton Miller had been teaching the country's first course on protected areas. Accordingly, one brief provision in the law was devoted to national parks to be created for "recreation and education of the public, tourism or for scientific investigation" (*Ley Forestal* 1969).

The provision on national parks attracted little attention or controversy during public hearings on the Forestry Law. Two groups did pay close attention, however. The first was the Costa Rican Institute of Tourism (ICT). The government agency was responsible for the few existing protected areas, which included Irazú and Poás volcanoes and Santa Rosa National Park, the historic battleground where the American invader William Walker was repelled by a volunteer army in 1856. The ICT was loath to cede these areas to the new park agency envisioned in the Forestry Law. According to Arturo Trejos, a technical consultant testifying before the Assembly, the institute had killed several earlier proposals to create a park service. "Why weren't these discussed in the Assembly? Because there has always been political pressure not to, and I am sure that this pressure was not from the timber industry, but from the same bureaucrats who have had responsibility for forest management for so many years" (Trejos 1969). Soon thereafter, Trejos was fired from his government position with the Institute of Lands and Colonization. Judging by the legislators' outrage at this development, the ICT apparently played a role in his dismissal. Political pressure against the creation of a park system was also in evidence when Congressman Vega Rojas proposed a motion, eventually defeated, to delete the bill's provision on national parks altogether.

The second group to take a special interest in the parks provision was the newly formed biologists' association. The Colegio de Biólogos took out paid newspaper ads (a common form of political communication in Costa Rica) in support of the law, establishing a precedent for the Colegio as a political force for the conservation of species. In letters to congress they warned that "the prevailing situation threatens the total extinction of valuable species of our fauna and flora,"[7] a message that stood in sharp contrast to the usual preoccupation with sustained production that characterized public debates on the Forestry Law. Colegio members drew on the financial resources of conservation allies overseas, and on their own familiarity with domestic politics, to advance this new ecological agenda and to provide the nascent national park system with sound legal footing. They challenged a proposal to divide administrative responsibility for national parks between the tourism agency and the new park service, employing a tactic used frequently throughout Costa Rica's environmental history: "We recently had the pleasure of meeting with Dr. Myron Sutton, Chief of the Division of International Relations at the U.S. National Park Service, and a world-renown expert in this field," they wrote in a letter to the president of the Assembly. "Dr. Sutton stressed that any aid provided by the U.S. Park Service to Costa Rica is conditioned on the park administration falling under the aegis of a single institution" (Sáenz 1969).

It is unlikely that this "condition" originated with Sutton, who had little knowledge of the ICT or of the intricacies of interagency politics in Costa Rica. More likely, the Colegio mapped out the political terrain for Sutton, explaining to their foreign ally that the ICT was a threat to the new park service, and in the course of those conversations arose the idea to use conditional aid for leverage in the bureaucratic struggle. This same tactic was used by Margarita Ortiz de Macaya, a close friend of Congressman Guardia Hurrero, in her testimony in support of the Forestry Law. Ortiz had just returned to her country after an extended stay in the United States, where she worked with the Sierra Club:

There is great interest in the United States in helping us in the area of natural resources, and I have learned that discussions are underway about where to invest funds for this purpose . . . Today we are living in a house of crystal. Your decisions, Costa Rica's decisions, are known immediately in other parts of the world which are interested in helping us, including the United States. They are looking to see whether we take an interest in natural resource legislation. . . . [The Sierra Club] is especially interested in national parks, and we have such beautiful areas, with a little effort they could be among the best in the world. (Ortiz de Macaya 1969)

As the 1960s drew to a close, all the pieces were in place for the dramatic increase in social activism and environmental policy reform that characterized the 1970s. Although there was nothing inevitable about the transition to come, policy entrepreneurs like Alvaro Ugalde and Mario Boza found an auspicious environment for reform when they entered the scene in the late 1960s. There was an organized cadre of biologists who could speak with authority on the plight of species and the need to protect intact remnants of habitat to ensure their survival. National parks had the legal backing of the government, and there was a new Park Service with a mandate, at least on paper, for expansion. Biology courses had been taught in the general education requirements of the country's major institution of higher learning, teaching many future leaders a fascination and respect for the scarlet macaws and hawksbill turtles, wild ginger and cream owl butterflies that comprise Costa Rica's natural heritage. Institutions such as the Organization for Tropical Studies and Tropical Science Center brought together foreign and domestic actors and resources, and they would facilitate a rapid transfer of information and enthusiasm from the American environmental movement in the early 1970s.

Creation and Expansion of the Costa Rican Park System, 1970–1986

Transnational relations played an essential role in the development of a national network of protected areas in Costa Rica. However, the relationship between Costa Rican environmentalists and their foreign counterparts has always been more complex than popular portrayals suggest. It is true that relative to a Saudi Arabia or Myanmar, Costa Rica is indeed a very cosmopolitan society, eagerly experimenting with ideas from abroad and generally welcoming of foreigners—what ecologist Daniel Janzen calls Costa Rican "xenophilia." But if Costa Ricans have embraced foreign influences, this has been done critically and strategically; their love of foreigners is not an unconditional one. Nowhere was this more apparent than in Costa Rica's first mass environmental protest, directed against the American Aluminum Company (Alcoa) in 1970.

The world's largest aluminum company, Alcoa sought to establish a bauxite processing plant in the Pérez Zeledón region south of San José. The proposal had the support of President José Joaquín Trejos, who sent a bill to the Assembly to approve a contract for this purpose.[8] But students at the University of Costa Rica raised concerns that the contract would grant foreign control over Costa Rican resources on terms benefiting the company at the expense of the nation. This took place during a period of heightened sensitivity to inequities in international economic relations, which would inspire developing countries to band together in 1974 to pass U.N. resolutions calling for a New International Economic Order. Fears of American incursions on Costa Rican sovereignty were fueled by the legacy of U.S. intervention in Central America, including William Walker's invasion of Costa Rica in the 1850s, military intervention in Nicaragua (1927–1933), the overthrow of Guatemalan President Jacobo Arbenz Guzman in 1954, and U.S. support for Nicaraguan dictator Anastasio Somoza who invaded Costa Rica in 1958.

President Trejos and legislators steadfastly supported the Alcoa contract, citing job creation, tax revenues, and the need for foreign capital, while student leaders mobilized the opposition. The spirit of student activism that swept across national borders beginning in 1968 animated university and high school students in San José. A series of protests culminated in widespread demonstrations on April 24, 1970, that constituted the largest civic disruption since the revolution of 1948. Students marched on the Assembly, some shattering windows and setting fires, while legislators who approved the contract were ushered out in Red Cross vehicles. Though the students had the support of many university professors, they were derided by the political establishment as idealists, romantics and communists, and they were ultimately unsuccessful in stopping the contract.

The relation between the Alcoa protests and environmentalism must be interpreted with care. The inspiration for the protests was primarily nationalistic. But it is accurate to identify this as the country's first environmental protest (as do many Costa Ricans) for two reasons. First, conservation did figure prominently in the rhetoric of movement leaders, who were concerned that the company would renege on its promise to restore landscapes destroyed by mining.[9] Thus in a fifteen-year retrospective on Alcoa, a university newspaper referred to "the ecological and political damage that Alcoa would bring to Costa Rica" (Ugalde 1985). Second, the relation between nationalist and conservationist discourses forged during that period—typified in the double entendre of the oft-heard phrase "defending our natural resources"—set the tone for contemporary controversies surrounding biodiversity prospecting and debt-for-nature swaps. The broader legacy of the Alcoa era is that it sensitized a generation of environmentalists and political leaders to foreign interference in domestic affairs. Reinforcing norms against political involvement by outsiders, Alcoa helped to ensure that the key figures in conservation policy reform in Costa Rica would be Costa Ricans.

Two of these figures, Alvaro Ugalde and Mario Boza, were especially important.[10] In 1968 Mario Boza was studying for a master's degree in forestry at the Inter-American Institute of Agricultural Sciences, where he took Kenton Miller's course on the design and administration of national parks. At the time Alvaro Ugalde was studying biology under Pedro León, a molecular geneticist at the University of Costa Rica who was an important figure in the Colegio de Biólogos. The two students met at a round-table discussion on natural resources, and Boza suggested that Ugalde join a field trip Miller was organizing to visit Great Smoky Mountains National Park in the United States. It was a radicalizing experience for both of them, and they returned to Costa Rica convinced that national parks were both essential and feasible in their own country. When the National Park Service was created by the Forestry Law in 1969, Boza was appointed by the Agriculture Ministry to be its first director—a position that he and Ugalde would occupy numerous times in the coming decades.

In the early years, the Park Service consisted of three people: Ugalde and Boza (both of whom were in their twenties), and one administrative assistant. Much of their work was voluntary. Deploying entrepreneurial skills that became their hallmark, they overcame staffing shortages by drawing on the National Youth Movement, the Civil Guard, the Costa Rican Boy Scouts, and the U.S. Peace Corps. "[E]fforts to establish the parks were met with indifference," recalled Boza (1993: 239). But what they lacked in public support, they compensated for with political connections. Of particular importance was their rapport with Karen Olson Figueres, the wife of the country's most prominent political figure, José "Pepe" Figueres, who had just assumed the presidency for the third time. Bipartisan alliances were another political asset they drew on to bolster their fledgling park system. Ugalde was associated with the National Liberation Party (PLN), his father having fought alongside Figueres in 1948. Boza, the son of a businessman, came from the more conservative Social Christian Unity Party (PUSC). This would facilitate a consistent and cumulative approach to park administration as the two parties alternated control of the government in the coming years, and would help environmentalism to gain acceptance among leaders of different political stripes. Of equal importance, the two men—Boza the technician and manager, Ugalde the charismatic leader—were personally dedicated to the cause.

Their entrepreneurial skills were very much in evidence during the expansion of the national park system in the 1970s, when the system grew from three units in 1970 to seventeen in 1978 (Wallace 1992). "This was a time with a lot of urgent problems, with the park agency running from one park to the next," recalled Pedro León (1997). "President Figueres was brilliant in many respects, but he had a blind spot when it came to conservation. He was from a different era. He viewed an undeveloped mountain as an enemy of civilization. The early 1970s were a difficult time because he appointed a cattle rancher, Fernando Batalla, as the Minister of Agriculture and Livestock." Against these political odds, Boza and Ugalde began their efforts at sites likely to attract popular support, including Poás Volcano, where thousands of Costa Ricans make an annual pilgrimage on Saint Joseph's Day, and at Santa Rosa National Park, established on lands the Costa Rican government had expropriated from the reviled Nicaraguan dictator Somoza in 1966. When Santa Rosa was transferred to the new park service, Ugalde found the area in disarray, slowly being cleared by neighboring ranchers and small farmers. In response he initiated a pressure campaign against the very agency in which he worked. He convinced Boza to publish a letter in the nation's premier daily newspaper, addressed to their superior, Agriculture Minister Batalla:

The first national historical park in the country, Santa Rosa, is about to disappear. . . . But this is not due to any great natural disaster nor to any supreme national necessity that obliges such sacrifice. It is due only to a few squatters who with fire, axes, and rifles are destroying the heritage of all Costa Ricans, of present and future generations. And what is the benefit to the country of this situation?

Nothing, except to demonstrate that the country's laws are worthless, if that is any benefit. (Boza 1970, cited in Wallace 1992: 18)

The campaign eventually paid off, with the government providing the necessary funds to make the park operational.

Negotiation and consultation are the bread and butter of Costa Rican political culture, and Ugalde employed these with finesse. He successfully negotiated with the families occupying the land, promising them he would resign from his position if he failed to meet their demands for relocation to new land elsewhere. Negotiation skills of a different sort were put to the test when Daniel Oduber, a ranch owner from the Santa Rosa area who was president of the Assembly, introduced a bill to transfer the park system back to the Institute of Tourism. Clearly Oduber believed that ranching interests would be better served if the park were taken out of the hands of these young crusaders. Boza and Ugalde launched a campaign to defeat the bill with the help of the Colegio de Biólogos. They mobilized the business community against the bill by pointing to a provision that would raise funds by taxing liquor. The first lady lobbied numerous members of congress on their behalf and reportedly wrote a letter asking Oduber to withdraw the bill, which she had the president hand deliver without knowing its contents (Wallace 1992). The bill was unanimously defeated, and Santa Rosa National Park was inaugurated in March of 1971 at a ceremony attended by Agriculture Minister Batalla, the president and first lady, and Oduber, who made a speech in support of the park.[11] This was not the last time the park would be threatened by the designs of bureaucrats or private interests, however. Protecting Santa Rosa and the rest of the park system would require the consistent application of this sort of political diligence over a span of decades.

Rather than simply declare a series of parks on paper, Boza was careful to make each area operational, with a budget and staff, before moving on to the next. Still the park system grew rapidly. Cahuita and Tortuguero were established to protect coral reefs and turtle hatcheries along the Caribbean coast, and Barra Honda National Park was created on the Nicoya Peninsula. In 1973 the geological formations and wildlife of the high Talamanca mountains were afforded protection with the creation of Chirripó National Park. Rincón de la Vieja was established for its scenic beauty and to protect the watershed of Tempisque River, while the islands of Guayabo, Negritos, and de los Pájaros were declared biological reserves, providing sanctuary for marine birds. This growing national system was complemented by privately owned and managed areas, including La Selva Biological Station, run by the Organization for Tropical Studies, and Monteverde Cloud Forest Preserve, which was established by a local Quaker community for watershed protection and later run by the Tropical Science Center.

By 1973 it was clear that something was going on in Costa Rica that differed markedly from the dismal record of "paper parks" common at the time in developing countries. That year Costa Rica was visited by a team of distinguished conservationists who touted the country as a model for the world. In 1975, on behalf of the World Wildlife Fund, Holland's Prince Bernhard bestowed a set of commemorative coins on Costa Rica, declaring "Cost Rica is the leading country in Latin America in the conservation of its natural resources."[12] While the international community conferred prestige on the national parks, Costa Ricans began to visit them in droves (Ugalde 1997a).[13]

The Rise of an Environmental Movement

While national park advocates were shoring up the institutional requirements of a protected areas system, outside the confines of the parks a larger social movement was under way. By the mid-1970s and for the first time in Costa Rican history, large swaths of the public were discussing environmental problems and pressing for solutions. Like earlier upwellings of conservation sentiment, the movement was led by conservation scientists. Unlike those earlier times, it was not confined to them. The movement's leaders were individuals with extensive international exposure, who were inspired by the incipient environmental movements of other countries. Pedro León, one of Costa Rica's most influential environmental advocates, encountered the book *Limits to Growth* while studying at the University of Oregon in 1973, which inspired his commitment to conservation (León 1997). Another important figure, Carlos Quesada, traces the origin of his concern to his experience as a student at Colorado State University, where in 1970 he happened across a demonstration during the first Earth Day:

I walked out of the engineering school and saw a big protest, with a group surrounding and burying some type of machine. As an engineer, I thought *qué stúpido*. But I went to see what was going on, and as I started talking with people,

I learned about problems of energy, pollution, chemicals, and oil spills. I began to question the prevailing system of consumption, and soon took more courses on water source management and the environment, and studied alternative models of development. (Quesada 1997)

The early 1970s also witnessed the rise of Costa Rica's first nongovernmental environmental groups. Costa Ricans' tradition of civic organizing[14] and the new resources available from foreign environmental groups facilitated the creation of a stratum of civic environmental institutions that would house environmental activists and spearhead political struggles throughout the 1970s. Prior to that period, the Colegio de Biólogos had been one of the only organized venues outside of government in which environmental advocates could press for change. There were earlier precedents like the "Garden Club" formed in the 1940s to monitor the park created along the Pan American Highway, but these were rare and their impact negligible. In 1971 the Costa Rican Audubon Society was created as an affiliate of the Florida chapter, its founding members including the botanist Luís Diego Gómez, Mario Boza, and a score of Costa Rican and foreign nature aficionados. In 1973 they helped launch a second group called Amigos de la Naturaleza, while the Costa Rican Association for National Parks and Zoos, a gathering of intellectuals and the wealthy, made a more "gentle" push for conservation, in León's words (León 1997).

The Tropical Science Center played a crucial role during this period, as a meeting place for environmentalists who went on to form advocacy groups like the Costa Rican Association for the Conservation of Nature (ASCONA). In the center's early years, foreign scientists played a prominent, if not predominant role. But the participation of a large number of politically active Costa Ricans, and the center's legal status as a Costa Rican organization, enabled its members to directly lobby political authorities. ASCONA, which was housed in the center and later had branches in Quepos, Puriscal, and San Carlos, emerged as the premier environmental advocacy group of the 1970s. The Organization for Tropical Studies (OTS) provided another important center for networking among advocates. But as an unmistakably American organization—and a consortium of research universities no less—OTS officials shunned direct political involvement (Schnell 1997). "OTS was very, very apolitical," was one advocate's telling assessment (León 1997).

In 1974 the Agronomy Department at the University of Costa Rica hosted the First National Congress on the Conservation of Renewable Natural Resources. Its organizers, which included Carlos Quesada, Alfonso Mata, Luís Fournier, and Rolando Mendoza, emphasized above all the importance of raising environmental awareness among the general public. In the ensuing months, conference participants made presentations to high schools, municipal governments, and professional organizations around the country in an effort to spread the word. In the summer of 1975 Rolando Mendoza, an ASCONA member and biology professor at the National University, organized an in-service training on environmental themes for college professors. Other activists who first met at the 1974 conference launched a campaign to pressure various government agencies to minimize the environmental impacts of their day-to-day operations. Boza, Mata, and Quesada wrote a letter to the general manager of the Costa Rican Electricity Institute, blasting the agency for destroying palm trees along Ballena Bay during an electrification project: "We direct our comments to you precisely because we know of your genuine concern for the environmental problems that are overwhelming the country," they wrote, "in the hope that, little by little, consciousness of these problems will spread throughout all the technical and political levels of the government, as the principal vector of progress in the country" (Boza, Mata, and Quesada 1976).

The efforts of these early activists went beyond consciousness-raising. While Boza and Ugalde concentrated on the park system, participants in the broader movement fought and won a series of environmental struggles. The first of these was in opposition to the construction of an intercontinental oil pipeline, which a domestic company planned to run from the Caribbean to the Pacific to transport oil from supertankers too large to navigate the Panama Canal. In common with most of the developing world, Costa Rica had been hard hit by the oil crisis. Considerable pressure mounted to develop the project, for which Costa Rica would receive a guaranteed supply of oil that would serve as a hedge against rising energy prices.

Carlos Quesada reacted to the proposal with the same amalgam of nationalist and environmental concern that characterized the Alcoa protests four years earlier. Quesada had become familiar with the anticipated environmental impacts of the Alaskan pipeline while at Colorado State and was quick to act. He warned of damage to the coral reefs of Cahuita National Park, the threat of oil spills, and the security risks inherent in making Costa Rican territory strategically indispensable for the energy supply of the Great Powers. He enlisted environmentalists he had met at the Tropical Science Center and at the recent national conference on renewable resources in a campaign to stop the pipeline.

Using tactics similar to those employed by Boza and Ugalde in the park agency, the pipeline protesters mobilized their networks of domestic political contacts. One of those who joined Quesada's campaign was a friend of Lena Terán, the wife of Richard Beck, who was the cousin of First Lady Karen Olsen Figueres. With these connections Quesada and his cohorts were able to arrange meetings with ministers and other high-ranking officials, explaining the oil development's double jeopardy to ecology and sovereignty. They pressed the case before legal advisers at the Legislative Assembly, offered seminars to the national organization of journalists, and enlisted the aid of the high school teachers union. The campaign eventually forced the president to annul the agreement. When the proposal resurfaced several years later, it was greeted by protests in the streets of San José and again defeated (Quesada 1997; Mata 1974; Acosta 1974).

In the context of the new environmental movement, lesser skirmishes were a fact of life in the 1970s over issues such as deforestation near Arenal Volcano, a proposed casino development on Caño Island, air pollution from a cement factory, and water pollution from a milk processing plant. One of the higher profile conflicts involved a government proposal to build a road connecting San José to Guápiles on the Caribbean coast. Though the road would provide an important addition to the country's transportation infrastructure, it would run through previously undeveloped rainforest northwest of San José. According to Wallace (1992: 79), "Conservationists feared a road would open the area to an Amazon-style land rush of settlers who would cut and burn the forest, destroying much of the Meseta Central's water supply in the process." Students staged sit-ins to protest the road construction. In response to concerns raised by a growing and increasingly vocal environmental community, in 1975 the World Bank, which was to finance the development, commissioned the Tropical Science Center to write an environmental impact study. The study concluded that the road would soon be washed out if measures were not taken to protect adjacent forested areas. Environmentalists eventually agreed to support the road, provided a national park was created on both sides. With the support of a $1.2 million loan from the United States, the government created Braulio Carrillo National Park, allowing resplendent quetzals and numerous other species to thrive in a large protected habitat located just outside a major urban center.

Transnational Linkages

No sooner did environmental NGOs emerge in Costa Rica than they began to seek allies beyond their borders, establishing linkages with like-minded organizations throughout the Americas. In 1978 ASCONA Executive Secretary José Luís Sáenz joined Latin American environmentalists from Mexico, Brazil, Columbia, Venezuela, and Bolivia on a month-long tour of the United States to learn of the strategies and accomplishments of the American environmental movement.[15] In December of that same year, ASCONA, CATIE (the successor of the Inter-American Institute of Agriculture), and the Guatemalan Natural History Association organized the First Regional Meeting of Non-Governmental Conservation Organizations, which took place in Guatemala City and was attended by numerous representatives from Panama, Nicaragua, Honduras, Mexico, El Salvador, Guatemala, Belize, the Dominican Republic, Ecuador, Peru, and Venezuela.

The origins of the Latin American NGOs attending the Guatemala City meeting were diverse. The Honduran Ecology Association was the product of the First National Seminar on Ecology, organized by the Honduran government in 1976. Friends of the Earth El Salvador, which had 900 members at the time, was formed in the mid-1940s based on the writings of William Vogt. Panama's Friends of Nature, one of eight environmental NGOs active in Panama at the time, was organized in 1969 in conjunction with the creation of Barú Volcano National Park. The conservation arm of the Guatemalan Association of Natural History was founded in 1960 by students and professors, with the slogan "For National Ecological Awareness." The Guatemalan Association for Defense of the Environment was established in 1974 in response to concerns over air pollution, toxic contamination of the food supply, and deforestation. The Belize Audubon Society was created in 1969 with support from Audubon's Florida chapter, while the Association for Caribbean Conservation was formed in the U.S. Virgin Islands in 1967.

The conference also featured a veritable who's who of Northern environmental groups interested in global issues. These included, among others, IUCN, the World Wildlife Fund, the Sierra Club, The Nature Conservancy, the Natural Resources Defense Council, and the Smithsonian Tropical Research Institute. The Natural Resources Defense Council began an international program in 1974, three years after its founding, to monitor environmental impacts of the American government's overseas activities and to provide information to foreign environmental groups. The Sierra Club, the oldest environmental organization in the United States, established its international program Earthcare in 1972. Earthcare's goal was to promote international environmental policy in collaboration with United Nations agencies, and four of five Earthcare offices were located in centers of diplomacy (de Blohm 1978). The Interamerican Council of Scouts was also present. Citing article 6 of their charter—"The Scout sees in Nature the work of God, and protects it"—Scout representatives noted that with 40,000 members throughout Central America, they could be a force for change in the new movement.

"Above all we must present conservation as an element in improving the conditions of life," said Costa Rica's Gerardo Budowski in opening the conference, "something positive rather than restrictive, capable of contributing to economic and social development. . . ." (Budowski 1978). His speech reflected the spirit of the gathering, where the emphasis was on spreading the word and affecting centers of power. The American ecologist Thomas Lovejoy, who a decade later would invent the concept of debt-for-nature swaps, touted the advantages of cross-border collaboration. With his invitation, however, came a warning against provoking fears of foreign meddling. "On some occasions the expert on a topic resides beyond the borders of the nation concerned, and while it is important to tap the greatest expertise possible it may also be important not to wave the foreigner around like a foreign flag" (Lovejoy 1978). The meeting adjourned after participants formed the Mesoamerican Federation of Non-Governmental Conservation Associations, with headquarters in ASCONA in San José.[16]

The Guatemala City meeting differed markedly from the 1948 conference in Colorado, in that it was organized by and for NGOs.[17] But this was not merely a push for social awareness. Participants hoped to affect the domestic and foreign policies of governments, and similar cross-border collaborations among NGOs during this period focused explicitly on the passage of international treaties. Amigos de la Naturaleza, organized as an "interamerican association for study and defense of the human environment," undertook a campaign to win ratification of the Convention on International Trade in Endangered Species (CITES). The organization had its headquarters in San José, while its president was the Bolivian conservationist Percy Baptista, operating out of La Paz, and its board included representatives from Columbia, Panama, Venezuela, and Mexico. In June 1974 Chaplin Barnes of the National Audubon Society's international division wrote a letter encouraging the group to lobby the governments of Costa Rica and other Latin American nations to ratify the treaty, which after a year had secured only two of the ten ratifications needed to enter into force (Barnes 1974). With additional encouragement from IUCN, Amigos took their case to the Costa Rican public. "We visited schools and talked to the students about the [ratification] bill and the importance of protecting animals from becoming extinct," said group member Manuel Cárdenas.[18]

Soon afterward, dozens of students representing fifteen Costa Rican high schools formed the "Working Group" that lobbied the president of the Legislative Assembly, Alfonso Garro, to push for ratification of CITES. The students promised that if Costa Rica ratified the treaty, "we will direct our efforts to [other] governments and students so that the case of Costa Rica catalyzes universal action in defense of the fauna and flora, founded on the law and with the backing of the consciousness of the youth." (Working Group 1974). Costa Rica was the first Central American country to ratify the treaty, and Amigos de la Naturaleza printed 1,500 copies of the Costa Rican legislation and sent it to decision makers and civic organizations throughout Latin America.

Building Institutions

If the Costa Rican environmental movement measured its success by its impact on the institutions of governance, it was Boza and Ugalde who led this charge. While forestry and wildlife administrations floundered for lack of esprit de corps and political support, the park agency continued to grow in prestige and effectiveness. These efforts came just in time. By the early 1970s Costa Rican wildlife was increasingly under threat, with alligators, manatees, and eagles in serious decline. Quetzals were being exported almost to the point of extinction, while jaguars and ocelots, once numerous, were becoming rare as a result of sales to Nicaraguan dealers who would then export their skins to the United States and Europe.[19] This was prohibited by Costa Rican law, but the wildlife branch of the government was so poorly endowed that it had no vehicles, and its small staff had to rely on public transportation when chasing wildlife traffickers.[20] Moreover, wildlife agency personnel complained that the greatest threat to wildlife was deforestation, while forestry officials proved unable to regulate timber extraction and were uninterested in protecting species habitats. The country's high deforestation rate and strong park system, cited today as the great irony of Costa Rican conservation, were in fact two sides of the same coin. Park advocates saw these protected areas as the last best hope for protecting biological diversity from the deforestation that continued unabated outside park boundaries.

Despite their early successes, Boza and Ugalde feared the worst when in 1974 Daniel Oduber—the rancher and congressman who had fought them over Santa Rosa—was elected president of the Republic. Oduber, however, had apparently undergone a change of heart, and he became convinced of the potential economic benefits of nature tourism. Ugalde believes Oduber was also won over by the Youth Movement volunteers he would bring by the president's office to talk excitedly about their work building trails in the parks. A legendary personal rapport soon developed between Oduber and Ugalde, who replaced Boza as director of the park agency after returning from studies at the University of Michigan (Ugalde 1997a; Wallace 1992).

Ugalde drew on this rapport in making another push for the parks. An exceptionally rich stretch of lowland evergreen rainforest on the Osa Peninsula had attracted the attention of the international scientific community, which urged Oduber to protect the area. The Osa Peninsula had also caught the attention of foreign timber interests, who had been clearing forests there for twenty years. Poverty-stricken miners and their families had also recently moved into the area to test age-old rumors of gold. With the backing of studies conducted by Joseph Tosi of the Tropical Science Center, Oduber declared Corcovado National Park on October 31, 1975, to save the remaining intact habitats. But the government was slow to allocate the funds needed to purchase land, hire park guards, and provide for relocation of the miners. Ugalde and Tosi were concerned that it would remain a park on paper only.

"I demanded more direct access to the president," recalled Ugalde, who is known for his forceful style. "Oduber told his secretary 'OK, Alvaro has access.' After that, nothing could stop me. I was pursuing money, and chasing after ministries. Having a president at my disposal was like having a toy. I had a dream, a plan" (Ugalde 1997a). Over the objections of other ministries, Oduber provided a large grant from a presidential discretionary fund and allocated $2 million to Corcovado over the next two years. With full support from the president, the park system expanded rapidly, adding Caño Island Biological Reserve, Palo Verde National Wildlife Refuge, Carara Biological Reserve, and Chirripó and Braulio Carrillo national parks. Foreign conservation interests provided some financial support for these early efforts, but most funds for land acquisition and management came from government budgets.

Under Oduber, park acreage nearly doubled, while the park service budget tripled and the staff increased to 400. International praise poured in. President Oduber, who declared 1977 the "Year of Natural Resources," received awards from the New York Botanical Society and the Animal Welfare Institute, and he was appointed an honorary board member of the World Wildlife Fund.[21] The second Conference of the Parties to the CITES Convention was held in Costa Rica in 1979. A few years later Boza and Ugalde would receive the J. Paul Getty Award for Wildlife Conservation, presented by Ronald Reagan in a ceremony on the White House lawn.[22]

Confronting Crisis

Park management was never an easy matter. Negotiations with gold miners in Corcovado were and continue to be heated and controversial, and while many parks enjoyed local support, relations with local communities on the Caribbean coast and indigenous groups in the Talamanca area were strained. The Park Service also had to fight a series of battles against the ambivalent support of Oduber's successor, President Rodrigo Carazo, who permitted Nicaragua's Sandinistas to conduct military exercises in Santa Rosa National Park and branded Ugalde a traitor for opposing him. Despite these challenges, up to this point the park system had continued to expand, adding Coco Island National Park and La Amistad National Park, an enormous area in the southern portion of the country that doubled the park system's land area.

In the early 1980s, however, the park system faced problems of a different scale as the Costa Rican economy went into a tailspin. Balance-ofpayments problems led to heavy borrowing, and in 1981–1982 gross domestic product dropped while inflation and unemployment soared (Hansen-Kuhn 1993). The Park Service staff was reduced by a fifth and in real terms the equipment and maintenance budget fell by an estimated 80 percent or more from 1980 to 1986. These events unfolded as landowners were demanding reimbursement for private lands declared as protected areas by the government, a right guaranteed under the Costa Rican constitution.

Facing economic crisis at home and a growing interest in global conservation abroad, Costa Rican environmentalists decided to launch a foreign fundraising campaign. Prior to 1979 international support comprised only 2 to 3 percent of the amount of support provided by the Costa Rican government (J. M. Rodríguez, cited in Wallace 1992). Boza and Ugalde had established the National Parks Foundation in 1979 to raise funds to pay for private inholdings in park lands. Meanwhile The Nature Conservancy, an American organization specializing in fundraising and land acquisition, opened an international branch with the goal of supporting similar organizations overseas. It did not take long for the two organizations to join forces. With a goal of raising $5.5 million for Costa Rica's parks in five years, The Nature Conservancy brought Ugalde north for training in the art of fundraising in America. Ugalde, whose first exposure to the international sphere was as a laborer in a candy shipping department in the United States, soon found himself navigating the arcane world of American philanthropy, touting the benefits of tropical conservation to the likes of the Gettys at art gallery receptions. "I emphasized the global aspects of Costa Rica's rainforests," he recalled, "pointing out the importance of preserving wintering habitat of North American migratory birds" (Ugalde 1997a). With coaching from the Conservancy's Spencer Beeby, Ugalde courted prospective donors by inviting them on guided tours of the new parks, where they could experience the country's natural wonders firsthand.

The fundraising campaign achieved its goal, raising the required $5.5 million in less than five years, and the National Parks Foundation staff grew from four to twenty-five, putting in place a professional team able to deftly handle foreign contributions. But Ugalde's American tour achieved something else that would prove far more significant over the long run. The campaign received extensive coverage in the newsletters of American environmental organizations, and for the first time large numbers of

[handwritten margin note: Nonprofits' key roles in funding]

[handwritten note at bottom: Media!]

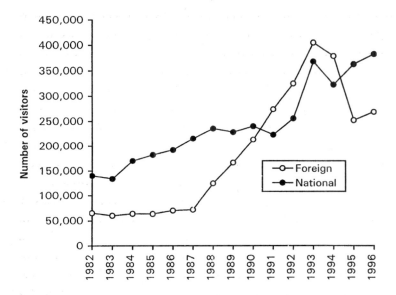

Figure 3.2
Annual visits to Costa Rica's national park system. Source. National System of
Conservation Areas, Central Office 1997; Burmúdez 1992.

people in wealthy countries learned of Costa Rican efforts to create a high-
quality protected areas system in the tropics. Moreover, by the mid-1980s,
Costa Rica's ecotourism industry was taking off at a pace that no park advocate or business entrepreneur had anticipated (figure 3.2). The park system had not only survived the financial crisis of the early 1980s, but was
now flourishing in a new era under the bright spotlight of international attention. The domestic players were essentially the same, but the economic
stakes were now much higher. When Oscar Arias assumed the presidential
mandate in 1986, these developments did not go unnoticed.

From Margin to Center: Institutionalizing Environmentalism, 1986–1990

Candidates for public office had debated environmental themes with reg-
ularity since the late 1970s, and by 1982 most parties had environmental
planks in their platforms. In 1986 there was even a Costa Rican Ecology
Party struggling to compete in various national elections. But the environment was not considered a strategic priority by the Arias campaign,

which ran on the promise of reforming domestic social policy and brokering peace in Central America at a time of heightened public concern over
the prospect of war with Nicaragua. Soon after taking office, however,
Arias backed a series of environmental policy initiatives that raised the
political profile of environmental protection far above anything seen in the
past. If the 1970s can be characterized as a time of sympathetic leaders
heeding the advice of a handful of dedicated reformers, under Arias in the
late-1980s a new environment ministry would broaden the scope of environmental policy, stimulate a series of innovative biodiversity conservation initiatives, and consolidate links with international supporters.

Environmentalists had been pushing for a national regulatory agency
since the late 1970s, when ASCONA protests against air pollution from
the National Cement Factory inspired a legislative proposal to create an
"environmental watchdog agency." The bill did not win legislative approval, but similar efforts under President Oduber set an important precedent for the actions of the Arias administration. Oduber had created a
Consultative Commission on the Environment led by none other than
Oscar Arias, at the time an ambitious young minister of planning. Park
advocates on the commission had pushed for the creation of a new environmental agency to house the park service. "It was very obvious that
having the park system under the Ministry of Agriculture and Livestock
[MAG] was an internal contradiction," recalled Pedro León. "MAG, as the
name implies, is fundamentally concerned with promoting ranching. Its
ministers were mostly ranchers or farmers, and lacked an environmental
perspective" (León 1997). The commission's recommendation for an environment ministry floundered for lack of support from Vice-President
Carlos Manuel Castillo, but a decade later the idea was revived under President Arias, who created a cabinet-level Ministry of Environment, Energy,
and Mines (hereafter the Environment Ministry) and appointed Alvaro
Umaña as its first leader.

Umaña symbolized environmentalism's shift from the margins to the
center of political power. While blue jean-clad park officials like Boza and
Ugalde were often preoccupied with finding a gallon of gas for a stranded
off-road vehicle, Umaña was more likely to be found in a three piece suit,
leading around coteries of international donors. His polished style and
intellectual stature benefited the agency in its early years, as he pushed
through a series of new policy initiatives for biodiversity conservation.

President Arias provided him with political support, but with the administration suffering from budget cutbacks, "he said 'You have my full support, but you won't receive any money—*no un cinco* (not a nickel)," according to an official close to the process (Obando 1997).

In 1987 Umaña secured full funding from the MacArthur Foundation for a new Office on Biodiversity to be led by Rodrigo Gámez. As Umaña's point man on biodiversity, Gámez had the right political credentials. A colleague of Pedro León at the University of Costa Rica, he had the respect of professional biologists and connections to the academic community. He knew Mario Boza from his agronomy studies at CATIE, and he had worked with Luís Fournier, who helped draft the 1969 Forestry Law. As the university representative to the Organization for Tropical Studies, Gámez had been introduced to internationally renown ecologists such as Thomas Lovejoy, Daniel Janzen, and E. O. Wilson. This combination of international and domestic contacts would serve him well in his efforts to strengthen the institutional foundations of biodiversity conservation.

To this end, from 1988 to 1989 the Office on Biodiversity organized a series of meetings involving prominent scientists, public administrators, and environmental advocates. Three pivotal ideas emerged from these discussions. First, participants saw the need for a comprehensive survey of the nation's species, most of which remained unnamed and unknown. Second, they wanted to explore the potential for nondestructive commercial uses of the biological riches protected in the national parks. Third, they saw the need for a major reform of the park system itself. These suggestions led to proposals for the creation of the National Biodiversity Institute (INBio) and the National System of Conservation Areas.

Despite the worldwide publicity accorded rainforest conservation in the late 1980s, the vast majority of the planet's species had yet to be identified (see May 1992). Individual researchers in Costa Rica had undertaken taxonomic studies of one or another species grouping for centuries, but these efforts were uncoordinated and did not provide readily available information on species diversity or biogeographic patterns at a national scale. Biologists associated with the Office on Biodiversity believed that a large-scale project could identify nearly all species in a large region in Costa Rica over a period of five years or more, provided adequate funding was available. In the latter half of the 1980s, the American ecologist Daniel Janzen had been engaged in a successful fundraising effort for the parks—a follow-up to Ugalde's earlier efforts—which demonstrated increasing interest abroad in financing biodiversity initiatives of this sort. Arias created a presidential commission to recommend how a species survey of this magnitude might be organized. Having just succeeded in creating a new ministry in the midst of budget-slashing measures imposed by the International Monetary Fund, commission members shied away from proposals for new governmental structures. An alternative proposal would create an organization within the universities, but Gámez was wary of this approach. Years before he and Pedro León made an unsuccessful bid to create an Institute of Tropical Ecology to coordinate taxonomic research within the university, and the experience convinced Gámez that university settings discourage the sort of broad scientific cooperation required of the new venture (Gámez 1997). Instead in 1989 the commission recommended a private, nonprofit, public-interest association for this purpose. The National Biodiversity Institute (INBio) was established in October of that year.

INBio was an innovative venture in several respects. The All-Taxa Biodiversity Inventory, to be undertaken in the Guanacaste region with a planned budget of $90 million, would be the largest taxonomic undertaking of its kind in history. INBio also sought to identify natural products of potential interest to the private sector, with the goal of generating new sources of funds for the park system and reducing its dependence on the vagaries of foreign donations. INBio adopted a novel approach to taxonomic surveys, hiring unskilled workers from rural areas and training them in the fundamentals of specimen collection. These "parataxonomists" provided high-quality mountings for identification by INBio systematists, who could on occasion draw on the advice of specialists flown in from around the world to help with fine-grain judgment calls.

INBio's extensive facilities and high international profile were big science for a small developing country. With a budget reaching $3.7 million in 1995, the INBio campus had numerous buildings filled with state-of-the-art laboratory equipment, educational displays, and dozens of researchers busily cataloguing their country's natural riches. INBio's Biodiversity Information Management Systems placed 9,000 pages of information on the internet, and scientists and environmentalists the world over came to visit its world-renown facilities (National Biodiversity Institute 1995; Lovejoy 1997; Rivera 1995). Soon INBio staff were providing workshops to share experiences with scientists and policymakers interested in undertaking similar initiatives in Indonesia, Kenya, Madagascar, and Central and South America.

The second major policy initiative emerging during the Arias years was the National System of Conservation Areas (SINAC) (see Vaughan and L. Flormoe 1995). The new conservation areas would resemble the core-buffer zone model long promoted by UNESCO's Man and the Biosphere program, with the old parks constituting the strictly protected core area, and surrounding populated regions comprising a partially protected buffer zone where economic activities were both allowed and actively promoted. Park advocates saw the need to create conservation areas larger than the traditional park design for both ecological and social reasons. Created as isolated patches of habitat, the parks were insufficient in size for the protection of many species including large animals, which often require vast stretches of territory (Newmark 1987). The major impetus for reform, however, was the protracted conflicts surrounding Corcovado National Park, where gold miners and park agency personnel had been embroiled in bitter conflict for years. Janzen, who was involved in the Corcovado debates and was experimenting with regional park management in Guanacaste (see Allen 1988; Lewis 1989), argued that Costa Rica's parks would not survive without greater efforts to involve local communities.

The SINAC idea generated opposition from some park officials, and they actively lobbied legislators to oppose the idea. After working for years to sell the idea of national parks to the Costa Rican public, they feared that replacing parks with conservation areas would dilute public understanding and support. In a political culture that both embraces and warily scrutinizes foreign involvement, there was also resentment surrounding Janzen's role. One of the few bilateral activists of foreign origin, through the INBio and SINAC initiatives Janzen had become more directly and energetically involved in environmental policy formulation than any foreigner to date. Some accused the outspoken ecologist of pushing decentralization to increase control over his "independent republic" in Guanacaste—a characteristic reassertion of the boundary defining the acceptable limits of foreign involvement in the domestic sphere. Nonetheless the conservation areas concept held a special appeal for many

Costa Rican environmentalists. The community outreach component meshed well with Costa Ricans' preference for extensive consultation and dialogue, and the administrative decentralization accompanying SINAC reforms would provide, at least in theory, greater opportunities for local input.

While INBio and park reforms were underway, Environment Minister Umaña solidified ties to the international donor community, and Costa Rica soon emerged as a leader in debt-for-nature swaps. Originally proposed by Thomas Lovejoy and first implemented in Bolivia, debt-for-nature swaps allow environmental organizations to buy private commercial debt at discounted rates and retire the debt in exchange for promises of domestic conservation investments. Though foreign donors had provided Costa Rican parks with short-term relief from the economic crisis of the early 1980s, Costa Rica emerged from those years with the highest per capita foreign debt of any developing country. With the National Parks Foundation in place, strong leadership from Umaña, and the support of Central Bank President Eduardo Lizano, Costa Rica established itself as the "star performer" in debt-for-nature swaps (Jakobeit 1996), receiving one-third of the funds provided to fifteen countries during the early stages of the transfer mechanism.

In February 1988 the seventeenth General Assembly of the International Union for the Conservation of Nature was held in San José, cementing the impression of Costa Rica as a world leader in conservation. Domestically, the political profile of environmental protection received a solid boost with the First Congress on Costa Rica's Strategy for Conservation and Sustainable Development, inaugurated by President Arias in the National Theater in October of that year (Quesada and Solís 1990). The planning document that was the focus of the meeting was ultimately ignored by subsequent administrations, but the process surrounding its creation generated enormous domestic publicity for the environmental cause. Of even greater significance, during this period the Environment Ministry reported that tourism had surpassed coffee and bananas as the country's greatest source of foreign currency and that most tourists came to see the country's national parks. The news undercut economic arguments by sectors unsympathetic to environmental protection. With this news and the support of the enormously popular Oscar Arias, the popular legitimacy of environmental arguments was firmly established.

A New International Ecological Order?

Rafael Calderón, who brought the Social Christian Unity Party into power in 1990, could not match Oscar Arias in profile or popularity. Arias was awarded the Nobel Peace Prize for his role in brokering an end to the conflict in Nicaragua, and he was a hard act follow for policymaking in general and environmental policy in particular. To launch the environmental program of his administration, President Calderón invited the nations of the world to join Costa Rica in establishing a New International Ecological Order. Although this ambitious initiative was later viewed as a flop, Calderón maintained what had become a tradition of presidential support for environmental protection. The Calderón years witnessed a continued ratcheting up of conservation's public appeal and political profile (Gonzales 1997; Vargas 1997).

In 1990 the Calderón administration created an environmental commission in the Ministry of Foreign Relations, to coordinate diplomatic activities in international environmental forums and to promote treaty ratification and implementation at home (Araya 1995). According to an adviser close to Calderón, the commission also aimed to keep Costa Rica in the international limelight where it enjoyed a reputation as a peacekeeper following the Arias Accords. With the end of the Nicaraguan war and the unexpected boom in ecotourism, Calderón saw the environment as a way to maintain the country's favorable image on the world stage. Gabriela Niehaus, the wife of the minister of foreign relations, was placed in charge of environmental policy for the commission, a charge she executed with authority. Prior to the commission's creation, Costa Rican delegates to international environmental meetings had neither concrete strategies nor the necessary coordination with domestic agencies to ensure implementation of international accords. The commission helped establish a professional presence at international meetings and also coordinated government relations with environmental donors (C. M. Rodríguez 1997).

Meanwhile, two congressional aides, Carlos Manuel Rodríguez and Gastón Vargas, came up with an idea for strengthening the administrative capacity of the legislature on environmental matters. Rodríguez was the nephew of the Legislative Assembly president, and he wielded political clout out of proportion to his formal position as an aide. "I realized that with my uncle as president of the congress, I had a chance to have some influence," he recalled. "With the fall of the Berlin Wall, I felt many congressmen were in search of a coherent ideology. I felt they needed an issue like the environment" (C. M. Rodríguez 1997). The two aides convinced one such congressman to introduce legislation creating the Environment Commission of the Legislative Assembly, which served as an important source of environmental policy initiatives in the coming years and inspired similar efforts in other Central American countries. One of the commission's first accomplishments was to pass a constitutional amendment guaranteeing that "every person has the right to a healthy and ecologically balanced environment. Therefore it is legitimate to denounce acts that infringe on this right and to claim redress of any harm caused."

The National Biodiversity Institute received continued, albeit cooler support from the Calderón administration. The institute had faced little political opposition during its formative years, other than some resentment by university scientists and museum curators who had worked for years on research questions and species collections now monopolized by INBio. With Rodrigo Gámez still at the helm, INBio was associated with the president's political opponents in the PLN, but its status as a private organization provided a measure of protection against political chicanery from the Calderón administration (Matamoros 1997). INBio also had Carlos Manuel Rodríguez of the Social Christian Unity Party as its legal adviser, which provided an extra layer of protection. But in September 1991 INBio ran into political trouble from an unanticipated quarter when it announced a "biodiversity prospecting" agreement with the American chemical firm Merck & Co. Under this innovative proposal, INBio would provide extracts from plants, insects, and microbes for drug screening, allowing the company to patent the resulting products. In return, INBio would receive a research and sampling budget of $1.1 million, royalties on commercial projects (half of which would go to the national parks, where most samples were collected), and training in pharmaceutical research (see Blum 1993).

"National Heritage Falls Into Private Hands," ran the headlines after announcement of the Merck deal (Sánchez 1992). With notable similarity to the Alcoa protests two decades earlier, critics argued that INBio was selling off the nation's resources on concessionary terms to a foreign transnational corporation. The controversy was amplified by the international attention given the Merck deal, which came just as delegates from

around the world were debating questions of sovereignty and conservation in preparatory meetings for the Earth Summit and the associated
Convention on Biological Diversity. Domestically, the negative reaction
was heightened by the secrecy surrounding the negotiations, which may
have been necessary to secure a deal with a private firm, but was a faux
pas for a public interest organization in a country obsessed with consultation. Moreover, the Merck agreement rekindled a debate on private
patenting of biodiversity for which the lines had already been drawn, several years earlier, in lower-profile conflicts surrounding a wildlife protection law.

For INBio supporters the public outcry was an ironic turn of events, because the institute was intended to generate commercial uses for biodiversity that would lessen dependence on foreign aid. But the biodiversity
prospecting agreement, like other Costa Rican policy innovations, was a
learning experience—the benefits of which accrue only to those advocates
who stay with the process, in a particular country, over the long haul. Carlos Manuel Rodríguez recalled the imbalanced nature of the early negotiations in Merck offices in the United States. On one side of the negotiating
table, Merck sent in a scientific team to scrutinize the natural products in
question, later a finance team, then a legal team. On the other side of the
table sat Rodríguez, with one INBio scientist at his side, bargaining with
successive waves of Merck negotiators. Ultimately INBio survived the controversy surrounding this first agreement (some argue that the enormous
publicity helped the institute), and indeed flourished, winning the support
of most Costa Rican environmentalists, securing additional biodiversity
prospecting agreements, and exploring ways to move up the chain of
value-added pharmaceutical research.

The Greening of Civil Society

While experts well-versed in the precepts of ecology and well-connected to
centers of power pushed through domestic policy initiatives, interest in environmental themes on the part of the broader Costa Rican public took off
as never before. Beginning in the late 1980s and continuing through the
1990s, hundreds of environmental organizations were formed around the
country, initiating thousands of environmental activities of every variety.[23]
With names like the Sarapiquí Association for Environmental Welfare, the
Children's Alliance for Environmental Protection, the Ecological Rescue

Brigade, Viva la Tierra Institute, and Arbofilia, these groups marched for urban water quality, protested pollution from mining, established environmental libraries in primary schools, led campaigns to reduce consumption of ozone-depleting chemicals, lobbied local governments for watershed protection, and staged theater productions to raise environmental awareness.[24]

Radio programs like "Listen to the Earth," "Nature and Life," and the weekly "Ecological Viewpoint" broadcast environmental messages over the airwaves, complementing a government-sponsored environmental soap opera in which the characters visited different national parks in each episode.[25] Magazines sponsored nature photography contests and the Costa Rican Aquatic Conservation Association set up a "blue telephone" line for citizens to report illegal dumping in fresh water and oceans. National congresses were held to coordinate the activities of dozens of high school and college environmental clubs springing up around the country. The Association of Protected Areas Volunteers led environmental education campaigns, while others formed a Humanist Ecology Party.[26] Particularly as the Earth Summit drew near, environmentalism was embraced by groups outside the environmental camp. Artists presented works celebrating the beauty of nature, the Federation of Professional and Entrepreneurial Women held a conference on nontimber paper sources, breweries ran television commercials against littering, and housing advertisements enticed potential buyers with the slogan "Live near to nature" (Arroyo 1996; Zuñiga 1991).

Against this backdrop of social interest, a dozen or so groups emerged as leaders of the nongovernmental movement. With professional staff in San José and ample foreign funding, the new NGOs shared a keen interest in affecting government policy. Staffed by a young generation in their twenties and thirties, these environmental advocates had little connection to the early struggles for national parks or the protests against the transcontinental pipeline in the 1970s. The new generation of environmentalists differed from their predecessors in another important respect: in addition to the traditional core of natural scientists, they held many attorneys in their ranks. The University of Costa Rica had established an environmental law emphasis for students in the late 1980s, and a cadre of committed graduates such as Roxana Salazar, Eugenia Wo Ching, and Jorge Cabrera were eager to turn governmental rhetoric into reality. They helped form organizations like the Environment and Natural Resources Law Center, which provided training seminars for judges, prosecutors, forest inspectors, and city officials—authorities whose ignorance of environmental laws and regulations impeded effective implementation of the country's environmental statutes (Wo Ching 1997). The Ambio Foundation undertook legal research and advocacy, while Justice for Nature focused on litigation, taking government authorities and private parties to court for environmental infractions.

While these groups pursued legal reforms, other environmental NGOs worked with or against government authorities to improve environmental quality. The Association for the Preservation of Wild Flora and Fauna began as a group of friends protesting construction of the Guápiles highway and went on to organize citizen patrols of national parks, bringing in hundreds of volunteers to monitor hunting and logging practices. The Organization for Tropical Studies arranged retreats for newly elected politicians and mid-level managers, providing instruction and facilitating bipartisan discussions of environmental themes. Later the organization trained environmental NGOs in Honduras, El Salvador, Panama, and Bolivia who were interested in arranging similar retreats for elected officials in their countries (J. M. Rodríguez 1997). The Neotrópico Foundation teamed up with agricultural credit institutions to provide farmers with incentives for tree conservation, and the Costa Rican Ecology Association led a successful campaign to prevent a subsidiary of Stone Container Corporation from establishing a wood chip mill in the Osa peninsula.[27] Before long these groups joined together to form FECON, a national alliance of environmental organizations.

A sign of maturity in the movement was its differentiation into various philosophical creeds and tactical preferences (Ramírez 1997; A. León 1997; Montoya 1997; Leach 1992). Some preferred grassroots mobilization of campesinos and shunned direct collaboration with the government, while others were more comfortable roaming the halls of congress with information packets in hand. Philosophically, those drawing on leftist traditions associated with liberation theology linked environmental concerns to a critique of neoliberal economics and social injustice. Others went to great lengths to distance themselves from the left, sensitive to accusations that environmentalists were simply *comunistas reciclados* (recycled communists). All of these groups lost at least as many battles as they won, confronted with a weak state regulatory apparatus and powerful lobbies from private interests in mining, bananas, coffee, cattle, and forestry. They suffered from the inevitable organizational challenges of nonprofit and volunteer work, and at times even their physical safety was in question.[28] Despite these challenges, by the early 1990s environmental NGOs were having a palpable impact on the creation and effectiveness of public policy.

While these events unfolded domestically, on the international stage tiny Costa Rica was only a marginal player at the Earth Summit. A small delegation led by INBio's Rodrigo Gámez steered a middle course in debates over the Convention on Biological Diversity, disagreeing with both the strict national control position favored by G-77 leaders and the open access position of the United States. Costa Rican delegates also felt the treaty placed too much emphasis on technology transfer and not enough on building domestic scientific capacity in poor countries. In the end Costa Rica signed the treaty for the simple reason that it was already doing most of what the convention required. Although Costa Rica was already a recognized environmental leader in 1992 (the renown plant systematist Peter Raven dubbed its park system "one of the great accomplishments of the human race over the last thirty years" [quoted in Wallace 1992: xvi]), Costa Rica lacked either the inclination or the ability to parlay its reputation into a leadership role at Rio. The North-South confrontations that dominated the Earth Summit were led, as Gámez (1997) put it, by "the United States, Brazil and India, with all their lawyers." International press coverage and academic analyses of the negotiation process understandably highlighted the traditional heavyweights of G-77 diplomacy (see Miller 1995), missing the story of those actually implementing the ideas contained in these international agreements.

Ecology Comes of Age: The Figueres Years

Although conservation had received fairly consistent presidential support since the early 1970s, environmental advocates the world over were taken by surprise when newly elected President José Figueres Ferrer, the son of the country's founder, announced that *desarrollo sostenible* (sustainable development) would be the guiding principle for his entire administration. As the first official act of his presidency, Figueres organized From Forest to Society, an all-day event celebrating environmental themes. Every mem-

ber of the presidential cabinet—from the minister of agriculture and livestock to the minister of transportation and public works—presented plans
describing how their respective agencies would promote development
strategies consonant with environmental quality. With foreign environmental dignitaries like Maurice Strong and Kenton Miller in attendance,
Figueres made sure that the country—and the world—understood his in-
tentions with respect to the environment.

"In the course of the campaign for the presidency, we saw that the traditional social democratic idea was no longer viable," explained Environment Minister René Castro (1997):

> So a group including campaign director Carlos Espinach, the second vice-
> president, the minister of education, president of the social security fund, myself
> and others discussed possible new strategies. Of all the new frameworks suggested,
> sustainable development seemed to make the most sense, both for the country and
> for the party. We needed an alternative vision of the future, and did not want to re-
> peat the story of APRA in Peru and all the other social democratic parties that have
> fallen by the wayside.

The strategy was also clearly intended to attract the attention of foreign
donors and tourist industries—to continue the influx of *oro verde* (green
gold) that began in the mid-1980s. But Figueres was not disingenuous, and
he held the respect of Costa Rica's leading environmentalists. His announcement caught them off guard, as environmental themes had not
figured prominently in his campaign, but organizations like INBio
quickly went to work helping the new administration to elaborate policy
strategies.

Bipartisan alliances were essential to the success of Figueres's ambitious
environmental agenda. Just as the alliance between Mario Boza and Alvaro Ugalde had ensured continued support for the park system, prior to
the elections a deal was struck between the PLN's René Castro and Carlos
Manuel Rodríguez of the rival PUSC. Castro was part of Figueres's inner
circle and was slated to become environment minister pending a PLN victory. Rodríguez, as the nephew of the PUSC presidential candidate, was
expected to occupy the same post if his party won. The two men shared a
similar outlook on environmental policy, and each would need support of
the opposition party when in power. They struck an informal agreement
that whoever won the election would bring the other along to work in his
ministry. True to the agreement, six months after the PLN victory, Castro
phoned Rodríguez to discuss a role for the latter in his ministry, in return

for Rodríguez's help in rallying conservative support in the congress, where the PLN lacked a majority (C. M. Rodríguez 1997).

The Figueres administration launched a number of new environmental policy initiatives. Castro explored new ways to finance conservation, and he hoped to eventually charge the national power company and private ecotourist outfits for ecosystem services provided by the national parks. He experimented with differential pricing for foreign and Costa Rican park visitors, provoking an outcry from the tourist sector that forced a partial reversal, but succeeding in generating new revenues. The administration also negotiated a series of joint implementation agreements allowing foreign companies to invest in tropical forest conservation in return for climate change mitigation credits. The Environment Ministry phased out leaded gasoline and launched the *Ecomárchamo* program to begin the arduous task of cleaning up San José's polluted air. President Figueres created the Advisory Commission on Biodiversity (COABIO), a group of experts providing guidance to the administration on implementation of the Convention on Biological Diversity. Housed in the National Biodiversity Institute, COABIO soon became the nation's most important source of biodiversity policy initiatives. Meanwhile park system administrators worked to consolidate the decentralization reforms initiated under Arias, while the Legislative Assembly was the site of hotly contested initiatives on forest management and biodiversity.

Policy Reforms of the 1990s
The 1969 Forestry Law underwent a series of reforms in the 1990s, prompted by a Constitutional Chamber decision invalidating certain of its provisions as unconstitutional infringements on private property. Environmentalists saw this as an opportunity to create a new piece of legislation to regulate timber use in sensitive areas outside park boundaries. Nominally, the old forestry law had established a permit system allowing state supervision of private forest practices, while in reality weak enforcement resulted in a dramatic reduction in primary forest cover. After several years of debate, the legislature approved the new Forestry Law in 1996 (see MINAE et al. 1996; Grosko and Ward 1996). From an environmental standpoint, the new law represented an improvement in certain respects. With funding from a recent gasoline tax, it provided tax credits to landowners willing to forgo timber activities for twenty years. But the law

was considered a defeat for environmentalists and a victory for the timber industry, which weakened penalties for infractions and defeated a strict "Ley Culpa" bill that would have banned logging in undisturbed primary forests.

The Forestry Law was a bitter learning experience for the new environmental groups. For years park advocates had protected species habitats without provoking an organized response from the timber industry. Confronted with proposals to regulate the sector as a whole, however, the industry threw its full political weight into the legislative ring. The national alliance of environmental organizations, FECON, had hired two specialists to lobby legislators full time, but they were outnumbered and outgunned by the forestry lobby. "The Forestry Chamber knows a lot of people in congress," lamented the young lawyer who led the fight for FECON. "They have the personal contacts" (Rolando Castro 1997). But FECON also lacked experience. They became involved too late in the process, had no proactive position, and were unpracticed in the art of congressional influence (Barquero 1997).

Efforts to pass a biodiversity law provided further evidence that in Costa Rica, conservation policies live or die by their proponents' ability to navigate the political terrain. In 1994 the Environment Commission of the Legislative Assembly had become, in its creator's words, "a rifle firing in different directions," as congressman Luís Martínez used it as a weapon in a personal rivalry with Environment Minister Castro. Martínez approached Vivienne Solís of IUCN, asking for help in drafting biodiversity legislation. They prepared a bill that would establish strong state controls over the use of biological resources and would have a chilling effect on future biodiversity prospecting agreements. It would also create a new biodiversity regulatory authority that would diminish the role of the Environment Ministry. Minister Castro was outraged and accused the international organization of interfering in domestic affairs. He threatened to revoke IUCN's charter in Costa Rica, prompting the director of what is arguably the world's most powerful environmental organization to fly in from its headquarters in Switzerland to make amends. The American Embassy in San José was notified of the incident (Obando 1997; Lahmann 1997; Petricone 1996).

Having neutralized the IUCN team, Castro put COABIO to work full time on alternative legislation. COABIO had several seasoned political veterans in its ranks, in contrast to the inexperienced group that lost the

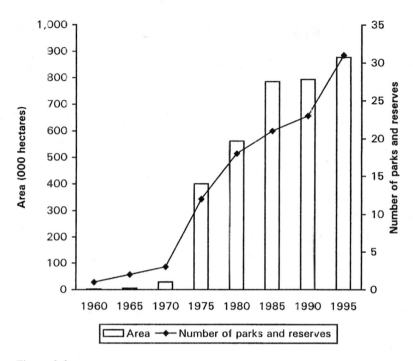

Figure 3.3
Cumulative growth of Costa Rica's national parks and biological reserves. Source.
Ministry of Environment and Energy 1997. Note. Includes marine areas.

fight over the forestry law. COABIO member Alfio Piva had long experience with congress and had many contacts among both the "generation of
'48" and the young political leadership. He had also grown up in the same
neighborhood as Martínez. When the congressman appeared unlikely to
agree to changes in the law favored by COABIO, Piva resorted to arm-
twisting Costa Rican style, talking with neighbors and business leaders in
Martínez's neighborhood. "I think everyone has a small group they care
about regarding their reputation," explained Piva (1997). Soon thereafter
Martínez introduced a new version of the bill incorporating several of
COABIO's suggestions.

The national park system had grown steadily over the years (figure 3.3),
but the administrative reforms first proposed under Arias were slow in
coming. Several legislative proposals to institute the transition from parks
to conservation areas failed to win support, and the Martínez-Castro rivalry made further legislative initiatives unlikely in the Figueres years.
So the national park service took the unusual step of proceeding with

sweeping administrative reforms absent legal backing. The wildlife and forestry departments were combined with the park service and placed under the new National System of Conservation Areas (SINAC). Earlier attempts to consolidate these agencies had met with fierce resistance from wildlife and forestry officials, but the new SINAC director, Raúl Solórzano, was a skilled political mediator who brokered a solution acceptable to agency leaders. SINAC reorganized the park system into ten conservation areas, each with a regional council designed to enhance community involvement.

By 1997 it was unclear whether Costa Rica's latest conservation experiment could meet its goals. The SINAC initiative amounted to a wish list of policy reforms, including administrative decentralization, popular participation, ecosystem management, species protection, and the integration of forestry and wildlife goals. Privately, ecologists expressed concern that foresters, with their traditional disregard for ecosystem integrity, now had greater say in the management of protected areas. It also remained to be seen whether the regional councils would provide meaningful opportunities for local input or simply rubber stamp the directives of park authorities.

President Figueres devoted more attention to the environmental cause than had any head of state in Costa Rican history. Indeed the political rhetoric of sustainability had reached such high levels that ordinary Costa Ricans—and more than a few environmental activists—began to roll their eyes in response to Figueres's ongoing environmental discourse, which more often than not appeared designed for foreign consumption. The Figueres administration unquestionably succeeded in attracting international attention. In addition to Costa Rica's leadership in debt-for-nature swaps, joint implementation projects, and ecotourism, it was among the first recipients of Global Environment Facility funds, received millions of dollars in foreign support for INBio, and was given $100 million through the Dutch Bilateral Convention on Sustainable Development to support the activities of NGOs. But while the environment had become big business and high politics, environmental advocates took it upon themselves to ensure that pronouncements were matched by practice. A poignant example is provided in a nine-page letter written to Figueres by one of the park system's founders, Alvaro Ugalde, in January 1997. Complaining of illegal hunting, staffing shortages, impacts of ecotourism, and the misappropriation of park entrance fees, Ugalde (1997b) wrote:

The prestige bestowed upon Costa Rica, which has inspired the tourism we are enjoying, the donations and rewards we receive, the prestige of INBio and other benefits, always has and always will be based on the presupposition that, beginning in 1970, Costa Rica has undertaken real, tangible, and measurable efforts to improve not only the protection, but every aspect of its protected areas system. . . . Mr. President, when in August of last year you dedicated national parks week to a celebration of the accomplishments of Daniel Oduber, I felt great pride and thanks for your gesture. . . . Nonetheless, I have no doubt that the best way to honor the work of Daniel, of [your father] and other presidents, is to maintain and improve these accomplishments, not just dedicate days, weeks and ceremonies.

Ugalde sent copies of his letter to former presidents and to the environmental community. Mobilizing his network of domestic contacts, he consulted Oduber's widow for advice on his dealings with the president and convinced former President Oscar Arias to press the case before Figueres's finance minister. Ugalde threatened to act through congress if necessary, and had students ready to mobilize on behalf of the parks (Ugalde 1997a). In April of that year Environment Minister Castro announced plans to mitigate the new threats to the parks (McPhaul 1997).

The foregoing history should make clear that conservation in Costa Rica has been neither a rosy picture nor an unqualified success (see Boza, Jukofsky, and Willie 1995). Bureaucratic infighting, incursions by powerful foreign firms, economic crises, population pressures, border skirmishes, congressional inertia, and weak judicial enforcement all have and will continue to challenge efforts to create effective institutions for the conservation of biological diversity. This is precisely why it is so impressive that despite these hurdles, Costa Ricans have been able to achieve what are on balance very impressive results. Nevertheless one wonders what conservation politics would look like if Costa Rica were not a major ecotourist destination. What would it look like in a country that lacks such an enormous foreign scientific presence, suffers levels of poverty more typical of developing nations and where political stability cannot be taken for granted? Insights into these questions can be gained by taking a close look at the history of conservation policymaking in Bolivia, where one of the poorest countries in the Western Hemisphere has emerged as a leader in tropical conservation.

Bolivia

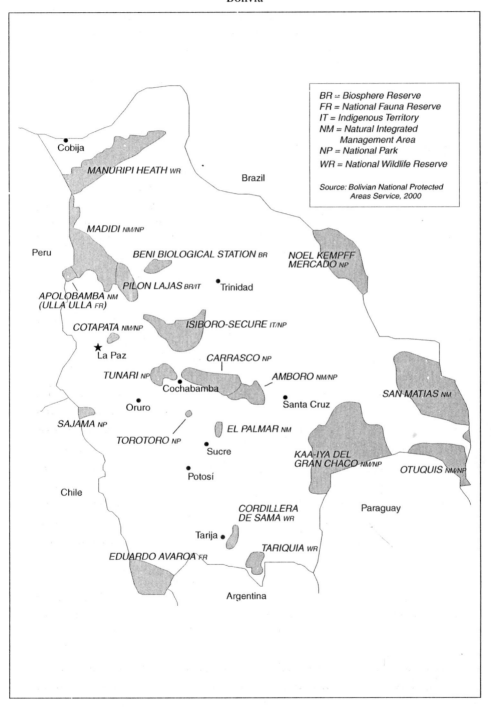

BR = Biosphere Reserve
FR = National Fauna Reserve
IT = Indigenous Territory
NM = Natural Integrated
Management Area
NP = National Park
WR = National Wildlife Reserve

Source: Bolivian National Protected
Areas Service, 2000

Cobija

MANURIPI HEATH WR

Brazil

MADIDI NM/NP

Peru

BENI BIOLOGICAL STATION BR

NOEL KEMPFF
MERCADO NP

PILON LAJAS BR/IT

Trinidad

APOLOBAMBA NM
(ULLA ULLA FR)

COTAPATA NM/NP

ISIBORO-SECURE IT/NP

La Paz

CARRASCO NP

TUNARI NP

Cochabamba

AMBORO NM/NP

SAN MATIAS NM

Oruro

Santa Cruz

SAJAMA NP

EL PALMAR NM

TOROTORO NP

Sucre

KAA-IYA DEL
GRAN CHACO NM/NP

OTUQUIS NM/NP

Potosí

Chile

Paraguay

CORDILLERA
DE SAMA WR

Tarija

TARIQUIA WR

EDUARDO AVAROA FR

Argentina

4

Environmental Leadership: The Bolivian Example

It is common in Latin America to say that we are in a profound crisis of creativity, that we have run out of paradigms, that we have run out of many of our dreams. . . . Suddenly, however, some windows have opened—not the great windows of the utopian '60s, but windows of a more pragmatic nature, with the arrival of environmental concerns. . . .
—Jorge Cortés, 1991[1]

[W]e recommend education and consciousness-raising among the general population; in the exercise of individual liberty we can accomplish through personal convictions that which the laws cannot achieve by force.
—Senators Eudoro Galindo and Enrique Quintela, 1991[2]

In 1990 a small charter plane circled over southeastern Bolivia, carrying several of the world's foremost biologists. Pilot Hermes Justiniano was bringing the researchers in for a closer look at the tropical dry forests of the Chaco region in one of the first missions of Conservation International's Rapid Assessment Program. The idea was to assemble an elite group of experts who could in a matter of weeks complete species diversity assessments that would usually require the efforts of numerous scientists over many years. Though the Chaco was known to be an area of exceptional biological diversity, the team was unprepared for what they found:

. . . the large area between the Río Parapetí and the Paraguayan border encompasses what is probably the last remaining nearly pristine chaco vegetation left on earth. None of us had previously seen chaco dry forest in such excellent condition. . . . Our findings on this trip lead us to believe that what is usually thought of as typical chaco elsewhere is actually greatly modified. (Parker et al. 1993: 8)

Bolivia is one of the world's most biologically diverse nations, with a rich variety of ecosystems ranging from cerrado woodland to thorn forests to lowland rainforests. It possesses up to a third of all the bird species found in the neotropics, and it has the seventh highest number of flowering plant species of any country in Asia, Africa, and Latin America. Just as Bolivia is rich in species, it is one of the most culturally diverse countries in Latin America. One can gain an appreciation for the complexity of Bolivian society and ecology with a perspective sweeping east to west across the northern half of the country. Viewed from that same small airplane, such a perspective would begin over the gallery forests and cerrado savannas adjacent to Brazil and move across the vast Bolivian Amazon, home to indigenous groups like the Movima and Yuracaré. It then reaches the Yungas, the lowland hills where Bolivian soldiers scour the land in search of coca plantations, at the insistence of the U.S. State Department. Continuing westward, a dramatic ascent into the Andes takes the viewer over peaks reaching 19,000 feet into highland plains inhabited by wild camelid species and dotted with Aymara villages, where people conduct their daily affairs in a language predating the Incan Empire. The view then descends into a large bowl containing the world's highest political capital, La Paz, site of the Burnt Palace (*Palacio Quemado*)—a fitting name for the seat of government in a country that experienced 188 coups d'état between 1825 and 1982. Returning eastward across the southern portion of the country, the ancient mines of Potosí come into view, where thousands of slaves died while extracting silver for Spanish overseers, and where today mining families live in poverty following International Monetary Fund (IMF) mandated closures of inefficient state mining operations. Then back to the dry expanse of the Chaco—home to Guaraní indigenous communities and the site of one of many territorial wars between Bolivia and its neighbors— and up finally to the Pantanal, South America's largest wetland. Such is the diverse panorama that Bolivian environmental policy reformers have to bear in mind.

From a social and political standpoint, Bolivia is as far removed from Costa Rica as one can get within Latin America. Costa Rica is a small, highly educated country where over 90 percent of the people are of Spanish or mixed Spanish-indigenous descent. In contrast, over 60 percent of the people inhabiting Bolivia's large territory identify ethnically and linguistically with indigenous communities. Bolivia is among the world's poorest countries, ranking 116 on the United Nations Human Development Index, and its social divisions—between highlander (*Kolla*) and lowlander (*Camba*), rich and poor, modern and traditional—are more palpable. Costa Rica has no standing army, while the military figures prominently in Bolivia's political history. The Costa Rican state was born on the fringes of the Spanish Empire, while Bolivia was at its center. By most measures, Bolivia is the "tougher" case—there are glaring examples of failed initiatives, and its successes have come against great odds. The two countries, however, share something in common: a remarkable record of policy innovation and leadership in biodiversity conservation. And in common with Costa Rica, the Bolivian policy reformers spearheading these efforts have always practiced the protean brand of activism central to this study—drawing on foreign ideas, well-connected in international circles, but at the same time deeply immersed in domestic politics and culture.

Bolivia's environmental history may be understood in the first instance as a series of dogged efforts by an environmental community navigating complex political developments—from indigenous movements to military coups, drug wars, and democratization—and parlaying these into opportunities for conservation. The other story running through the history to follow is the changing shape of the environmental community itself. What started as a few isolated individuals evolved into a small but tight-knit group in the late 1970s and within a decade developed into a social movement attracting the participation of thousands, from high school students to union organizers, military leaders, business magnates, and Catholic priests.

Green Quixotes: The Early Years

Government decrees for natural resource conservation date back to the earliest years of the Bolivian Republic, when the revolutionary leader Simón Bolívar banned all hunting of wild vicuñas in 1825 (Heinrich and Eguivar 1991). Numerous such decrees were issued throughout the nineteenth and early twentieth centuries, and while the historical record is too scant to conclude that these were entirely ineffective, it is clear that this steady march of paper proclamations left no institutional foundation for the wildlife conservation advocates of the 1960s. The small number of Bolivians concerned with conservation during this period had to start from scratch.

One remarkable early accomplishment in this regard was an effort spearheaded by Armando Cardozo in the 1960s to protect the remaining populations of vicuñas, a wild camelid species related to the domesticated llama. Cardozo received his training in animal physiology and livestock management in the United States and at the Inter-American Institute for Agricultural Sciences in Costa Rica. He had been studying the timid creatures in the Bolivian Andes since the 1950s, and he was alarmed to learn in the mid-1960s that their populations were declining rapidly throughout the mountainous habitats of Bolivia, Peru, and Ecuador. The primary threat in Bolivia was overhunting, often by peasants using automatic weapons distributed during the National Revolution of 1952. Concerned that the vicuña was headed for extinction, in 1968 Cardozo traveled to Argentina to learn more about national parks at a conference sponsored by the International Union for the Conservation of Nature (IUCN). In the cafes of Barilochi, Argentina, he engaged in a series of discussions with three South American colleagues: the Chilean botanist Carlos Muñoz, an Argentinean agricultural expert, and most importantly, Felipe Benavides, the wealthy and well-connected pioneer of Peru's conservation movement.

The four men sought to launch a coordinated international effort to protect remaining vicuña populations, and they debated the specific form this might take. They agreed that a major obstacle was the ease with which hunters could manipulate customs regulations and move the animals across borders to evade regulatory authorities. "We decided to do something through the government," recalled Cardozo (1997), and this particular group stood in a good position to do just that. Cardozo was director general of the ministry of agriculture in the military government of General René Barrientos. Benavides, very much Cardozo's senior, had friends stretching from the Dutch royalty to the presidential palaces of South America.

Cardozo's plan to regulate vicuña exports received lukewarm support from the minister of agriculture, and he was unable to gain an audience with General Barrientos. But if the norm was stiff resistance against foreign lobbying on matters of conservation, Benavides was clearly the exception:

Early one morning Felipe Benavides came from Peru and visited my office, asking me whether I had spoken with General Barrientos regarding the vicuña. I explained that I had not, because I held an inferior rank. Felipe said "Okay, I'll speak with

Barrientos," and by 10 a.m. he had arranged a meeting with the president. At 1:30 p.m. I was at home having lunch with my family, when the phone rang. It was the minister of agriculture, saying "*Doctor,* I received an urgent call from the president, who tells me you have a proposal regarding the vicuña." A presidential decree banning the export of vicuña was issued within ten days. (Cardozo 1997)

Cardozo and Benavides worried that the decree was insufficient—what was needed was an international treaty banning all trade in vicuñas. The opportunity arose in 1969, after General Barrientos died in a mysterious plane crash and the national populist General Alfredo Ovando assumed the presidency. Ovando supported the idea of an international convention, leading Bolivia and Peru to conclude the Treaty of La Paz, which spawned subsequent treaties involving Chile and Argentina. This initiative predated the well-known Convention on International Trade in Endangered Species (CITES), which the South Americans agreed to join on the condition that it would not supersede their treaty. The Treaty of La Paz was enacted despite protests from European zoos, which argued that they needed to import vicuñas for their collections and threatened to retaliate by banning animal exports to the zoos of treaty signatories (Cardozo 1997).

As in Costa Rica, the 1972 United Nations Conference on the Human Environment—often claimed by scholars to mark the beginning of a broad-based international environmental movement—went unnoticed by Bolivia's early environmentalists. Instead they focused their attention on the creation of a protected area devoted exclusively to vicuña conservation. This effort was initiated by a little-known figure, Juan Nogales, who sought to protect the animals from extinction. Though the nature aficionado had little interest in military affairs, to receive logistical support from the government of General Hugo Bánzer, Nogales would need to secure some form of military rank. As is the case throughout Bolivian environmental history, personal contacts made all the difference. Nogales's brother was a retired military official, the same minister of agriculture under whom Cardozo had served some years before. The former minister approached Cardozo on his brother's behalf, and Cardozo arranged to have Nogales appointed as a police captain and assigned a vehicle for patrolling the new Ulla-Ulla National Fauna Reserve, which remains an important protected area for vicuñas.[3] As a result of the reserve and the ban on international trade, vicuña populations rebounded from roughly 1,000 individuals in the late 1960s to 4,493 in 1981 and 33,844 in 1996 (DNCB 1996; Cardozo 1997; U.S. Department of Interior 1999).

Actions to save the vicuña were a rare success story during a period of scant domestic interest in conservation. The few who voiced such concerns had been exposed to environmental ideas from abroad, often as science students in foreign universities. One of these early pioneers was Wagner Terrazas, who in 1973 wrote a book entitled *Bolivia: Pillaged Country.*

Most nations, even those considered conservative, have put into place appropriate measures for the defense of their natural resources. These policies have translated into militant actions for the "conservation of renewable natural resources," a position that clearly contrasts with that of Bolivia, where the indiscriminate sacking of these goods is permitted—a situation, moreover, that alarms no one. (Terrazas 1973: 91)

As a fisheries expert trained at the University of Michigan, Terrazas frequently pointed to the experiences of other nations, warning of an impending "dust bowl" in eastern Bolivia and complaining that "in Bolivia, we have been late to create reserves for defending plants and animals from extermination, the only functioning reserve to date being the Ulla-Ulla Fauna Reserve." Terrazas sought, however, to develop a conservation ethic appropriate to his country. He complained that Bolivian elites "try to imitate other peoples, as occurred earlier with the French, then with the Germans and lately with the North Americans, Russians and Chinese" (Terrazas 1973: 134, 94). To make conservation resonate with popular domestic concerns, he touted a new conception of land reform,

. . . based on the idea that "the land belongs to those who work it and take care of it," complementing the oft-repeated slogan of the Mexican leader Emiliano Zapata. However, because our campesinos need measures corresponding to the reality in which they live, it seems necessary to revitalize the concept of *Pacha Mama*, Eternal Mother of the Earth, explaining that she will not be eternal if she is destroyed as is currently the custom. (Terrazas 1973: 135)

While Terrazas and other agricultural experts like Percy Baptista and Manuel Posnansky tried with little success to push a conservation agenda within the Ministry of Agriculture, far away from the mountainous capital the naturalist Noel Kempff led a one-man campaign from his home in the eastern frontier city of Santa Cruz de la Sierra.[4] Founder of the Santa Cruz Municipal Zoo, Kempff is best remembered for his work as the director of Urban Parks and Gardens, covering the city with thousands of trees to delight residents with tropical blooms of every color and variety. When not planting trees, Kempff planted the seeds for a national parks movement. In 1964 he warned of "the danger of unrestricted exploitation" of wildlife, arguing that "we must regulate this exploitation without further delay . . . establishing forest reserves in which hunting is banned at least during the reproductive season."[5]

Kempff had the domestic political connections needed for such an undertaking. One family member was vice-president of the Senate, a contact Kempff used in an attempt to introduce legislation creating three national parks in the late 1960s. When his bill floundered for lack of congressional support, he turned to his brother, Rolando, who in the early 1970s occupied a high post in the government of General Hugo Bánzer. Kempff used the opportunity to propose two new national parks. In a series of written correspondences during this period, Rolando reported on the status of the proposals within the Bánzer administration, advising his brother on matters of political strategy (Kempff 1972). Using yet another channel, in 1971 Kempff wrote to his friend Baldemar Melgar, urging him to use his connections to Trinidad mayor General Vaca Medrano, to push for the creation of a tropical bird refuge near Trinidad in the Bolivian Amazon (Melgar 1971; Kempff 1971).

Kempff melded his domestic political resources with the assets of conservation allies abroad. He maintained regular correspondence in French, Spanish, and Portuguese with scientists from around the world, including María Buchinger in the United States and the prominent Brazilian environmentalist Paulo Nogueira-Neto. "I was recently elected member of the board of IUCN," wrote Nogueira-Neto in June 1970, "which could be useful for the cause of nature conservation in Bolivia." Kempff encouraged foreign conservation experts to visit Bolivia to help with his plan. In October 1967 Harold Edgard Strang, a natural resource consultant in the Brazilian Institute of Agrarian Reform, recommended that "really you should travel to the United States to take a course on national parks," and Jean-Paul Harroy of IUCN wrote from Brussels in 1968 to suggest they meet. This was apparently a time of increasing transnational collaboration among South American conservationists, as Strang mentioned an upcoming roundtable on nature conservation to take place in Río in December 1967 and another in Argentina the following year. From Argentina, Wilhelm Kenning sent Kempff a bibliography on national parks and an address list of North American environmental groups that he might contact for help (Nogueira-Neto 1970; Strang 1967; Harroy 1968; Kenning 1970).

The culmination of Kempff's international networking was the Fourth Conference on Amazonian Fauna and Flora, which he hosted in Santa Cruz de la Sierra in October 1971 to focus national attention on the need for protected areas in Bolivia. "The Amazon must be preserved," declared Kempff in a speech before the assembly of foreign scientist-activists.[6] María Buchinger shared experiences from conservation in the United States, while Cristóbal Bonifaz, founder of the Charles Darwin Foundation in Ecuador, "promised to send from Ecuador copies of all current legislation in order to provide ideas to the government of Bolivia when it legislates for the protection of Amazonian fauna and flora."[7] The scientists publicized earlier findings that outbreaks of hemorrhagic fever in the Amazon were precipitated by overhunting of wild feline species, which boosted populations of pathogen-carrying rodents. After the conference Kempff escorted a group of foreign scientists to Trinidad to talk up the importance of his proposed bird refuge.

Articles and letters in support of conservation filled local Santa Cruz newspapers over the coming weeks. An editorial in *El Deber* expressed the hope that demands for government action to protect Amazonian wildlife would "not fall on deaf ears,"[8] and the political impact of the conference was significant given the general lack of support for conservation during this time. Two government ministers attended, including Colonel José Gil Reyes, minister of agriculture and campesino affairs, who promised to search for solutions to deforestation and unregulated hunting. More importantly, the effort inspired the municipality of Trinidad to propose to the central government the creation of Kempff's long-sought bird sanctuary. The 1,500 hectare reserve was created by order of President Bánzer and inaugurated in 1971 in a ceremony attended by the president and Kempff's contact, mayor General Vaca.[9] Kempff also attributed to the conference Bánzer's decision to support his second pet project, declaring Germán Busch Nature Reserve (later renamed Amboró National Park) in 1973.

These sporadic accomplishments were the exception in the 1970s, which may be considered the lost decade for conservation in Bolivia. At a time when Costa Rica was cultivating foreign financial and technical support for a wide variety of conservation initiatives, little occurred in the heart of South America. These were the years of the Bánzer dictatorship (1971–1978), followed by a period of political instability and government crackdowns on the democratic opposition from 1978 to 1982. It was not that autocracy was incompatible with advances in environmental policy; although popular mobilization would have been difficult, it is clear from earlier efforts to protect the vicuña that with the right political connections, environmentalists could make gains. (Indeed, ratification of the Treaty of La Paz was an uncomplicated matter absent an independent legislature.) Rather, it was more difficult for Bolivian environmentalists to receive support from the nascent environmental movements of Europe and the United States. Foreign environmental organizations were loath to establish relations with a dictatorial regime, whether for philosophical or logistical reasons.[10]

This was clearly the case with the Ecology Institute, the organization that would help lay the foundation for a national environmental movement and corresponding changes in government policy in the years to come. During a meeting of the United Nations Man and the Biosphere Program held in La Paz in 1974, Bolivians made important contacts with biologists from Germany's University of Göttingham, who offered to fund and train a Bolivian organization devoted exclusively to the study of ecology. The proposal was postponed for years, however, because students at the University of Göttingham protested the idea of providing aid to the Bánzer dictatorship. Isolated during the formative years of environmental movements in industrialized countries, Bolivia lacked an institutional basis for transnational environmental relations until the early 1980s.

Laying the Institutional Foundation for an Environmental Movement

When asked about the origins of their country's environmental movement, Bolivian observers will typically begin by describing the historical development of academic programs in the ecological sciences. The founding of Bolivia's first degree-granting programs in biology in La Paz and Cochabamba in the early to mid-1970s created a cadre of citizens who not only cared about conservation, but had the ecological training to back it up. Many of those who would later become leading figures in the Bolivian environmental movement—including Mario Baudoin, Arturo Moscoso, Alexandra Sánchez de Lozada, Juan Pablo Arce, Carlos Quintela, and Carmen Miranda—first met through these new programs in the biological sciences. Moreover, for the first time these classmates and professors constituted an interacting community of concern, whereas the earlier generation of conservationists had only minimal coordinated planning among them.

The institutional pillar of this community was the Ecology Institute, established at the Universidad Mayor de San Andrés in 1978 with support from the University of Göttingham after General Bánzer announced plans for elections. Over the next two decades the Ecology Institute would serve as a central meeting place for foreign and domestic scientists, and it would provide a new generation of Bolivian environmentalists access to international scientific and financial networks. The country's environmental history cannot be divorced from its political history, however, as Ecology Institute scientists learned in their struggle to survive the coups and countercoups of the post-Bánzer period. When García Meza took power in 1980, the military shut down the university, confiscated equipment and materials, and replaced the Ecology Institute's leaders, accusing them of collaboration with the democratic opposition movement (UDP). Cecile de Morales, director of the institute when the coup occurred, recalled the events of July 17, 1980:

At the time I was leading a group of students in field studies near La Paz. We left early in the morning and didn't know about the coup. There had been a coup in Trinidad, but not in La Paz. We returned to the city at 2:00 p.m., to find barricades and tanks in the streets. I was responsible for the students, and was concerned about getting them home safely. With twelve students packed in my car, I drove them to the university in the center of town so that they could at least walk home. (de Morales 1997)

In the early years, the institute's scientists focused on research rather than activism, undertaking species surveys, revamping taxonomic collections, and contributing to agricultural projects. Scientists did try to raise public environmental awareness through a series of conferences held in Cochabamba, Cobija, and La Paz in the early 1980s. But if the Ecology Institute spawned a community of conservation-oriented scientists, the watershed event for the development of a community of activists per se was the founding in 1985 of the Environmental Defense League (LIDEMA), one of the first national alliances of environmental organizations to appear in Latin America. From that point on a growing number of scientists "came out of the laboratories, to also get involved in changing society" (de Morales 1997).

There were a few scattered precedents for civic environmentalism prior to this period. The Bolivian Ecology Society (SOBE), established in 1973, included students, urban professionals (particularly architects), and agricultural scientists like Terrazas, Baptista, Posnansky, and José Lorini (Lorini 1997). A second group, PRODENA, adopted the name of a Peruvian organization founded by Felipe Benavides, and it included an elite coterie of journalists and persons of influence (including Armando Cardozo) who wrote letters to protest government mismanagement of natural resources. In the east, Noel Kempff formed the Association for the Conservation of Natural Resources which, interestingly enough, shares the name of a prominent Costa Rican environmental group from the 1970s. These early citizens groups were quite small, however, and their influence under the vertical lines of command of the dictators was limited.[11]

As in Costa Rica, a protoenvironmentalism can be found in social concern over foreign control of natural resources. In the late 1970s several of Bolivia's future environmental leaders, including Carlos Brockmann, José Lorini, and Guido Capra were members of the Center for the Study of Natural Resources, an arm of the prodemocracy movement that opposed policies encouraging foreign ownership of Bolivian resources. Their initial concern was domestic sovereignty over oil and minerals, following the lead of earlier university groups like the Bolivian Committee for the Defense of Natural Resources[12]—"but this evolved, bit by bit, to become a theme of conservation of biotic resources," according to one participant.[13] Likewise the Defenders of Renewable Natural Resources, founded in 1930 at a time of heightened nationalist sentiment,[14] wrote to Noel Kempff in 1982 of their new common cause: "conservation of the landscape, which is the face of God."

The influence of these early groups paled in comparison to that of the national environmental alliance that took shape in the 1980s. The initial impulse for the Environmental Defense League was a cooperative agreement among the Ecology Institute, SOBE, PRODENA, and the National Museum of Natural History, signed in 1983 in the office of Wagner Terrazas at the Ministry of Agriculture (LIDEMA 1995). Two years later, Diana Wood, a World Wildlife Fund consultant to the U.S. Agency for International Development (USAID), visited Bolivia and energetically promoted the idea of a national alliance. Carlos Brockmann, a Bolivian scientist working with USAID, likely had a hand in the agency's decision to divert several hundred thousand dollars of PL-480 food aid funds to support the new alliance.

The Environmental Defense League enabled dispersed environmental groups to jointly pursue three goals: changing government policies, raising environmental awareness among the general public, and soliciting foreign funds to help accomplish these goals. It was this last category of activity that became the league's comparative advantage. It served as a conduit for the swelling stream of foreign funds pouring into the tropics as Northern publics became aware of the plight of the rainforests in the late 1980s. In the coming years several of its member organizations would develop professional staffs, diverse conservation project portfolios, and independent fundraising capabilities. Other groups, wary of the "professionalization" of the environmental movement, opted to remain volunteer organizations.

One of these volunteer organizations was the Ecology Association of Eastern Bolivia. The association was the product of a conference entitled "Impacts of Development on the Ecology of the Bolivian Tropics," held in Santa Cruz de la Sierra in April 1986 and attended by some 200 participants, including a who's who of Bolivian environmental activists. As the number of environmental groups increased throughout the 1980s, the roster of Environmental Defense League affiliates grew to include the Conservation Association of Torotoro, the Ecology Association of Sucre, the Center for Conservation Data, the Friends of Nature Foundation, Environmental Protection Tarija, the Bolivian Pro-Nature Defense Association, and the Center for Integrated Studies of Ecology and Development, among others.

In the previous chapter we saw that in Costa Rica the first serious government efforts to conserve biological diversity preceded the development of widespread social activism. In Bolivia the opposite occurred, as environmental NGOs took the lead in defining issues and priorities that would only later make their way onto government agendas. The series of policy initiatives that followed from the mid-1980s onward—the new legislative initiatives, protected areas, and regulatory agencies—were of a qualitatively different nature from the government efforts of earlier decades, both for their technical merits and the administrative and political support they received.[15] These new, more effective institutions resulted when an increasingly well-organized network of environmental groups turned its sights to government policy.

Greening Government, 1985–1989

The Beginnings of a Protected Areas Network

The institutional successes of Bolivian conservation have resulted from shrewd opportunism by environmental advocates turning larger political developments—triumphs and tragedies alike—into opportunities for institutional strengthening. One of these opportunities arose in September 1986, as Noel Kempff led a team of scientists conducting species surveys in Huanchaca National Park, situated in a remote area in northeastern Bolivia. Huanchaca had its origins in 50,000 hectares that General Bánzer had granted to a small group of military men in 1975, in an area containing one of the richest assemblages of natural diversity in the country. Declared a national park in 1979, the area is home to maned wolves, black howler monkeys, freshwater dolphins, and more bird species than exist in all of Canada. Absent a significant budget, the park survived only because of low population pressures in the region. Kempff hoped to convince the Brazilian government to create an adjacent park across the border.

Kempff's team landed their plane on a small airstrip which, as it turned out, was frequented by Brazilian drug runners. Upon landing, Kempff and most of his party were murdered. When news reached Santa Cruz de la Sierra, thousands took to the streets protesting the drug trade, which they believed could only operate with government complicity. The national legislature passed a resolution honoring Kempff's conservation work, but Santa Cruz newspapers demanded a more tangible state response. The powerful Santa Cruz Civic Committee, the quasi-governmental entity that led the historic fight for fiscal decentralization in Bolivia, took action to commemorate "the great defender of our ecology, fighter against all of those who would harm our fauna and flora."[16] The committee, led by representatives from agribusiness, industry, academia, unions, and the army, spent several hundred thousand dollars to expand Huanchaca, which park authorities renamed Noel Kempff Mercado National Park. The effort remains one of the few examples of a local government in a developing country providing significant funding for a national park.

Kempff National Park was the flagship park in a growing system of protected areas pushed by the network of biologists associated with the Ecology Institute. These efforts, however, were not without their setbacks. A more problematic protected area was Amboró National Park, one of the original areas Kempff had fought for in the 1960s. Home to eight species of monkey and more than 600 types of birds, the area was upgraded to national park status under President Siles Zuazo, the UDP leader who ushered in the democratic system that has prevailed in Bolivia since 1982.

"This was one of the first protected areas in which people were actually told they could not do something," recalled national park system director Alexandra Sánchez de Lozada (1997). At the vortex of the conflict in Amboró was park director Robin Clarke, a British ornithologist who arrived in Bolivia in the early 1980s, attracted by one of South America's premier centers of avian diversity. The area was also home to a large number of Quechua farmer settlers who opposed the park, citing agrarian reform laws that grant title to those who work fallow land. The campesinos accused park proponents of recklessly cordoning off economic options from poor families; Clarke countered that most of the settlers were of recent origin and would stop at nothing short of destroying the entire area before moving on. In 1984 Clarke wrote, "It is my opinion that if the Park is to have a future these people have to be removed *now*, before they become too well established and form a powerful group" (Clarke 1984, emphasis in original). The farmers did indeed organize into disciplined farmers unions, and Clarke's fierce advocacy was not well received in a political culture wary of foreign interference.[17] Clarke was the target of death threats, and on one occasion foreign tourists visiting the park were assaulted by angry locals. In the coming years Amboró would see a steady improvement in administrative capacity and some tentative agreements among farmers and park authorities.[18] But Amboró would serve as a poignant reminder that "Without community participation, you will not be able to achieve a thing" (Baudoin 1997), and it would inspire subsequent policy reforms to promote local involvement in park administration.

Each of Bolivia's protected areas is unique in its biological endowment as in its political trajectory. This is certainly true of the Beni Biological Station, founded in 1982 by Dr. Ovidio Suárez and later conferred the status of International Biosphere Reserve by UNESCO. Located in the Beni Province—a region almost four times the size of Costa Rica—the reserve is situated near a tributary of the Amazon that seasonally floods the low-land rainforests of the area. The Beni reserve provides habitat for more than 2,000 types of vascular plants and over 100 mammal species, including jaguars, giant anteaters, armadillos, Azara's night monkeys, and three-toad sloths.

The influential Suárez—physician, diplomat, and president of the Bolivian National Academy of Sciences—was well-suited to the politically complex task of establishing a protected area. To locate a site for the reserve, Suárez enlisted the help of Edmundo Chávez, a wealthy rancher who knew the area well, and that of Spanish scientists from the nearby Doñana Biological Station. They decided on the northern portion of the Chimanes Forest, which already had legal protection—on paper, at least—as a forest reserve. Suárez rallied support among local legislators and soon received the blessing of the president, who issued a decree creating the Beni Biological Station (Miranda 1997).

Suárez arranged for the biological station to be administered under the aegis of the National Academy of Sciences. Given the station's emphasis on scientific research, there was a certain logic to this arrangement. But there was also an unstated political logic that would serve the biological station well in coming years. According to station director Carmen Miranda (1997),

The Doctor established it within the academy, which is a state institution under the ministry of education but enjoys a great deal of management autonomy. That's quite important. It is the ideal umbrella for research and conservation programs because it is within the state structure [receiving budgetary support], yet over the long-term, because it is on the margins of politics, it is not subjected to the big changes that occur every four years.

The fate of the Beni reserve was closely tied to the historical evolution of transnational environmental organizing. The mid-1980s represented a turning point in this history, as a number of well-established environmental organizations in the United States and Western Europe expanded their scope of activity to include international issues. A major player in this transition was The Nature Conservancy, a powerful American nonprofit specializing in fundraising and land acquisition for conservation. In 1984 the organization's international program provided financial and technical support to develop facilities and a management plan for the Beni Biological Station. In early 1987, however, an internal dispute developed within

The Nature Conservancy regarding the scope of its new international role. Eventually its international program split off to form a new organization, Conservation International. Having alienated one of the world's most influential and well-funded environmental groups, Conservation International was eager to prove itself as a major player on the international scene. Bolivia was to be the testing ground, and the test was the world's first debt-for-nature swap.

First proposed by ecologist Thomas Lovejoy (1984) of the Smithsonian Institution in an editorial in The New York Times, debt swaps allow environmental organizations to purchase developing nations' debt and retire it in exchange for domestic investments in conservation. Designed to simultaneously reduce debt burdens and leverage funds for conservation, their major contribution is toward the latter goal. They enable the purchase of debts at deep discounts from financiers eager to dispense with what turned out to be poor investments. Moreover, because the conservation investments are made in local currencies, they are politically palatable to countries eager to save foreign currency reserves.[19]

Behind every widely publicized story of international funding for tropical conservation is a low-profile tale of the domestic political networks used to bring this about. The world's first debt-for-nature swap was no exception, as it required support from the Bolivian Central Bank and from President Paz Estenssoro, the revered national leader responsible for agrarian reform and women's suffrage, who returned to the presidential pulpit in 1985. Carlos Brockmann, who presided over PL-480 funding for the Environmental Defense League, was approached by representatives of the Beni Biological Station and Conservation International. Brockmann was well-connected in the Paz Estenssoro administration, and he arranged for the environmentalists to meet with Planning Minister Gonzalo Sánchez de Lozada. The planning minister was sensitive to environmental concerns due to the influence of his daughter, a biology student associated with the Ecology Institute. He supported the debt swap proposal and in a subsequent meeting with the president, environmentalists emphasized the "value of an agreement that would so dramatically place the country in a leadership role" (Ortiz 1989). The president gave Conservation International the go-ahead, and in 1987 the group purchased $650,000 of Bolivian debt from Citibank. In return, the Bolivian government established a three million acre buffer zone adjacent to the Beni Biosphere Reserve in the

Chimanes Forest, and with matching funds from PL-480 established a fiduciary account to support the biological station (Campos-Dudley 1992).

Combating the International Wildlife Trade

Shortly before Bolivia gained notoriety in the 1990s as a leader in biodiversity conservation, it was known as the site of one of the world's most voracious illegal markets in exotic species. Exports of Bolivian wildlife had already reached an alarming scale in the 1960s, when trappers killed birds and primates daily as fresh bait to lure jaguars, ocelots, and other felines whose furs could command a handsome price in wealthy countries. Large reptiles, particularly caiman, were exploited in large numbers beginning in the 1940s, and in 1966 the Beni and Santa Cruz provinces exported approximately 325,000 reptile skins. From 1979 to 1984, just as Bolivian environmentalists were beginning to organize, the wildlife trade intensified, reaching an annual export of hundreds of thousands of furs and skins, in addition to live exotic birds and primates for scientific experimentation. In 1978 the United States alone imported 3,166 live monkeys from Bolivia. From 1983 to 1984 Bolivia exported an estimated 58,776 live birds, 262,000 monkeys, and close to one million reptile skins (Marconi 1992; Kempff 1986).

Much of the trade was illegal, either surpassing allowed limits or dealing in species like jaguars and otters specifically prohibited under the Convention on International Trade in Endangered Species. Bolivia also served as a conduit for illegal wildlife trafficking from other South American countries. The agency that presided over this scenario was the Center for Forestry Development. Created by forestry legislation issued during the Bánzer dictatorship, the center had regulatory responsibility for forests and wildlife, and it was widely viewed as a corrupt and incompetent agency. With a total of six employees in 1980, it would have been difficult for the center's Department of Wildlife and National Parks to play a constructive role even if it had so chosen (Freeman et al. 1980; Moscoso 1997).

The wildlife trade reached such alarming proportions that in 1985, Parties to the CITES Convention meeting in Buenos Aires voted to ban all wildlife imports from Bolivia within ninety days if the country did not clamp down on the falsification of trade permits by government authorities. Tarnishing Bolivia's reputation in matters of foreign relations helped focus the minds of the country's political leadership. A broad Bolivian environmental movement was still a few years away, so it was a small but influential group that used the CITES fiasco as an opportunity to convince President Paz Estenssoro to take additional measures to curb the wildlife trade. The group included Armando Cardozo, with what one observer described as his "multiple connections in the intellectual, cultural, and political spheres of the country"; Ninon de Illanes, the wife of the Bolivian ambassador to the United States; Tamara Sánchez, whose sister was secretary of the presidential cabinet; and Andrés Szwagrzak, a wildlife trade expert and Polish émigré who would lead the Bolivian delegation to CITES in 1989. According to Szwagrzak (1997),

The president was convinced of the need to do something. But as the second democratically-elected president, he had concerns about how to issue a decree in a manner that was rapid and effective yet conformed with the law. It would require legal work within the Ministry of Agriculture, and then the decision of the entire cabinet, including some who were not crazy about the idea.

In response to this combination of international pressure and domestic lobbying, in June 1986 Paz Estenssoro issued a near-total ban on wildlife exploitation. This was followed by a tightening of export restrictions in the Paz Zamora administration, which declared a total ban on the hunting or export of all Bolivian wildlife in 1989. The domestic ban was unenforceable and overreaching, given the subsistence needs of rural inhabitants. The ban on exports, however, had a salutary effect in that foreign customs officials no longer needed to investigate the legitimacy of Bolivian export permits, knowing that all such exports were banned. Parallel to these efforts, Szwagrzak and Carlos Brockmann of PL-480 joined forces with European environmentalists in a series of lawsuits against wildlife importers in Germany. Although a significant amount of clandestine trade persists in Bolivia, the combined effect of the lawsuits, the total export ban, and the establishment of national parks in areas previously exploited has been to slow the trade considerably from the levels attained in the early 1980s (Baudoin 1997; Szwagrzak 1997).

In the challenging political landscape of Bolivian conservation, by the late 1980s a patchwork of successes, however qualified, were beginning to add up to a pattern of accomplishments. At this time environmentalists also began consolidating the sporadic institutional successes of the previous ten years' work into a more comprehensive process of national planning for environmental protection. With support from the U.N. Food and Agriculture Organization, in 1987 the nongovernmental Bolivian Network on National Parks, Protected Areas, and Wildlife, established under the leadership of Carmen Miranda, drew up plans for a national system of protected areas. President Paz Estenssoro also created a Sub-Secretariat of Renewable Natural Resources and the Environment during his final year in office—the first step in what would be a gradual strengthening of environmental administrative capacity within the executive branch. These developments laid the foundation for a more ambitious environmental policy agenda in the 1990s. They also attracted the attention of international donor organizations with a new mandate to support tropical conservation.

The Bolivianization of the Environmental Movement

By all accounts, when Jaime Paz Zamora assumed the presidency in 1989, the Beni Biological Station was one of Bolivia's conservation success stories. The debt-for-nature swap had provoked a national debate about debt repayment and sovereignty, but this had the effect of raising public environmental awareness to unprecedented levels. The swap also made a name for Bolivia within international conservation circles. With support from prestigious foreign and domestic organizations, the Beni reserve inspired hope among the enthusiastic young group of biology students surveying the area under the guidance of professors Guillermo Mann and Mario Baudoin. In their enthusiasm, however, they neglected to investigate one critical element of the Bolivian Amazon: people.

Among the Chimane, Moxeño, Yuracaré, and Movima indigenous groups of the Chimanes Forest area, survival strategies vary from subsistence hunting and fishing to wage labor for the region's cattle owners. What the people of the Chimanes Forest share in common is a long history of exploitation and political marginalization at the hands of economic and political elites (see Jones 1995). In keeping with this tradition, indigenous leaders were never consulted during the creation of the Beni Biological Station or the UNESCO Biosphere Reserve, which were established on traditional Indian lands. Nor were they consulted in Paz Estenssoro's decision to open up the Chimanes Forest to logging, or in subsequent negotiations to protect the area through the creation of a buffer zone financed by the debt-for-nature swap.

Absent indigenous participation, from 1986 to 1989 management decisions in the Beni were made by a commission with representatives from the Center for Forestry Development, the Ecology Institute, the biological station, the Environmental Defense League, Conservation International, the provincial Beni government, and the local association of timber companies. During negotiations over land use strategies for the region, environmentalists were overrun by the timber industry and its government allies. The process took on a life of its own when the International Tropical Timber Organization—itself the focus of intense criticism from the international environmental community—joined the fray, investing over a million dollars in a project touting the Chimanes as a model for multiple-use forest management. "It was very sad," recalled Beni Reserve Director Carmen Miranda (1997): "Bolivia and the ITTO were presenting the Chimanes Program to the outside world as an example of sustainable management for Latin America, indeed for the entire tropics. . . . ITTO technical consultants would mention parenthetically that it was a disaster. But their conclusions were to go forward with the project." With the reserve opened up and environmental opposition neutralized, timber companies fanned across the forest felling mahogany and other valuable species in indigenous homelands.[20]

Few could have predicted the events that followed. Indigenous political organizing in Bolivia traditionally had been a highland affair. The Katarista movement that spawned independent worker and campesino unions in the 1970s was organized by Aymara peasant leaders from the high Andean plains (*Altiplano*). When CONDEPA party leader Remedios Loza Alvarado caught national attention by walking into the legislature in her traditional attire in 1997, it was the colorful dress and stylishly tilted top hat of the Aymara community that splashed across the front pages of national newspapers. In contrast, the lowland Indians had long since been dismissed as a viable political force. This changed in the 1980s when, in conjunction with an unprecedented increase in indigenous organizing throughout Latin America (Yashar 1996), indigenous communities across eastern Bolivia formed political organizations within and across ethnic groups. Local organizations like the Center for Beni Indigenous Peoples and the Assembly of the Guaraní People took shape, while seventy delegates from Chiquitano, Chiriguano, Guarao, and Ayoreo communities launched the Eastern Bolivian Confederation of Indigenous Peoples (CIDOB), which soon counted a quarter million members (Ströbele-Gregor 1994; Delgado 1994).

It was in this context that in 1990, during the Second Encounter of Unity of Beni communities, indigenous leaders Olinda Echave, Ernesto Noe, Antonio Coseruma, and Marcial Fabricano planned the March for Territory and Dignity. On August 15, 1990, marchers departed from Trinidad in a demonstration that eventually attracted the participation of hundreds of indigenous people in a 500 mile trek from the Amazon to the Andes over the course of thirty-three days. Though their immediate concern was to halt timber and ranching operations on indigenous lands in the Chimanes Forest, the larger goal was nothing less than territorial recognition and a greater role for lowland indigenous peoples in the political life of the nation. The march captivated national attention as protesters were greeted by powerful Aymara and Quechua organizations as they ascended the Andes. National newspapers were flooded with letters of support from every quarter of Bolivian society—with the notable exception of the National Chamber of Forestry and Bolivian Society of Forest Engineers, which tried unsuccessfully to discredit the marchers and their cause.

Beyond the novelty of political mobilization by lowland *indígenas,* the March for Territory and Dignity was unique in two respects. First, it was part of a larger transnational political movement among indigenous peoples. Organizations like the South American Indian Council, the Indigenous Coordinating Committee of the Amazon Basin, and the World Council of Indigenous Peoples were making important gains in international law (notably International Labor Organization Convention 169 on Indigenous and Tribal Peoples) and facilitating cross-border exchanges of information and strategies (see Brysk 2000). Political strategy comprised the second novel element of the march; indigenous leaders explicitly tied their arguments to the ecological concerns voiced by Bolivia's rapidly growing environmental movement.

The latter half of the 1980s had witnessed a rapid proliferation of environmental groups in Bolivia. In 1985 the Environmental Defense League could easily track the country's dozen or so environmental groups; by 1990, the true number of such organizations was anyone's guess, as the environmental cause was taken up by church groups, campesino organizations, city councils, and professional organizations of every stripe. Leaders of the March for Territory and Dignity wasted no time in making the connection. "We Benianos wish to defend our natural resources," explained Noe, and the idea found a receptive audience.[21] "[T]hese communities maintain a harmonious relationship with their environment and are therefore the most qualified to protect it," argued environmental journalist Marthadina Mendizábal de Finot.[22] Another columnist wrote, "Today, as all of humanity is concerned with the destruction of the Amazon, the indigenous peoples of Eastern Bolivia, placing themselves at the forefront of this worldwide response, have decided to make their long-forgotten voices heard in order to defend one of the most important forest zones of Bolivia."[23]

When the marchers reached La Paz in mid-September, indigenous leaders entered into direct negotiations with President Paz Zamora, his cabinet, legislators, and the military. In response to their demands, the president issued executive decrees recognizing indigenous territories in portions of the Chimanes Forest and the whole of Isiboro-Securé National Park. He provided the Sirionó people with legal recognition for 30 million hectares of land in Monte San Pablo and Ibiato, and leaders of the march accepted the president's invitation to help draft a special Law on Indigenous Peoples.

Although these institutional gains were not a panacea for the longstanding problems faced by indigenous communities, the March for Territory and Dignity placed indigenous rights squarely on the environmental agenda and forged a lasting alliance between two emerging national movements with strong transnational ties. The Eastern Bolivian Confederation of Indigenous Peoples became a member of the Environmental Defense League, while Conservation International hired anthropologist and indigenous rights advocate Guillermo Rioja as the new director of its Bolivia Program. Environmentalists benefited from their association with a high-profile human rights issue, which shielded them from criticism that they were more concerned about flowers and beetles than about people; indigenous groups, in turn, gained access to the technical and financial resources streaming in from Northern environmental organizations. While the alliance was mutually beneficial, it represented more than a voluntary meeting of minds. Whatever their personal concern for indigenous rights, from a strategic standpoint environmentalists faced the choice between supporting the indigenous cause or courting political irrelevance.

Navigating the State

While environmentalists continued to search for ways to blend their concerns with broader currents in Bolivian history, behind the scenes they engaged in a series of struggles to create effective government institutions. The years of the Paz Zamora administration (1989–1993) represented a watershed in this regard. High on the environmental agenda was the creation of a government agency specifically devoted to environmental policymaking. In the final months of the previous administration, President Paz Estenssoro had created a Sub-Secretariat of Renewable Natural Resources and the Environment. The agency survived into the Paz Zamora administration under the leadership of Gerardo Aguirre, a close relative of the new president. In 1991 a movement was afoot within the administration to reduce the number of sub-secretariats. Faced with the prospect of removing a family member from power, and sensitive to the publicity surrounding the upcoming Earth Summit in neighboring Brazil, Paz Zamora upgraded the agency to the status of full-fledged secretariat.

Armed with greater political clout, Aguirre invited Ecology Institute Director Mario Baudoin to head a new National Directorate of Protected Areas and Wildlife. The new agency would be in charge of implementing the plans designed by Baudoin and his former biology students, who now held leadership positions in the country's major environmental organizations. Baudoin had misgivings about leaving his university post to work for the government, where it could be difficult even for well-meaning individuals to avoid entanglement in corruption. But he could not resist the opportunity to put into practice the ideas that he and his students had been pushing for the past decade: "In the university we are always saying 'this must be done, and that must be done.' How often in one's lifetime does one get the chance to really do something? It would have been cowardly to say 'no'" (Baudoin 1997).

Over the next two years Baudoin's primary concern was to secure an agreement with the Global Environment Facility of the World Bank, which provided several million dollars for Bolivia's national park system in 1994. The funds were channeled through a new national environmental endowment, FONAMA. The brainchild of biologist Carlos Quintela, FONAMA was the latest in a growing list of Bolivian policy innovations, its semiautonomous status and professional fundraising staff serving as a model for similar initiatives throughout Latin America.[24]

Baudoin (1997) attributed the success of these early institutions in part to the caliber and commitment of the environmental activists who entered government during this period:

Lilian Villalba was the first person in charge of the Global Environment Facility project. She is a hard-working biologist who has worked with vicuñas, and her heart is in conservation. Carlos Quintela, who formed FONAMA, is a biologist. [FONAMA director] Carlos Arze was one of the first to push for the creation of the Ecology Institute. So these are people who were both competent and personally interested in the topic. This situation is very different from the typical CDF [Center for Forestry Development] bureaucrat, who wants his salary paid and no problems.

Such *corazón* would be put to the test in clashes with powerful government adversaries. In addition to the usual budgetary fights within the agriculture ministry, Baudoin's new parks and wildlife agency succeeded in wresting regulatory authority from the Center for Forestry Development, which was loath to relinquish control of its lucrative wildlife use permits. To win these sorts of struggles required the strategic mobilization of networks of personal contacts. On one occasion, Baudoin enlisted the personal support of Secretary Aguirre to stop a powerful forest official and leader of the ruling ADN party from illegally extracting timber from Amboró National Park. On another occasion, Baudoin and his colleagues sought to remove a park director accused of financial mismanagement, but the director was backed by a powerful alliance of local officials in Santa Cruz de la Sierra. Baudoin turned to Santa Cruz Senator Enrique Quintela, the father of Baudoin's former student; the park director was replaced shortly thereafter.

These initiatives took place within the larger framework of the Historic Ecological Pause declared by President Paz Zamora in January 1990. The policy was intended to temporarily slow the pace of natural resource exploitation, in effect buying the government time to get its regulatory house in order. The Historic Ecological Pause included a five-year ban on new timber concessions and a national environmental charter to guide administrative reforms and environmental planning. To combat the continuing illegal trade in species, the president declared the total ban on wildlife use described earlier, and he created a wildlife trade investigative commission that included Andrés Szwagrzak and representatives from the Ministry of Interior, INTERPOL, and the Bolivian Armed Forces.

While these developments unfolded in the executive branch, a coalition of environmental advocates and sympathetic politicians advanced the environmental agenda within the legislature. The General Environmental Law of 1992 was the most important piece of environmental legislation adopted to date in Bolivia, both for its comprehensiveness and the wide public participation and debate it inspired. Guiding this process were a handful of activists well-known in the environmental community and well-versed in the workings of the legislature. One of these was Freddy Heinrich, a former legislator and Bolivia's first environmental lawyer. If anyone knew how to navigate the state it was Heinrich, who had also served for twelve years as a legal expert within the Ministry of Planning and Coordination, under a series of dictators and into the post-1982 democratic regimes.

"I became an environmentalist by accident," said Heinrich, tracing the origin of his environmental concern to a note that came across his desk in the late 1970s. It was an invitation to a conference on Latin American environmental policy to be held in Costa Rica.

So I traveled to Costa Rica, and soon faced one of the greatest personal crises of my life, because the Costa Ricans were already taking these matters very seriously, and there were numerous experts with a good deal of training. On the first day when they asked for my opinion regarding a legal framework for Bolivia, I had nothing to say. . . . That evening, they had some books on environmental law for sale. I did not sleep that first night, and instead read an entire book. . . . I left the conference with a great deal of concern for the environment. (Heinrich 1997)

With the environmental movement gaining momentum in the early 1990s, Heinrich's expertise was quickly put to use. Environmentalists debated and ultimately lobbied against an earlier draft of a national environmental law, which had been based on a compromise between Paz Estenssoro's MNR party and the ADN party of dictator-turned-democrat Hugo Bánzer. In 1991 Representative Jorge Torres, head of the new Ecology Commission in the lower legislative chamber, assembled a small group of environmental advocates to help design a new law. The group included Heinrich, Ricardo Cronembold (head of the environmental law division within the secretariat), Arturo Moscoso, Carmen Miranda of the Beni Biological Station, forestry expert Javier López, Juan Carlos Enríquez of FONAMA, and Alexandra Sánchez de Lozada, the influential daughter of former planning minister (and presidential hopeful) Gonzalo Sánchez de Lozada (Moscoso 1997). Cronembold argued for an environmental legislative code similar to that of Columbia, but Heinrich convinced the group otherwise: "I was opposed, because I used to be a congressman so I knew the process. It's not easy approving a code," he explained. "A code has all the norms, regulations, and principles all in one document, and includes numerous articles, so it is hard to move through the legislature. So I was opposed because of my familiarity with parliamentary practice" (Heinrich 1997).

While Representatives Torres and Roca led the fight in the lower chamber, a parallel process in the Senate was initiated by Enrique Quintela. Senator Quintela had served as president of the Friends of Nature Foundation before entering the legislature. He attributes his environmentalism to the influence of his son Carlos, the biologist who created the national environmental endowment.

When I arrived in the Senate in 1989, there was no environment commission—there was really nothing regarding the environment. I spoke with the others to get that moving along. We were only twenty-seven senators, so it was more of a club. We were not friends—but even though we were adversaries on controversial issues, the environment wasn't terribly controversial. . . . The parties fight for control of commissions, and the majority party tends to win these fights. We were in the opposition. But there were three commissions that were not of particular interest to the majority: human rights, environment, and science and technology. Since that time, of course, the level of interest has changed. (Quintela 1997)

As president of the new Commission on Ecology and the Environment, Quintela formed a bicameral commission with environmental allies in the lower chamber. With financial support from foreign donors, the lawmakers established regional consultative commissions to initiate discussions across the country and thematic commissions to attract input from technical experts, environmental NGOs, and affected economic sectors. The General Environmental Law was passed in 1992, providing legal backing for the national environmental endowment and the new secretariat and establishing an ambitious legal framework that would spawn subsequent legislation on forestry and biological diversity.

The Sánchez de Lozada Administration, 1993–1997

Bolivian environmentalism has never been monopolized by any single political party—a fortuitous development given the half dozen major parties and the Byzantine coalition politics that follow elections every four years. Instead, environmental advocates have forged connections with a wide spectrum of political players at all levels of government, which has helped maintain the momentum of environmental policy reforms against the vagaries of Bolivian politics. In the campaign for the general election of 1993, the Environmental Defense League organized a forum in which candidates from every political party, from the Revolutionary Left Movement (MIR) to the indigenous-led Conscience of the Patria (CONDEPA), pledged to advance environmental policymaking if elected. With characteristic political savvy, environmentalists were spreading their bets. When the electoral dice were tossed they came up winners, as MNR candidate Gonzalo Sánchez de Lozada—father of longtime environmental activist Alexandra Sánchez de Lozada—was chosen to succeed Paz Zamora in the presidential palace.

The environmental agenda for the new administration was crafted by a contact group led by Alexandra Sánchez de Lozada, in consultation with the Millennium Foundation (a think tank with close ties to the MNR) and experts from the U.S.-based World Resources Institute and the office of American Vice-President Al Gore. President Sánchez de Lozada created a new Ministry of Sustainable Development and the Environment—one of the first of its kind in the world—to incorporate environmental concerns into multisectoral development planning. He appointed his daughter as head of the parks and wildlife agency first led by her former professor, Mario Baudoin, and it was renamed the National Biodiversity Conservation Directorate.

A Movement for Parks

In 1993 Baudoin had finally secured several million dollars from the Global Environment Facility for the consolidation and expansion of a national park system. This and other foreign aid enabled environmental policy reformers to implement plans that would have been unimaginable to the previous generation of conservation advocates. Technical support for conservation came from a variety of foreign universities and research organizations. Financially, the $422,000 that the National Biodiversity Conservation Directorate received from the national treasury was augmented by $5.5 million from Holland, Germany, Switzerland, the United States, the Global Environment Facility, the Inter-American Development Bank, The Nature Conservancy, and Conservation International. The directorate used these funds to create five new protected areas and to expand others, adding roughly 11.5 million hectares to the system, with varied degrees of administrative infrastructure.

International support was only part of the inspiration for the expanding national park system. The other was a steadily growing domestic environmental movement. In La Paz, citizens held demonstrations that halted toxic waste imports from Europe; in Sucre, Archbishop Pérez denounced deforestation, while the Christian Solidarity Movement launched an environmental education campaign and mobilized 2,000 students to clean up city streets. Residents of the Chaco region undertook a march to Tarija to protest deforestation, and in Santa Cruz citizens protested fish kills provoked by pollution of freshwater streams. With conservation now politically popular and financially remunerative, the government was unable to keep pace with local demands for protected areas. The mayor of Oruro welcomed an increase in administrative support for Sajama National Park, hopeful that this would attract tourist dollars to his economically depressed region. The Ecology Association of Sucre, working with local government and universities in Chuquisaca province, forwarded several proposals for national parks that led to a protected area in the region's high elevation dry forests.

One of the most important protected areas created during this period was in the Chaco, where indigenous leader Bonifacio Barrientos joined forces with American ecologist Andrew Taber of the Wildlife Conservation Society to propose a park in the area surveyed by Conservation International's Rapid Assessment Team several years earlier. The Environment Ministry greeted the idea with skepticism, concerned that it would conflict with plans for a natural gas pipeline in the area. But Alexandra Sánchez de Lozada won her father's support for the proposal and with several million dollars from USAID, Barrientos and the Izoceño-Guaraní people assumed administrative responsibility for a new 3.5 million hectare park—the world's largest protected dry tropical forest (Sánchez de Lozada 1997; Painter 1997).

The Chaco project was at the leading edge of another of Bolivia's environmental policy innovations—a move to delegate management responsibility for national parks to local community organizations and NGOs. First proposed by former parks director Mario Baudoin, it was a propitious moment for this experiment. In response to long-standing political demands, in 1994 President Sánchez de Lozada pushed through sweeping reforms for popular participation and administrative decentralization that enjoyed broad public support (see Grindle 2000). And foremost among the demands of the March for Territory and Dignity was indigenous control over traditional lands.

As with other policy innovations, local participation in park management was not an unmitigated success. Few indigenous communities were as well organized and politically skilled as the Izoceño-Guaraní in the Chaco. Indigenous participation in forest management in the Beni suffered from a lack of coordination and was still burdened by the conflicts and mistrust that inspired the indigenous march. Environmental management was an impossible feat in the indigenous territory covering Isiboro-Securé National Park, where impoverished campesinos growing coca crops for export engaged in violent exchanges with the Bolivian military.

Elsewhere, however, positive strides were being made. With financial support from The Nature Conservancy, Bolivia's Friends of Nature Foundation assumed management responsibility for Noel Kempff National Park, bolstering its administrative capacity and successfully deterring illegal incursions from Brazilian timber companies. In 1997 the list of Bolivian policy innovations grew, as these two groups worked with the Sánchez de Lozada administration to broker the world's largest forest-based carbon offset agreement. Under carbon offset programs, a polluting firm can earn credits under the international Framework Convention on Climate Change by investing in measures to reduce atmospheric carbon dioxide abroad (see Hamwey 1998). In this case, The Nature Conservancy convinced American Electric Power to provide $7 million to support the expansion of Kempff National Park. The agreement enabled the company to sequester atmospheric carbon through forest conservation, in lieu of the more costly alternative of reducing emissions from its own smoke stacks.

The deal also enabled environmentalists to expand the park by several hundred thousand acres.

Unfinished Business: Reforming Foreign and Domestic Conservation Policy

The growing strength of the domestic environmental movement affected the bargaining positions of Bolivian delegates participating in international environmental negotiations. In preparation for the 1992 Earth Summit, the Bolivian Forum on Environment and Development brought together nongovernmental groups to review the official positions of the Bolivian government. When in the heat of Earth Summit negotiations the United States came out against the Convention on Biological Diversity, members of the Bolivian forum lobbied to ensure that their government would not adopt the American position (Moscoso 1997). In December of 1996 Bolivia raised its profile in international environmental diplomacy by hosting the Summit on Sustainable Development in the Americas. Six months later, under the leadership of Alexandra Sánchez de Lozada, Bolivia cosponsored a proposal with the United States to list big leaf mahogany as a species requiring export permits under the CITES Convention. The proposal was defeated by the Conference of the Parties, but it represented a significant development in Bolivia's foreign environmental policy, reversing the stance of the previous administration and signaling strong support for conservation from one of the world's major mahogany-exporting countries.

Domestically, the most high-profile environmental initiative of the Sánchez de Lozada years was a sweeping reform of the nation's forestry policies—a contentious political fight that produced one of the most environmentally oriented national forestry laws in Latin America. Although the Forestry Law involved many of the same Bolivian players who had dominated environmental policymaking over the previous decade, it was unique for the unusual degree of direct foreign involvement in the political process, particularly by USAID forestry experts.

In the view of reformers, the forestry law decreed by General Bánzer in 1974 was conceptually sound but lacked effective tools for implementation. It created the famously ineffective Center for Forestry Development, which had since lost regulatory authority over wildlife and national parks to Baudoin and his network of former students, but the center retained responsibility for forestry activities, which went essentially unregulated. To remedy the situation, in 1992 a new forestry bill was drafted under the leadership of Representative Neysa Roca, one of the cosponsors of the earlier General Environmental Law. She formed a multipartisan alliance with three other lawmakers, who defined their parties' positions on the new bill and helped move it through the lower chamber. Pavez and Bojanic (1998: 53) describe the complexity of the political task faced by the "Group of Four":

First they had to reach agreement on the content, then develop an "esprit de corps," maintain loyalty within the group, demonstrate multiple protagonists rather than a single one, obtain the support of their respective parties, use their ability to intervene at various decisionmaking levels . . . threaten to defeat the bill in the lower house if basic provisions were modified, solicit technical advice from international organizations (FAO, BOLFOR[25] and The World Bank), work closely with NGOs, and engage in ongoing lobbying of their parliamentary colleagues. Additionally, as part of their strategy to mitigate the influence of those representatives sympathetic to the position of the timber industry, they labeled them as "sell outs."

The National Forestry Chamber and its 150 member organizations had strategies of their own. They mobilized their contacts in regional civic committees and in the National Chamber of Commerce and Industry, and they lobbied individual lawmakers, successfully stalling the bill until the 1993 elections. In national news media they portrayed themselves as technicians who took a more balanced approach to conservation than their radical environmental adversaries; in turn, the Environmental Defense League and eastern indigenous organizations portrayed the timber industry as "termites" prepared to sell the country short for personal gain.

The team leading USAID's Project on Sustainable Forest Management (BOLFOR) arrived in Bolivia in January 1994, at a time when a revised forestry bill had been approved in the lower chamber but was stalled in the Senate. Initially BOLFOR's political influence was insignificant, as the team had no inside contacts with members of the Senate, and their proposals had to first pass through the Ministry of Sustainable Development and the Environment. Their influence increased over the coming months, as they bolstered their technical credentials by producing a series of economic analyses of the forestry sector. But the real change came when BOLFOR officials borrowed a page from Costa Rica's book of political influence. In November 1995 BOLFOR organized an educational retreat for decision makers, modeled after the policy courses of the Organization for Tropical Studies in Costa Rica, which sent José María Rodríguez to help organize the session. "Without that workshop, there would not be a forestry law today," concluded a BOLFOR consultant close to the process (Andaluz 1997). BOLFOR invited a select group of ministry officials and key legislators from both chambers to the retreat, which was followed by a one-day seminar for the entire legislature. In the course of these meetings BOLFOR officials made the political contacts they needed. The most important new ally was Senator Antonio Sánchez de Lozada, the president's brother, who had replaced Quintela as head of the Senate environment commission (Andaluz 1997; Nittler 1997).

BOLFOR drafted a new bill in close consultation with the president, whose personal involvement in the final months helped push the legislation past its previous impasse. By the time the Forestry Law was finally approved in 1996, the timber lobby had achieved a good number of their aims, including provisions for exclusive and transferable harvesting rights and the defeat of a proposal that would restrict exports. Nevertheless it was environmentalists who were most satisfied with the outcome. The Environmental Defense League (LIDEMA) capitalized on personal relations with lawmakers, forged years earlier during passage of the General Environmental Law; the legislators, in turn, looked to LIDEMA to rally public support.

"Senator Sánchez de Lozada called us and asked us to get involved," according to LIDEMA Director Luis Alberto Rodrigo (1997). "Antonio knew that LIDEMA could help stop the pressure of the loggers." Though the constellation of environmental groups under LIDEMA had trouble presenting a unified position, they raised public concern through conferences and protests, culminating in the March of the Green Flags, a series of public environmental demonstrations that took place across the country from October to December 1995. Among their concerns incorporated in the final legislation were the maintenance of state dominion over forest lands, the requirement that timber companies write harvest management plans, and provisions for citizen inspection to ensure compliance with the plans. Environmentalists formed an alliance with indigenous advocates, helping them to secure exclusive rights for forest exploitation within indigenous territories (Rodrigo 1997). And the new law created an independent Forest Superintendency, designed to provide training and regulatory oversight with insulation from political manipulation. To prevent whimsical appointments by agency directors, the superintendent was to be nominated by the Senate and approved by the president. To promote policy consistency over time, the appointment would last for six years, spanning two four-year political administrations.

The major environmental setback of the Sánchez de Lozada administration was the failure to pass a law on biological diversity. The same network of biologists and policy experts who led the other legislative efforts had proposed several versions of the bill to lawmakers since the early 1990s. The idea was to provide a legal framework for the evolving national park system, including its innovative local management committees, and to broaden the biodiversity mandate beyond wildlife conservation to cover topics like genetic resources and ecosystem integrity. The biodiversity legislation faced none of the fierce opposition encountered by the Forestry Law, but languished simply for a lack of sustained interest by political leaders. Environmental attorney Antonio Andaluz (1997) expressed his frustration:

The odd thing is that the president of the Senate Commission on Environment, Agriculture and Watersheds was Senator Antonio Sánchez de Lozada, the president's brother. And the president was the chief of the MNR Party. And Antonio is the uncle of Alexandra, director of the National Biodiversity Conservation Directorate. Theoretically, it should have been the ideal moment for passage of the law. . . . But if no one is pushing strongly, it stops there—and there it stopped.

The fate of Bolivia's biodiversity legislation underscores the importance of policy entrepreneurship. Favorable political and social circumstances never constitute a sufficient condition for policy change. A skilled and sustained commitment is required to overcome the innumerable sources of inertia present even when conditions are ripe for reform. Given the sustained energy needed for major institutional changes in developing countries, the remarkable point from the Sánchez de Lozada years and the history preceding them is not that many policy efforts failed, but that so many others succeeded.

Conclusion

In late 1997, as former dictator Hugo Bánzer occupied the Burnt Palace once again—this time as a democratically elected president—the uncertainty and unease in the environmental community was palpable. Would the Forest Superintendency maintain its political independence? What would become of the National Biodiversity Conservation Directorate? Would the nascent national park system continue to grow? To flesh out these concerns, I ended several interviews with the following question:

Imagine that twenty years from now I write, "Beginning in the mid-1980s, Bolivia saw the rise of an active environmental movement and corresponding changes in government institutions. A series of laws were passed, innovations tried, and parks created. By the turn-of-the-century, however, public interest and political support for environmental issues began to wane, as the nation turned its attention to other matters." What is your reaction to this scenario? Do you think this could occur?

The question evoked heavy sighs from veterans of Bolivia's environmental movement. Juan Pablo Arce based his assessment on the country's international commitments:

Impossible. Bolivia is participating in the international desertification program and in climate change negotiations. Bolivia is part of a network of laboratories measuring the ozone layer through the university, and is Party to the Basel Convention on international trade in toxic waste, as well as a series of bilateral agreements on tropical forest management. Bolivia is Party to the Amazon Cooperation Treaty and to the Convention on Biological Diversity. . . . To just do away with these? . . . It would be quite radical. (Arce 1997)

From his office in the Ecology Institute, Mario Baudoin (1997) provided a more cautious assessment, one that is as much historical retrospect as prediction. "Anything could happen, sure," he answered. "But not without a fight." A more systematic examination of the resources used in this fight is the subject of the chapters to follow.[26]

III
Explaining Policy Change

5

Domestic Political Resources

We must face the fact that many protected areas are the result of political maneuvers and through political manipulation they may also disappear.
—Luis Diego Gómez, 1988[1]

The idea was to seize any favorable opportunities or circumstances that came up, even unexpectedly, to invent a thousand and one tricks to get what we needed. . . . We copied it from insects, whose antennae are always waving back and forth to test the environment for food. We captured opportunities.
—Mario Boza, on the origins of the Costa Rican national park system, 1993[2]

Why have Costa Rica and Bolivia emerged as leaders in the creation of institutions to protect biological diversity? In this and the next chapter I elaborate a theoretical structure—*the spheres of influence framework*—to address this question.

Before doing so, let me reiterate that policy reformers in these countries have faced numerous obstacles in their decades-long efforts to create effective institutions. As documented in the preceding chapters, they have had to overcome corruption, bureaucratic rivalries, and the designs of high-ranking officials beholden to economic interests. Park officials have faced successive occupations by foreign and domestic military forces, by campesinos with families to feed, and by multinational firms looking to develop gas pipelines, private casinos, and timber empires. The policy context is one of budget cuts, slothful legislative procedures, and political parties with a thirst for export revenues. Add to this list drug trafficking, economic crises, military coups, and the insatiable overseas market for exotic furs and feathers, and it becomes clear that policy reform has been no easy feat.

Despite these challenges, Costa Rica and Bolivia have managed to create a series of environmental institutions that work reasonably well. Some

Table 5.1
Representative policy accomplishments

Costa Rica	National Biodiversity Institute (INBio)
	Among the world's best national park systems
	Strong environment ministry
	Env. commission of the Ministry of Foreign Relations
	Environmental legislation/constitutional amendment
	Pioneer in the development of nature tourism
	Advisory Commission on Biodiversity (COABio)
	Leader in joint implementation projects
	Leader in debt-for-nature swaps
	National Parks Foundation
	Administrative reform of park system
Bolivia	World's first debt-for-nature swap
	World's largest forest-based carbon offset initiative
	Experimental local/indigenous park management
	Rapidly growing protected areas system
	National Environmental Fund
	Leader in international efforts to protect vicuña
	Innovative forestry legislation
	Gradual strengthening of environment ministry
	National biodiversity conservation agency
	Leader in efforts to list mahogany under CITES
	Total ban on trade in domestic species

of the more important institutional accomplishments detailed in the previous chapters are shown in table 5.1. In their totality, these have unquestionably led to the conservation of more biodiversity than would have survived in their absence. A few counterfactuals amply illustrate this point.

Observers readily agree that without Costa Rica's national parks, the habitats they protect would resemble the stump-ridden pastures that prevail outside park borders. Without Bolivia's Noel Kempff National Park and the domestic ban on trade in species, the jungles of the northeastern part of the country would be the target of intense exploitation by timber interests and skin traders. In southeastern Bolivia, indigenous communities worked with the National Biodiversity Conservation Directorate to create Gran Chaco National Park because they recognized that these government institutions would bring greater benefits to both their people and their natural surroundings than would the status quo. Were it not for the Treaty of La Paz and subsequent efforts to protect the vicuña, populations of these graceful wild camelids would be greatly diminished.[3] Without Costa Rica's National Biodiversity Institute (INBio), the biological diversity of the Central American isthmus would be less understood and the parks that protect it would have less funding. Counterfactuals such as these beg the question of how the facts came to pass, and it is to this question that we now turn.

Domestic Responses to Global Environmental Problems: The Spheres of Influence Framework

The spheres of influence framework derives its explanatory power from the unique nature of global environmental problems, which are the subject of widespread international concern but whose resolution ultimately depends on decisions made by public and private actors at the domestic level.[4] Where global outcomes depend on the actions of developing countries in particular, the resources brought to bear on domestic policy are profitably categorized into those of domestic and foreign origin, for these differ in kind. As discussed in chapter 1, those with access to the resources of the international sphere affect national policy by providing scientific expertise and financial aid, and by sharing policy ideas from abroad. Those with access to the domestic sphere affect national policy through the deployment of political resources—the focus of this chapter—and by reshaping international policy ideas to fit the contours of domestic culture and politics, a process described in chapter 6.

The institutional accomplishments shown in table 5.1 owe their success to bilateral activists—policy reformers who have simultaneous access to domestic and international spheres of influence. Before we examine in detail the domestic political resources at their disposal, let us first take a closer look at the nature of bilateral activism itself.

Bilateral Activists

To better appreciate their position, we may contrast bilateral activists with individuals who operate purely in one or another sphere. With respect to any given developing country, an American director of a group like the World Wildlife Fund operates purely in the international sphere of influence. Based in Washington, D.C., the director has access to all the trimmings of this modus operandi, including exposure to an enormous stock of international policy ideas and access to world-renown scientists, prominent philanthropists, and high-ranking officials in overseas aid organizations. But this figure lacks the wealth of domestic resources necessary for creating effective institutions in such a country. Even the field staff of international organizations rarely spend more than three or four years in a given developing country—hardly enough time to acquire a sophisticated understanding of domestic channels of influence or to see major policy initiatives through to completion. Other individuals operate purely in the domestic sphere. Many politically influential actors in a given society have minimal contact with the world beyond their nation's borders. They know all the right people at home, but they have little exposure to the experiences of other countries, are fluent in only one tongue, and would just as soon keep it that way.

Bilateral activists face incentives to stay in the middle, to occupy the cultural borderlands[5] between these two spheres of influence. Cosmopolitan Bolivians who choose to spend the better part of their lives in places like Geneva or London stand to lose political resources like extensive personal contacts at home, and they are therefore less valuable to international environmental organizations with a stake in the decisions of the Bolivian government. Those who operate purely on the domestic scene, shunning international exposure altogether, are in less demand by domestic environmental groups seeking foreign resources. Many people do choose to operate purely in one or another sphere, and the purpose here is not to judge their actions. But it is important to note that these choices have the effect of removing them from the ranks of those most influential in national environmental policymaking.

Not everyone with access to the resources of the international and domestic spheres engages in bilateral activism. To actually deploy these resources for the purposes of policy change requires the will and skill of an activist. Bilateral activists are among the small minority of individuals who devote a great deal of time and energy to political life—the *Homo politicus*, in Dahl's (1961: 225) formulation, who "deliberately allocates a very sizable share of his resources to the process of gaining and maintaining control over the policies of government." For example, there are a number of scientists whose tenure in a particular developing country is sufficient to acquire a measure of political savvy, but who simply choose to focus on scientific research as their contribution to environmental protection.

Senior officials in developing countries, particularly presidents and ministers, meet the criterion of simultaneous access to domestic levers of power and international circles of influence (see Putnam 1988), and they often have a decisive impact on environmental policy change. What distinguishes them from bilateral activists is that they are generally involved only for the short term, typically the four or so years corresponding to their tenure in office. Although their support is often crucial, the individuals occupying these posts have not been the primary catalysts for the accomplishments listed in table 5.1 because these initiatives evolved over the long term.[6] Bilateral activists are the ones responsible for an overall pattern of accomplishment. Power brokers with short-term involvement open a window of opportunity here, provide some money and initiative there. But it is bilateral activists who combine and synergize these disparate efforts, who lend consistency, institutional memory, and learning—who order the effort into something more than a collection of fits and starts. They are the ones who, after losing a political struggle, can say with honesty "we'll be back."

Political Resources and Policy Change

Foreign scientific expertise and financial capital have been indispensable for the success of nearly every national park, government agency, and regulatory reform described in the previous chapters. Indeed, few issue areas rival environmental protection for the level of transnational collaboration it has inspired. But the fate of the rainforests—and that of the coral reefs, tropical deserts, and local communities that depend on them—has been equally shaped by the timely application of domestic political resources of the sort described in the remainder this chapter. I devote a separate chapter to domestic political resources not because these are more important than foreign science and finance, but because they are less understood.

As Haas (1992) has cogently argued, the technical uncertainties inherent in environmental management bolster the influence of communities of like-minded experts who can define the relevant set of questions and provide guidance to policymakers. But the uncertainty of environmental management arises not just from the difficulty of understanding atmospheric chemistry or the dynamics of extinction. Ever-changing configurations of political power at the national level render highly uncertain the place and timing of opportunities for policy change. Domestic political resources may be thought of as assets for the management of this political uncertainty. Environmental advocates with expansive domestic social networks can maintain a relatively consistent influence despite the vagaries of national politics, while those with a long-term domestic presence can endure periods of political resistance and strike fast when the time is ripe for change.

I categorize domestic political resources into four types: process expertise, social networks, agenda setting resources, and political learning. While there are important distinctions among these, they share a common requirement: to obtain them, one must spend many years in the country of interest. Moreover, as we shall see, the resources acquired in one country are generally of little use in another. This structural constraint goes a long way toward explaining the nature of transnational environmental relations—who participates, how, and with what effect—and the role of bilateral activists in mediating these relations.

Thinking Long-term

Why should it be that with such intense foreign interest in conservation in tropical countries, the most influential policy entrepreneurs are typically nationals of these countries? The immediacy of the colonial experience—chronologically, psychologically, and as manifested in continued relations of dependency—is one of the defining characteristics of developing nations. Therefore it comes as little surprise that formidable barriers exist against direct political involvement by foreign environmental actors. As Stephen Krasner (1995) reminds us, even the smallest and least powerful of nations retain the power to expel foreigners from their territory. In the environmental realm this power has been used with effect. In 1996 The World Conservation Union (IUCN), arguably the world's most powerful environmental organization, was nearly evicted from Costa Rica following accusations of political meddling.[7] The U.S. Peace Corps was expelled from Bolivia after allegedly participating in a coercive population control campaign in 1968. The environmental movements of both countries share roots with earlier social movements against foreign control over natural resources, and such concerns nearly proved the denouement of the first debt-for-nature swap and of biodiversity prospecting agreements. The greatest objection raised by campesinos disputing the legitimacy of Bolivia's Amboró National Park is that the park's manager and most vocal proponent is a British scientist, who wrote in 1986, "Let it be stated once and for all that gringo involvement in Amboró National Park must be kept to an absolute minimum for the immediate future because the local population is very touchy about this issue. . . ." (Clarke 1986: 143). It is noteworthy that this sensitivity to national sovereignty circumscribes the activities of expatriates even in two countries that are quite open to foreigners and foreign influences compared to many other developing nations.

Resistance to foreign meddling in domestic affairs provides only a partial answer, however, to the question of why most bilateral activists are cosmopolitan nationals rather than acculturated foreigners. Equally important is the fact that it takes many years to acquire the political skills needed to usher through major policy reforms, and the precise nature of these skills differs from one country to the next. I would argue that it takes a Costa Rican student less time to earn a doctorate abroad in conservation genetics than it takes a foreign scientist to acquire the domestic political contacts and expertise needed to effectively promote policy change. Moreover, the policy process in which these resources are applied typically stretches over a decade or more. To illustrate, figure 5.1 shows the gestation period for some representative policy reforms. If we start the clock at the time proponents first attempted to establish these institutions, and keep it running for as long as these undergo major reforms, the pattern is clear: Environmental policy change is a long-term undertaking. Because many of the initiatives shown in figure 5.1 built on one another and on earlier events, the overall process of institutional reform is even longer than this figure suggests.

Let us recall the timeline for the political struggles that gave rise to Costa Rica's national park system. The process began during legislative debates over forest policy in the late 1960s, when proponents of species conservation overcame agency opposition and inserted a provision on strictly protected areas in an otherwise production-oriented forestry law. The process intensified throughout the 1970s with the creation of the country's first operative parks; survived the financial crisis of the early 1980s, when park

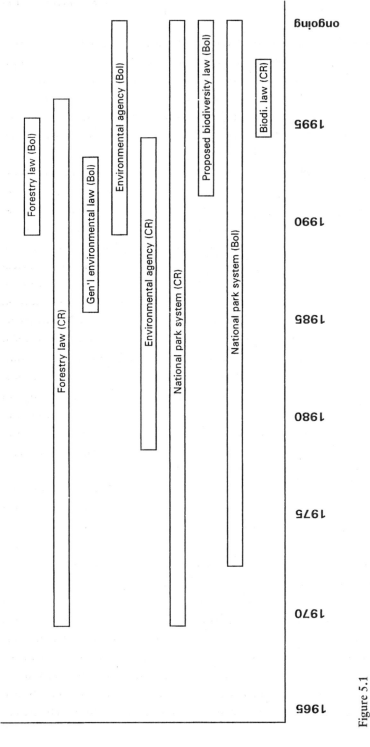

Figure 5.1
Timelines for major policy reforms. Note. CR = Costa Rica, Bol = Bolivia. Many of these initiatives had much earlier precedents: forestry legislation, for example, dates back for centuries. Timelines shown here extend back only to those efforts that had a direct and immediate bearing on later initiatives, such that they are properly considered part of the same reform effort.

advocates resorted to international fundraising campaigns; and included a major decentralization initiative in the late 1980s, which environmentalists fought to institutionalize in legislative proposals throughout most of the 1990s. Not surprisingly, many of the most effective environmental advocates are those who have stayed involved over a quarter-century or more, while the most effective institutions are those benefiting from such diligence.

It takes time to foster the political constituencies needed to protect new institutions against possible reversals in political fortune. Social movements are not built overnight. Moreover, elected officials may choose to lend their support only after an institution has proved its worth some years down the line. Although Costa Rican park officials enjoyed high-level support in the 1970s, this was purely at the personal discretion of political leaders. By the late 1980s, however, any Costa Rican president hoping to ignore national parks could do so only at a significant political cost. It took the better part of two decades to create a social constituency for the parks at home and abroad, and to establish a general expectation for continuity.

If it is true that all major policy reforms require a long-term commitment, this is especially true of biodiversity conservation, given the time scales intrinsic to ecological concerns. A single sea turtle may require half a century just to reach sexual maturity; the assemblages of species found in relatively undisturbed ecosystems are the product of evolutionary processes spanning millions of years. If it is perpetuity you care about, every victory is temporary.

This brings us to the central point of this chapter. The temporal requirements of conservation policy stand in sharp contrast to the short tenure of foreign environmental advocates. Most individuals in this category—whether they are field biologists, representatives of prominent international NGOs, World Bank consultants, or government officials—spend a maximum of two to four years in any given developing country, which sharply limits their influence over the policy process. Their sponsoring organizations do often maintain a continued presence; if personnel turnover were accompanied by the seamless transfer of political contacts and accumulated wisdom, this might provide for a consistent influence—but it is not and does not. The World Bank, for example, which is a major source of environmental aid to Bolivia, played an active role in early discussions concerning proposed forestry legislation in the 1990s. The bank's influence waned, however, once its representative transferred out of the country for his next assignment (Pavez and Bojanic 1998). The financial accounts that the official had managed remained for his successor; any political resources he acquired during his tenure boarded the plane with him. Expatriate staff turnover also attenuated the ability of the U.N. Food and Agriculture Organization, which provides technical assistance for Bolivia's national parks, to shape the content of the Forestry Law.

Thus we can see why there emerges a division of labor between foreign and domestic environmental advocates. Foreign environmentalists share a great interest in conservation outcomes in developing countries, but they lack not only the political legitimacy but the long-term presence needed to be major players in the policy process. Instead, they concentrate on their comparative advantage, namely technical and financial aid. Exploring the potential for a constructive international role, the contributors to *Institutions for Environmental Aid* conclude,

... a long-term commitment to policy dialogue, in which persuasion plays a larger role than coercion, is more promising than strict conditionality, but only in conjunction with a commitment by funders to develop strong local knowledge and long-term ties to recipients. ... Unfortunately, such commitment and coordination are rarely observed for sustained periods of time, let alone over the five- to fifteen-year period required to institutionalize major policy reforms. (Keohane 1996: 18)

It is bilateral activists who provide the enduring link between global concerns and national outcomes. Because of the dual requirement of international exposure and lasting domestic presence, these activists tend to be cosmopolitan nationals rather than foreign visitors. Let us now explore more systematically the domestic subset of their entrepreneurial skills.

Political Learning

Policy entrepreneurs accumulate over the course of their experience a stock of strategic wisdom about domestic politics and institutions. Political learning occurs when individuals draw on this store of past experience to improve the prospects for future success. Such "learning across time" (see Rose 1993; Neustadt and May 1986) is especially pertinent to the study of policy leadership, because many of the policy innovations described in previous chapters—including debt-for-nature swaps, national biodiversity agencies, and pharmaceutical prospecting agreements—were implemented with little or no precedence in other nations, precluding learning across space. Accordingly, bilateral activists have drawn on past experiences with other policies in their own countries to decide what to do and how to do it.[8]

Often they miscalculate. Sometimes errors are committed by the young and inexperienced, as when Costa Rica's newly minted environmental attorneys were outmaneuvered by the timber lobby during passage of national forest legislation in the mid-1990s. But even the most experienced advocates are prone to fundamental errors in program design or political calculation. The information most pertinent to institutional designs—such as underlying causes of environmental problems, or the dimensions of coalitions of support and opposition—may emerge only after the first steps are taken, often in the wrong direction. Indeed, the string of successes detailed in the previous chapters may be interpreted as enlightened responses to a long string of failures. It was in response to the bleak history of ineffective "paper parks" in Costa Rica that Park Service Director Mario Boza decided to provide each new park with administrative and financial backing before moving on to declare new areas. Likewise, Bolivian environmental advocates were responding to a long history of ineffective government decrees when they inserted into the new Forestry Law provisions for timber harvest plans, citizen oversight, and a politically autonomous regulatory agency. "We don't need new concepts—we need new tools," proclaimed one of its authors, waiving in the air a compendium of centuries of enlightened but ineffective environmental legislation. The Forestry Law's emphasis on regulatory tools springs directly from historical evaluation.

Behind every institutional edifice in Costa Rica and Bolivia today is a shadow of what did not work yesterday. Past failures to include local communities in decisions affecting protected areas provided the inspiration for today's widely lauded policy innovations in community participation. The design of Costa Rica's successful National Biodiversity Institute was informed by the earlier, unsuccessful efforts of Rodrigo Gámez and Pedro León to establish a tropical research institute within the University of Costa Rica. It was precisely because of these failures that INBio was created independent of the universities. The 1969 Treaty of La Paz, which successfully banned international trade in vicuñas, was born as a response to the failure of isolated national initiatives. In both countries, specialized environmental ministries were created in order to depart from the poor historical record of environmental management under agriculture ministries. "History shows," said a former Bolivian parks director, "that the agricultural sector has treated the environment in terms one could hardly describe as positive."

An important variant of political learning is "venue shopping" (Baumgartner and Jones 1993), a process of trial-and-error in which advocates experiment with diverse venues of political influence. When Professor Mario Baudoin grew weary of trying to promote conservation from the ivory tour, he experimented—quite successfully—with a government role as director of Bolivia's parks and wildlife agency. Conversely, when reformers hoping to introduce environmental themes into Costa Rica's national curriculum encountered opposition in the Ministry of Education, they created a nongovernmental organization to take environmental education directly to the communities. One of the most indefatigable of venue shoppers was the Bolivian naturalist Noel Kempff whose efforts to establish protected areas from the early 1960s until his death in 1986 resembled a three-ring circus, with simultaneous feats in local, national, and international arenas. He worked with local governments in Trinidad and Santa Cruz, with the national legislature and the presidency (under both military and democratic regimes), and internationally, lobbying the Brazilian government in the hope of creating a binational park. After many failures, he finally prevailed by using international nongovernmental contacts to persuade local military leaders to convince a national dictator to create a park that ultimately survived the transition to democracy.

Agenda-Setting Resources

The chronic uncertainty that characterizes national-level politics also carries certain advantages, as when it produces unexpected opportunities for policy reform. In 1994 José María Figueres caught Costa Rica's environmental community by surprise when he announced plans to structure his administration's policies around the concept of sustainable development. South American environmentalists experienced a similar jolt when the father of environmental activist Alexandra Sánchez de Lozada was elected president of Bolivia. Such windows of opportunity arise only once in a great while, and remain open only for a short time (see Kingdon 1984). Accordingly, to exploit these opportunities requires policy entrepreneurs on the ground, with plans in hand, over the long haul.

At first blush, it would appear that the very purpose of environmental institutions is to render windows of opportunity less important. A park agency is designed to create routine and predictable opportunities for conservation, making environmental outcomes less reliant on chance alone. But the ability of these organizations to take advantage of irregular and unforeseen opportunities goes a long way toward explaining their success or slothfulness. For those with political acumen and the will to use it, a tax windfall, a reshuffling of the presidential cabinet, or an unexpected call from a private donor can create sudden and unexpected opportunities for increasing budgets, strengthening agency administrative capacity, or acquiring new land for parks.

At times political developments unrelated to conservation provide an opportunity to hitch environmental protection onto other institutional reforms. The site where the invader William Walker was defeated in 1856 provided Costa Rica's Park Service with a politically attractive option for historical preservation in the early 1970s. Park advocates seized the opportunity and protected not only the hacienda where the battle occurred but 12,000 surrounding hectares in what is now the Guanacaste Conservation Area. A similar opportunity arose in 1972, when the Costa Rican Communist Party organized the citizens of Quepos to demand public access to local beaches controlled by North American developers. The Park Service acquired the beaches and piggybacked onto the proposal a plan to acquire the surrounding jungles, thereby creating Manuel Antonio National Park. With proper vigilance, dozens of these small, day-to-day openings can be shaped into larger patterns of accomplishment. On rarer occasions, sweeping social changes unrelated to conservation can open new opportunities for environmental policy reforms. An emboldened political movement for indigenous land rights in Bolivia made possible the establishment of the world's largest protected dry tropical forest, managed under the aegis of an indigenous organization in the Bolivian Chaco.

More predictable windows of opportunity are opened by high-visibility events designed to focus the attention of political leaders on questions of environmental quality. The signing of the Convention on Biological Diversity at the Earth Summit in 1992 inspired lawmakers in Costa Rica and Bolivia to introduce biodiversity legislation into which environmental advocates inserted long-sought administrative reforms. Whereas most windows of opportunity are unforeseeable, requiring rapid responses by players close to domestic politics, planned events like international summits allow even distant actors, like foreign environmental groups, to seize the moment. In a letter written to President Sánchez de Lozada in 1996, The Nature Conservancy and its Bolivian counterpart used this strategy to goad the president to take timely action for the expansion of Noel Kempff National Park. In a show of diplomatic finesse they wrote: "Finally, if you believe it would be appropriate to complete these steps in time for you to announce the project at the December Summit for the Americas on Sustainable Development in Santa Cruz, we are prepared to work with your appointees to that end" (Watson and Justiniano 1996).

If foreigners unfamiliar with domestic politics in a particular developing country have any political resource at their disposal, it comes in attracting the attention, however briefly, of heads of state. Presidents and prime ministers relish their role as national representatives before the community of nations. In charge of foreign affairs, they are attuned to the affairs of foreigners. Accordingly, on occasion prominent foreign actors may capture the attention of national leaders, directing their attention to conservation needs or bestowing medals and awards to recognize past accomplishments and encourage more of the same. Compared to the intricate machinery of influence used by domestic advocates, this is a blunt if heavy tool and is used infrequently.[9] It is significant, however, in that it briefly opens opportunities for domestic advocates to push through their pet proposals.

Windows of opportunity also arise as a result of unforeseen changes within the political apparatus of the state.[10] Elections and coups provide the most dramatic illustrations, but more mundane developments—a new congressional committee chair or agency director, for example—can mean a green light for reformers long waiting in the wings. The replacement of agriculture minister and cattle rancher Fernando Batalla had this effect for Costa Rica's fledgling park system in the 1970s. Similarly, from his vantage point within the military government of Hugo Bánzer, in 1972 Rolando Kempff advised his conservation-minded brother that a change in agriculture ministers would provide a propitious moment for creating new national parks in Bolivia (Kempff 1972). Changes in legal structures may produce similar opportunities, as occurred in 1990 when the Costa Rican courts ruled that portions of the existing forestry law were unconstitutional, which catalyzed efforts to revise outdated forest policies.

It may take many years for such political openings to present themselves. In the 1970s a proposal for a national environmental regulatory agency in Costa Rica emerged in discussions organized by Planning Minister Oscar Arias, but was rebuffed by the vice-president. It was only a full decade later, when Arias assumed the presidency, that an environmental ministry was created. Rarely do foreign actors have the presence or patience to wait so long. A World Wildlife Fund program assessment concluded in 1996 that among the group's few policy-oriented projects in Latin America, "Some of these are not viewed as cost-effective or successful, especially those whose implementation depended on timely government actions or continuity in government leadership" (Pielemeier 1996: 30).

Networks of Social Influence

In every society personal acquaintances with individuals in positions of influence can provide policy advocates with important points of access to the political system. In developing countries, where it is common for frail legal institutions to exist alongside pressing needs for coordinated social action, interpersonal bonds of trust often provide the "glue" that institutions cannot. As documented in chapters 3 and 4, these interpersonal relations are a meticulously cultivated political resource deployed frequently by bilateral activists. In common with the patron-client relations driving deforestation in Southeast Asia (Dauvergne 1997), the social networks that environmental leaders in developing countries rely on to advance their agenda are personal, reciprocal, and noncontractual. In contrast with patron-client exchanges, they are less material-based and less vertical, more apt to take the form of symmetrical relations among friends, colleagues, and kin. Sometimes these personal contacts provide access to decision makers, allowing bilateral activists to present a point of view or to serve in a formal advisory capacity. In other instances, they use their domestic social networks to dole out punishment to their adversaries. Sullying the reputation of opponents—publicizing their deeds to close relatives and mutual friends, or publishing open letters of protest in public media—is a frequently used strategy of influence. The targets of these attacks rely on their social networks for employment, loans, and favors in times of need; they may shrug off such threats, but often these hit the mark.[11]

If a long-term domestic presence serves as a hedge against the uncertain timing of opportunities for change, it is widespread personal contacts that hedge against their uncertain locale. The most effective bilateral activists know people in multiple political parties and in numerous towns and villages throughout their country. This allows them to shop around policy proposals, increasing the odds of finding a sympathetic legislator to introduce a bill or a mayor to push for a local protected area. And when an obscure figure suddenly rises to a position of authority, there is a good chance that among a hundred well-connected environmental activists, someone knows someone who can gain an audience with the new political boss. Schoolmates, coworkers, and fellow members of church groups, unions, and social clubs are all important—but family and ethnic ties are especially so.[12] This is one major difference between nationals and the rare long-term foreign visitor. Despite their years of experience in a particular developing country, these expatriates rarely have the breadth of social connections of their domestic counterparts. Expatriates frequently confine their domestic social networks to those with shared professional interests, and they almost always lack the family connections. When President Bánzer appointed someone from outside Bolivian conservation circles to head the Ministry of Sustainable Development, an expatriate environmentalist expressed to me his dismay: "I've been working in Bolivia upward of twelve years. I know every person in the country who works in biology and conservation. I have taught at four Bolivian universities. And now the minister is a physician, accompanied by many others I have never encountered in the environmental field."

To be most efficacious, these personal connections should be not only wide-ranging but redundant. Multiple connections to an organization or influential set of individuals—such as city council members, presidential candidates, university administrators, or peasant union leaders—provide advocates with consistent leverage at key decision-making points that is less susceptible to disruption from staff turnover or changes in personal loyalties. Compared to the thick webs of connections possessed by long-term residents, the few sinews of social influence possessed by foreigners are thin and tenuous. Officials of foreign environmental organizations often experience the frustration of spending months establishing good contacts in an agency or organization in a developing country, only to see these contacts evaporate with a change in personnel.

A poignant example of the power of domestic social networks is found in the efforts of Bolivian environmentalists to inject conservation concerns into the policies and practices of the national forest agency (CDF). When a dispute arose between environmental advocate Lincoln Quevedo and the timber industry in the late 1980s, the industry prevailed on the government to remove him from his seat on the regional governing board of the CDF in Santa Cruz de la Sierra. Quevedo turned to fellow conservationist Francisco Kempff, who served as a university representative on the board. Kempff made a few phone calls, arranging for Quevedo to receive an academic appointment and to be designated as a university representative on the forestry board, all within a span of twenty-four hours. "You should have seen the face of the CDF representative," he recalled, when Quevedo took his seat at the board meeting the following day (Kempff 1997).

The importance of social networks in efforts to strengthen national institutions is immediately apparent in smaller nations with their provincial politics. "It's a small country," noted a Costa Rican reformer. "It's who you know, that's number one" (Madrigal 1997). But even in much larger nations these networks of influence come into play. To illustrate, we might imagine a diagram showing a dozen of the key organizations shaping conservation policy in Bolivia—the legislature, the presidency, the major universities, the Environmental Defense League, political parties, the Ecology Institute, and so on—represented by circles arranged around the perimeter of the page. Next imagine drawing a line between two of these circles whenever a bilateral activist has occupied positions in both organizations, and for every instance in which an activist in one organization has a longstanding personal relationship with someone in another. The resulting picture would resemble a dense spider web, representing a tightly intertwined network with multiple and overlapping linkages. These linkages go a long way toward explaining the political impact of bilateral activism.

Process Expertise

A fourth category of political resource—process expertise—includes knowledge of the complex formal rules and routines of government as well as more tacit and informal knowledge concerning the conventions of political engagement. Bilateral activists know the political terrain—the contours of partisan and ethnic alliances, and the history of rivalries among agencies, groups, and individuals. They are sensitive to the larger political picture and how a particular environmental policy initiative may or may not fit into this picture. They have a sense of what "sells," what does not, and why.

Although scientific expertise is widely (and rightly) lauded as an indispensable resource for global conservation, domestic process expertise is equally important but rarely recognized in scholarly works or popular portrayals. The rapid expansion of Bolivia's national park system in the 1990s, for example, was facilitated by the process expertise of its first director, Mario Baudoin. Baudoin insisted that the new agency have its own legal department, knowing that if it had to rely on the lawyers of the larger ministry, this would create bureaucratic bottlenecks slowing the process of park creation. Process expertise was also at play when Costa Ricans first debated proposals for an environmental regulatory agency in the 1970s. The younger environmental activists participating in these discussions were wary of partisan manipulation of government agencies, and they argued for an autonomous, quasi-state institution; the more seasoned members of that debate prevailed, arguing that only a full-fledged ministry could enter the ring with enough throw weight to confront powerful established ministries.

There is no column in agency ledgers to record investments of this sort of political savvy, yet such investments are routine and the dividends are paid regularly—sometimes in cash, as when the founder of the Beni Biological Station placed its administration under Bolivia's Education Ministry to ensure regular access to government accounts. More often than not, process expertise is the product of long personal experience. Bilateral activist Carlos Manuel Rodríguez drew on his experience as a former congressional aide when introducing environmental legislation in Costa Rica: "The way I work with the Assembly is to get the support of the aides," he explained, "who then provide their legislators' signatures. Besides, one day they will be legislators themselves—It's a better investment" (C. M. Rodríguez 1997).

Beyond this familiarity with the nuts and bolts of policymaking, process expertise includes facility with the finer points of political influence. "In our culture, one of the nuances is personal interaction," explained Costa Rica's Pedro León (1997). León and his allies have used these interactions to their advantage in countless instances of face-to-face persuasion. At times the nuances of political influence turn on a single word or phrase. When the director of the Costa Rican Park Service, Alvaro Ugalde, sent President Carazo an urgent telegram objecting to the establishment of a police post in Santa Rosa National Park, he referred to the president's "soldiers" (Wallace 1992)—a sharp rebuke in a country with a proud tradition of antimilitarism. Twenty years later, when Ugalde sent President Figueres a letter protesting his neglect of the country's protected areas, he made a not-so-subtle reference to the conservation legacy of the president's parents. The importance of a word did not escape the attention of bilateral activist Daniel Janzen, who in 1991 suggested that his colleagues change the park agency's name from "service" to "system" to send a clear signal to park employees resisting administrative reforms (Janzen 1991).

To build a movement for environmental policy and institutions requires a knowledge of likely sources of support and opposition. In 1978 bilateral activist Gerardo Budowski identified some promising allies for the new movement in a speech delivered at the First Regional Meeting of Non-Governmental Conservation Organizations in Guatemala City (Budowski 1978):

I do not know a single ornithologist who is not profoundly conservationist. . . . [Fishermen] are our best allies for defending the fragile coastal zones. . . . There are so many additional alliances: scientists who need natural areas for investigating the components or processes of nature, geneticists who wish to save materials for future experiments . . . urban inhabitants, tourist promoters who depend on such regions . . . in order to avoid killing the hen that lays their golden eggs.

These efforts also require an appreciation for the types of arguments likely to play well in political circles. According to Mario Boza (1993: 240), "The answer was to create parks in areas of stunning scenic beauty, on historic sites commemorating heroic exploits of the past and in areas of demonstrated importance for conservation. In other words, the idea was to merge historical, scenic, and natural values so that no one could object, making it easy to sell the public on the idea of conservation."

Supportive alliances notwithstanding, rare is the policy initiative that does not inspire at least some form of opposition. Mental maps of likely sources of resistance, while not recorded on parchment like their cartographic counterparts, are no less real for it (see Grindle and Thomas 1991). At times these maps reveal themselves explicitly. In the course of one interview, without prompting, a participant walked over to a drawing board and sketched a diagram of the opposition to clean air policy in Costa Rica, which included the Ministry of Public Works and Transport, elements within the Environment Ministry, the San José bus drivers union, and the taxi drivers—who, he explained, are not as politically potent as the bus drivers, but display ingenuity in subverting regulations. Demonstrating that domestic political resources are most powerful when used in combination, he explained how he hoped to overcome the opposition pending upcoming elections: "The PUSC candidate is my brother-in-law."

Political Resources and Bilateral Activism

It is a fair question why the actors dispatching these resources are bilateral activists and not trilateral or multilateral activists. Is there no one with significant domestic political resources in more than one developing country? As a rule, the answer is no. The political resources acquired from forty years of residence in Egypt—the family ties, familiarity with the political culture, and knowledge of the ins and outs of policymaking—are of little use in neighboring Sudan. Analysts use terms like "the Third World" or "developing countries" with more than a little unease, given the bewildering diversity of polities gathered under these labels. Many and varied policymaking styles exist within the conceptually contiguous political regimes categorized as military, bureaucratic-authoritarian, populist, corporatist, or democratic.[13]

In some cases influential family and ethnic ties span borders, but legal and normative barriers against foreign interference are erected to keep out more than the citizenry of former colonial powers. For obvious reasons, nations are particularly sensitive to incursions on sovereignty by their immediate neighbors. Costa Ricans are fiercely suspicious of other Central American nations, and a Nicaraguan activist accused of political meddling would be viewed with at least as much scorn as an American committing a similar transgression. Access to the domestic political resources of more than one developing country, while not logically impossible, would be an exceptional feat.

Many of the bilateral activists described here were trained in the natural and physical sciences, which raises the question as to how the present study relates to research on epistemic communities (Haas 1992). The contribution of the epistemic community literature is not to show that scientists are important to international environmental efforts—for this much is plain to the casual observer—but to explain why. This literature helps us to understand why scientists act cohesively to further common ends, arguing convincingly that the shared normative and evaluative standards of their professions serve as an ideational basis for overcoming the difficulties of sustained collective action. This explanation provides considerable leverage for understanding the motivations of many bilateral activists, but it provides less for understanding their strategies and causal impacts. The epistemic communities literature emphasizes substantive expertise, privileging the role of scientists, whereas I emphasize process expertise as well, which brings into the fold attorneys and others who "speak the same language" as government officials, as one policy reformer put it. Importantly, bilateral activism is often undertaken by scientists because they are among the most cosmopolitan of citizens in developing countries, while among expatriates, ecologists are the most likely to commit to a long-term stay, due to the site-specific, longitudinal nature of their field work. Scientific credibility certainly counts in policy circles, but the influence of the scientists described in this study is only partly a function of their science.[14]

Finally, it is worth asking why this coupling of international and domestic resources should take place within an individual person, rather than in the context of a long-standing alliance among domestic and international actors each specializing in their respective sphere of influence. Where government institutions are weak—as is often the case with new and innovative policy initiatives in developing countries—individuals are the primary source of institutional memory (Sikkink 1991). The lack of institutional continuity endemic to policymaking in most developing countries (Sloan 1984) is compounded by the erratic and uncoordinated nature of overseas aid. Trends in the donor world come and go, and when an institution that was the darling of the international donor community suddenly dries up for want of international support, it is up to committed individuals to carry the torch to some other arena. The project focus of most overseas aid further compounds the problem, leaving it to individuals to carry out the cumulative and integrative functions necessary for a sustained effort at policy reform. Extensive and ongoing transnational relations enhance these individuals' abilities to carry out this function effectively.

The political resources detailed in this chapter enhance the capacity of domestic reformers to strengthen national environmental institutions. But this technology of social influence might be applied toward any number of social goals. To understand why politically engaged citizens in Costa Rica and Bolivia have used these resources to advance environmental ends in particular, the following chapter explores the origins of national environmental concern, including the timing and nature of changes in public preferences, the international origin and transnational diffusion of policy ideas, and the impact of these ideas on state institutions.

6

Policy Culture

Our cause must be a majority cause, not that of a small sector.
—Gerardo Budowski, opening remarks at the First Regional Meeting of Non-governmental Conservation Associations, Guatemala City, 1978[1]

Ladies and gentlemen, in recognition of the global environmental movement, there is no smoking permitted on this flight.
—Announcement on all flights of Aero Sur airlines in Bolivia, 1997

Domestic policy responses to global environmental problems are shaped by changes in ideas and institutions, occurring in a context of intense transnational exchange. The previous chapter considered the politics of institutional reform, particularly the political resources used by bilateral activists hoping to enhance the ability of government to respond to environmental problems. In this chapter the ideational component of this process is explored in more depth. Specifically, to understand the central question of this study—how Costa Rica and Bolivia emerged as leaders in biodiversity conservation, and the roles played by foreign and domestic actors in this process—we must now take a closer look at how the very idea of environmentalism has spread across borders.

The goals of this chapter are threefold: to demonstrate the importance of a broad public constituency in matters of environmental policy; to document the rise of popular support for environmental protection in Costa Rica and Bolivia; and to explain how this surge of popular interest came about, with particular reference to its international origins. Central to this discussion is the concept of *policy culture*—a term first introduced by Almond and Powell (1978: 39–46), which I revive and further develop to characterize the emergence of widespread, enduring public interest in a particular issue area in a given society. Building on recent research on the phenomenon of rapid cultural change, I argue that policy culture provides analytic leverage for understanding the transnational movement of environmental policy ideas and the interaction between international environmental norms and domestic cultures.

Dynamics of Cultural Change

To the handful of Bolivian environmentalists present in the 1970s, the notion that a major commercial airline would one day broadcast environmental messages like the one introducing this chapter would have been unthinkable. It is precisely the speed with which concepts move from the unthinkable to the commonplace that justifies studies of cultural change.

Culture refers here to the conceptual component of social organization (see Eckstein 1988: 801–803). The shared concepts with which societies make sense of reality can show considerable resilience, evolving slowly, if at all, over the course of generations (Abramson and Inglehart 1995; Inglehart 1990). In other instances, however, elements of these shared understandings can change quite rapidly. As Rochon (1998: 9) points out,

[C]ommonsense beliefs are not universal, but are instead typically bounded by time as well as by space. Today's orthodoxy may be the heterodoxy of yesterday and tomorrow. Although cultural change is not usually perceptible from day to day, when we look over a longer time span it becomes apparent that even the most fundamental assumptions about morality and the standards by which quality of life should be evaluated are subject to change.

Although the processes driving the pace of cultural change are complex,[2] two factors stand out. First, culture is a hotly contested terrain, one filled with social activists, religious reformers, and revolutionaries agitating for change in the dominant modes of thinking and interpretation (see Alvarez, Dagnino, and Escobar 1998). Second, culture is not merely a product of *public opinion*—a term that suggests an aggregation of individually formed preferences—but of *social opinion,* formed in the course of interactive dialogue and debate. At times these interactions efficiently restrain innovative thinking, as when they assume the form of sharp community censure. In other instances, the highly interactive nature of culture can have the opposite effect, exhibiting the properties of tipping models. Tipping models describe scenarios in which the costs and benefits of individual behavior change as a function of the preferences and behavior of others—as, for example, when there exist strong pressures for social conformity. These circumstances can promote entrenched stability as well as dynamic "bandwagon effects" in social beliefs. The earliest proponents of a new idea often face castigation or indifference, which act as negative feedbacks protecting the integrity of the old belief system. Once a certain threshold of social interest is reached, however, the balance of social opinion may tip rapidly toward a new stable point. The stability of this new point stems from the fact that detractors of the new idea are subject to the same mechanisms of social censure as were the early innovators. In concrete terms, as more people join the environmental cause, for those individuals still uncommitted, the cost of gathering information about environmental problems lowers and the cost of ignorance, apathy, or opposition is raised.

Policy Culture Defined

Of the many matters on which societies develop predominant views— from artistic tastes to sexual mores to standards of sanity and reason— policy culture pertains to the subset of views concerning matters of public policy. Accordingly, whether an issue is considered an appropriate matter for government policy—or better left to markets, parents, or pastors—is an important determinant of whether or not a policy culture exists. Almond and Powell first elaborated the concept in 1978 in an effort to decompose political culture into a series of smaller, more manageable analytic categories. Policy culture itself was never adequately defined, however, referring alternately to the preferences of mass publics or of policy elites, to views regarding specific issue areas as well as the performance of political systems. Let us then make some needed refinements before proceeding.

Policy culture is used here to refer to the level and type of attention accorded an issue area by any given society. Alternatively, it can be thought of as what a society wants and expects its government to do with respect to a specific issue. Whereas *political culture* refers to deep cultural orientations about the political process (Can government be trusted? Do we control our destiny? Is liberty or equality the higher good?), policy culture is issue-specific and more subject to periodic change. Policy culture is a

necessary concept precisely because research on political culture has little
to say about change—about the dynamic relationship between changing
social concerns and institutional reform.[3]

While more dynamic than political culture, policy culture is less capri-
cious than many elements of "public opinion" writ large; policy culture
denotes a set of social beliefs and attitudes that are relatively stable over a
period of a decade or more. To illustrate these distinctions, when there
arises in the public a general expectation that government should provide
a safety net to protect its citizens against extreme economic hardship, one
can speak of a policy culture in support of social welfare. Popular notions
about the appropriate role of government generally (political culture) will
affect views concerning its specific role in promoting social welfare (policy culture). And from month to month public opinion may fluctuate
wildly on a particular government initiative in support of this goal. It is the
long-term, issue-specific set of beliefs that comprise the terrain policy culture is intended to map.[4]

Before moving on to consider the specifics of environmental policy
culture in Costa Rica and Bolivia, two final clarifications are in order.
First, policy culture is a mass phenomenon.[5] It does not describe the beliefs of small groups of committed actors (advocacy coalitions, epistemic
communities, issue networks, iron triangles, and so forth), although the
interaction between these specialists and the larger citizenry is a central
question for studies of policy culture. Second, to speak of "a" policy culture with respect to an issue area is not to downplay the contested nature
of a country's dominant policy ideas. But the fact remains that Canadians
think differently about national health care than Americans do, and the
latter differ from the British in their assessment of the risks posed by genetically modified foods (see also Jasanoff 1990). Because policy culture is
defined with reference to government policy, there is an end game: an identifiable arena in which some ideas win out, others lose, and observers can
readily identify the outcome.[6]

The Political Relevance of Policy Culture

Studies of state-society relations typically focus on the ways in which powerful social actors circumscribe the effectiveness of government (see, e.g.,
Migdal 1987). Similarly, the literature on social movements pays the greatest attention to civic actors at those moments when they act in opposition

to the state.[7] However social interest and involvement in state affairs can also increase the capacity of government to deliver public goods (Press 1998; Putnam 1993). This is especially true of environmental policy. Most of the information relevant to environmental policy decisions—hunting practices, the health of watersheds, or the latest toxic plume from a nearby factory—is diffuse and decentralized. This provides a rationale for a wide range of citizens and nongovernmental organizations to bring environmental problems to the attention of government.

It is impossible for a citizen to develop expertise in strategic air defense policy without a government affiliation. This is not true of environmental expertise, however; many of the central ideas underpinning national environmental policy agendas are first developed in the nongovernmental sector. Costa Rica's National Biodiversity Institute was the brainchild of academic scientists, while many protected areas in Costa Rica and Bolivia were first proposed by religious organizations, peasant unions, indigenous groups, and amateur naturalists. In the implementation of policy, citizen involvement is again particularly germane to environmental issues. While the major parameters of military and trade policy—the troop movements and weapons stockpiles, exchange rates and tariffs—are readily subject to central government control, environmental policymaking aspires to regulate innumerable private activities undertaken by millions. Only at an exorbitant administrative cost can states undertake such activities unaided.

Nongovernmental actors often work directly with their government counterparts to improve policy outcomes. One wildlife protection group in Costa Rica organizes cohorts of volunteers to patrol the national parks, documenting illegal game hunting. The Ministry of Justice provides group members with badges to give them the legal backing needed in confrontations with poachers. In some instances these state-society collaborations are initiated by government agencies themselves. Costa Rica's Environment Ministry has established a "green line" to encourage citizens to make phone reports of environmental crimes, while the Bolivian government has gone so far as to hand over administrative responsibility for its national parks to environmental groups like the Friends of Nature Foundation and indigenous organizations like the Capitanía of Upper and Lower Izozog. At other times, civil society takes the lead. Because weak enforcement of environmental laws is often the result of inadequate training of judicial authorities, a group of environmental attorneys in Costa Rica (CEDARENA) publishes compilations of environmental statutes and organizes training workshops for judges and public prosecutors.[8]

While some citizens' groups in these countries work closely with government, others have improved policy implementation through confrontations with state authorities. The most common form of public protest is the *denuncia:* a complaint, often publicized in major news outlets, intended to goad reluctant authorities to action. On a larger scale, citizens have engaged in mass marches and civil disobedience to protest government mismanagement of natural resources. Examples include the March of the Green Flags, which Bolivian activists timed to coincide with legislative debates over national forest policy, and the indigenous March for Territory and Dignity, which spurred reforms in the country's national park system. In Costa Rica, protests against Alcoa Aluminum Company, inspired by a mix of nationalist and ecological concerns, constituted the largest civil disruption in the history of the modern republic, while sit-ins to protest construction of the Guápiles highway resulted in the creation of Braulio Carrillo National Park.[9]

The above examples demonstrate the relevance of an environmental policy culture to efforts at institutional reform. Increasing the public profile of environmental ideas is not, however, uniformly advantageous for environmental advocates. Heightened public awareness may also raise awareness among the intended targets of regulatory policies, causing them to scrutinize proposed policies more closely than they might have absent a vocal public campaign. Nonetheless, most countries with a sustained pattern of accomplishments in environmental policymaking have experienced high levels of popular mobilization for environmental initiatives. Viewing government policy as central to their concerns, leaders of environmental movements have rarely passed up the chance to couple their efforts with those of government officials, whether in an adversarial or cooperative capacity. Viewing the environmental cause as a planetary one, environmental movements have been quick to reach out across borders, helping to spread the word and to enlist allies transnationally.

Documenting the Rise of Environmental Policy Culture

Bolivian and Costa Rican societies have undergone important transformations over the last four decades regarding popular concern for environ-

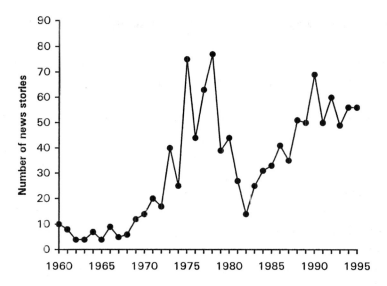

Figure 6.1
Environmental news in Costa Rica.

mental issues. Prior to the 1970s few Costa Ricans bothered themselves with questions concerning the fate of tropical forests. In Bolivia, the connection between public apathy and the tepid state response to environmental degradation was direct. "Unfortunately conservationism in this society is not understood," wrote Noel Kempff in a letter to a Brazilian colleague in 1968. "[M]y proposal to create three national parks was presented as a bill before the Senate, was sent to an economic commission, and there it lay in slumber" (Kempff 1968).

This public indifference was soon to change, as reflected in news coverage of environmental themes from 1960 to 1995.[10] Figure 6.1 shows a sudden increase in the attention accorded environmental issues in Costa Rica in the mid-1970s.[11] A similar change, also quite sudden, occurred in Bolivia in the mid-1980s (figure 6.2). These data do not merely reflect a growing interest among a few journalists; the rise of environmental policy cultures in these countries is reflected in increasing numbers of letters-to-the-editor on environmental topics during this period (figures 6.3 and 6.4), and the news stories themselves feature the activities of several thousand individuals and organizations. Nor can these results be attributed to a surge in international news stories on the environment: Environmentalism

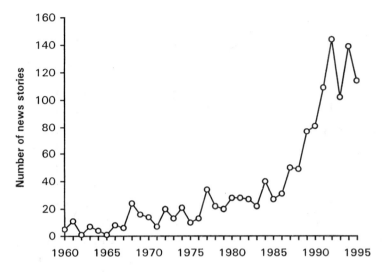

Figure 6.2
Environmental news in Bolivia.

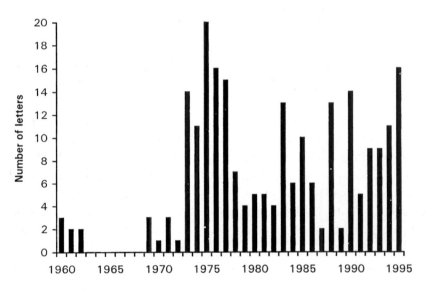

Figure 6.3
Letters on environmental topics in Costa Rica.

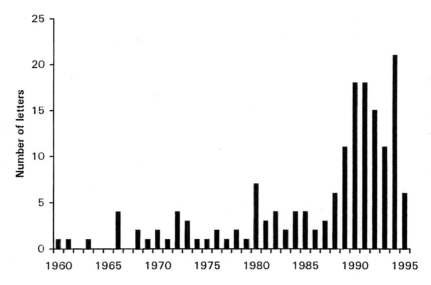

Figure 6.4
Letters on environmental topics in Bolivia.

did not become a "hot topic" in Bolivia until a full decade after its emergence in Costa Rica, despite the fact that their media had equal access to foreign environmental news during this period. More to the point, most of these news items were written by and for Costa Ricans and Bolivians, as shown in figures 6.5 and 6.6.

Importantly, the extent and timing of the changes revealed by these summary quantitative measures is corroborated by interviews with long-term observers of the environmental movements of these countries. As documented in chapters 3 and 4, Costa Rica witnessed the birth of an environmental movement in the mid-1970s, while Bolivia experienced a similar phenomenon a decade later—a point of variation to which the argument will return shortly.[12] For now, this simple but central result serves to remind us that there is nothing automatic in the transnational spread of environmental ideas. The existence of a vocal international environmental movement with global media networks and diplomatic channels at its disposal can neither ensure, nor explain, the adoption of environmental ideas by a given society at a given moment in history.

Today the level of social interest in environmentalism in these societies starkly contradicts the stereotype that developing societies are too poor to

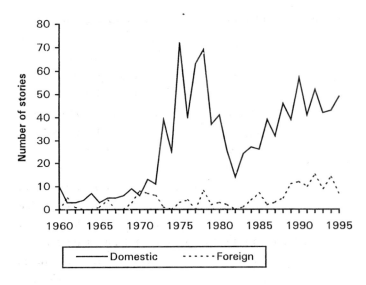

Figure 6.5
Sources of environmental news in Costa Rica.

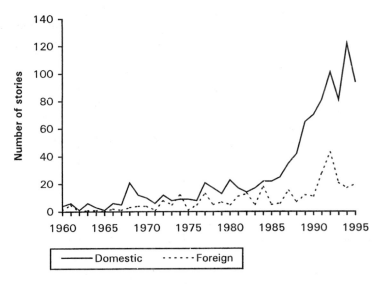

Figure 6.6
Sources of environmental news in Bolivia.

care about the environment. At least 86 citizens' environmental groups exist in Bolivia, while in Costa Rica the figure has reached roughly 245 environmental groups.[13] Museum exhibits celebrating environmental themes are commonplace today in cities like San José and Santa Cruz de la Sierra, and environmental studies programs have been established in many universities. Radio and television airwaves are filled with environmental messages, advertisers tout the ecological benefits of their products, and it is common to find murals on the walls of elementary schools and city thoroughfares exhorting passersby to save the planet.

To what extent have these public concerns entered into the universe of concepts and concerns held by political elites? One place where social discourses intersect with the formation of political elites is in the top law schools, where many of these nations' future political leaders are trained. Figures 6.7 and 6.8 show the number and percentage of graduate theses from these schools focusing on environmental protection.[14] From the mid-1980s onward in Costa Rica and to a lesser extent in Bolivia, interest in environmental themes has increased among the elite who go on to assume positions of leadership in government.

The increasing salience of environmental themes among political elites is also reflected in a longitudinal analysis of presidential inaugural speeches.

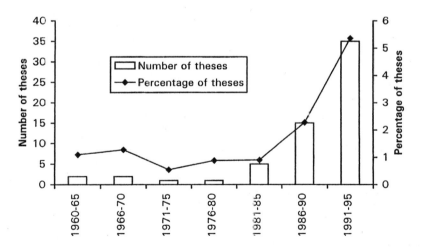

Figure 6.7
Law theses on environmental topics in Costa Rica. Source. Universidad de Costa Rica, theses for graduating law students.

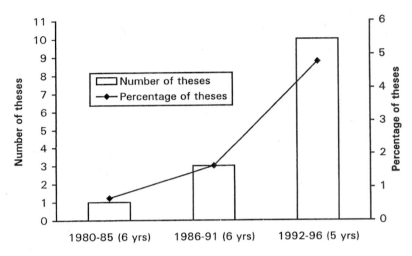

Figure 6.8
Law and political science theses on environmental topics in Bolivia. Source. Universidad Mayor de San Andrés, theses for graduating students in law and political science. Note. Data prior to 1980 not available.

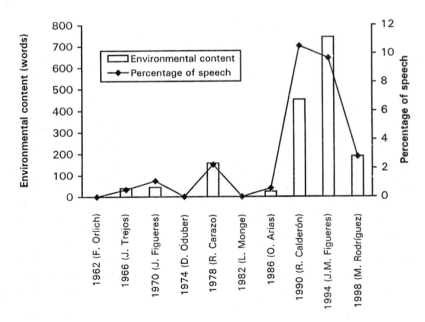

Figure 6.9
Attention given environmental issues in presidential inaugural speeches in Costa Rica. Note. Includes all words in sentences or phrases about environmental protection. J. M. Figueres speech is the first annual report to the legislature rather than the inaugural speech.

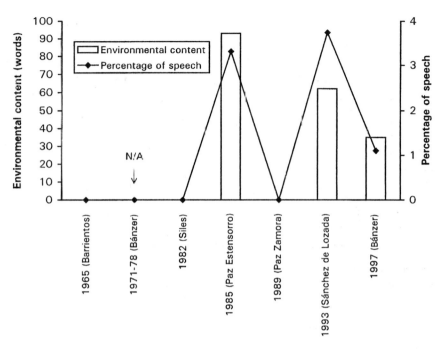

Figure 6.10
Attention given environmental issues in presidential inaugural speeches in Bolivia.
Note. Only presidents who governed for two or more years are shown here. In-
cludes all words in sentences or phrases concerning environmental protection.
N/A = not available.

Figure 6.9 shows that no Costa Rican president of the 1990s opted to
ignore environmental protection when publicly defining the priorities of
government. (Indeed, in 1994 Figueres chose to make sustainable development the conceptual basis of his entire program of government.)
Although longitudinal trends are harder to identify in the Bolivian case
(figure 6.10), due to data limitations during the 1970s and an extraordi-
narily high level of political turnover from 1978 to 1982, what is clear is
that most presidents from 1985 onward have devoted a significant portion
of their rhetorical attention to environmental themes. Some presidents
who ignored environmental themes in their campaigns and inaugural
speeches (such as Oduber, Arias, and Paz Zamora) were convinced after
assuming office to devote significant resources to environmental protection, while others who spoke of conservation (such as Trejos) devoted little
subsequent effort to this area. But holding apart the question of whether

words have been followed by action (the subject of chapters 3 through 5), as a measure of public discourse these figures suggest that the rise of environmental policy cultures has been paralleled by a change in the level of rhetorical attention given the environment by political leaders.

The Changing Content of Environmental Discourse

While the preceding discussion documents changes in the level of attention given environmental issues over time, the rise of environmental policy cultures is also reflected in the changing content of public deliberation on environmental themes. Much of what is new about contemporary environmentalism is the ecological emphasis on connections among problems previously considered in isolation. This provides another methodological vantage point from which to view the rise of environmentalism. Static measures of media attention accorded various environmental problems are provided in figures 6.11 and 6.12. But it is the dynamic change in the way these issues are represented that is most revealing. News articles from the early 1960s expressed alarm over issues like deforestation, water quality, and soil erosion—but rarely were such issues discussed together in the same article, because they were not recognized as related components of a larger syndrome. By the 1990s, however, these issues were tightly bound together and considered in relation to each other as part of the litany of problems placed under the environmental banner. This increase in issue bundling is reflected in figure 6.13, which shows a steady increase in the average number of environmental issues appearing in any given article over time.[15] Figure 6.14 shows the same phenomenon from a different angle. Here we see an increase in the frequency with which so-called "green issues" (relating to land use and nature preservation) are found in the same news item as "brown issues" (concerning pollution).

The political implications of issue bundling are several. For one, the conceptual linkage of these issues shapes the composition of political demands pressed by environmental advocates. It is often the case that single-issue environmental campaigns expand over time to cover other conceptually contiguous "environmental" issues. As Leonard and Morell (1981: 293–294) have observed, "Significant effects often spill over from one type of environmental concern to another. The movement against nuclear power is a good example. In the Philippines, Spain, and other countries, groups which had originally organized to combat proposed

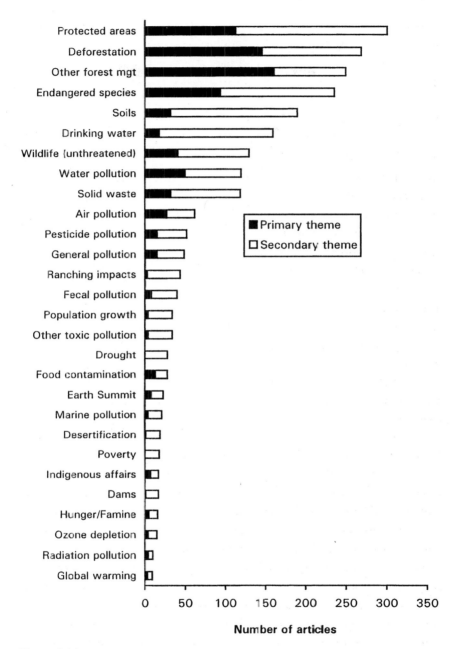

Figure 6.11
Content of environmental news in Costa Rica. Note. Excludes topics with eight or fewer articles. The number of articles on "deforestation," "other forest management," and "indigenous affairs" may be biased upward due to collection procedures. (See methodological appendix for details.)

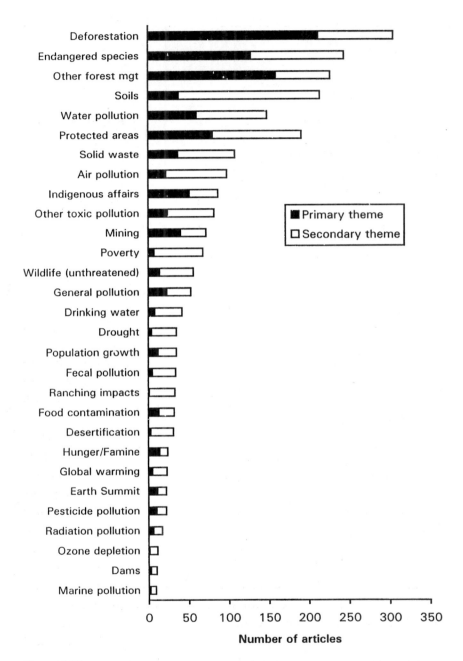

Figure 6.12
Content of environmental news in Bolivia. Note. See notes accompanying figure 6.11.

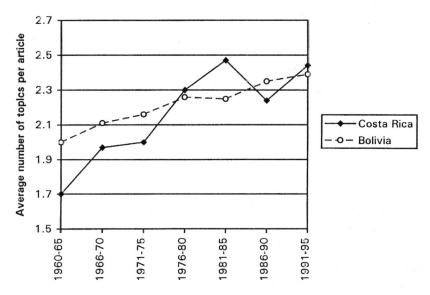

Figure 6.13
Issue bundling: Topics per article.

nuclear power plants have subsequently expanded to deal with other issues." Conversely, a Costa Rican group established for the purpose of
wildlife conservation later held demonstrations in opposition to French
nuclear testing.

Issue bundling can also help steady the inevitable vagaries of public interest in matters of policy (see Downs 1972). If environmentalism were
synonymous with (and limited to) concern for species extinction, the
chances of sustained, widespread public interest in environmental policy
would be slim. In contrast, the dozens of physical and social issues bundled
together under the environmental rubric today increase the likelihood that
at any given moment one or another environmental issue is in the public
eye. More significantly, extinction itself is more likely to be the focus of
sustained attention when bundled with these other issues. During periods
when no high-visibility species conservation events capture public attention, other elements of the environmental problematique keep an environmental policy culture alive, sustaining a social movement and political
institutions that may again turn their attention to biodiversity. The ability
of a topic to ride the coat tails of a conceptually related issue is apparent
in the attention given species extinction in the news. Fully half of the time

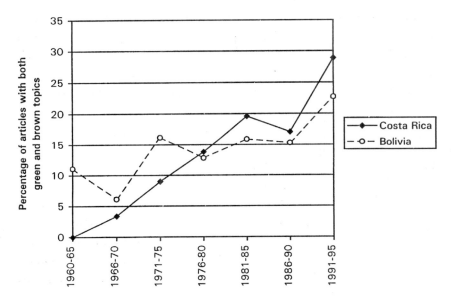

Figure 6.14
Bundling of "green" and "brown" issues. Note. Data includes all articles and letters covering "green" and/or "brown" issues, using domestic news sources only. The figure shows the percentage of these that cover both types of issue in the same news item. "Green" issues = topics dealing primarily with nature and land use, specifically: deforestation, endangered species, other forest management, soils, protected areas, wildlife, drought, ranching impacts, desertification, and the Biodiversity Convention. "Brown" issues = all forms of pollution, solid waste, mining, food contamination, latrines, global warming, and ozone depletion. Subject categories that could not be readily categorized as green or brown (such as military impacts, indigenous affairs and the Earth Summit) were excluded from the analysis.

that threats to biodiversity were mentioned in the newspapers, this was raised as a secondary theme in articles primarily concerning some other environmental issue.[16] The other environmental issues were equally dependent on such associations.

Issue bundling of this sort has directly influenced the design of institutions and the allocation of government resources. The conceptual bundling apparent in public discourse is firmly established in Bolivia's General Environmental Law, which contains language on air pollution, species extinction, energy, water quality, forest management, soils, national parks, and mining, among other issues. Issue bundling also brings to light asymmetries in the performance of government institutions. Contrasting Costa Rica's leadership in biodiversity conservation with its dismal record on urban air pollution, an adviser to President Figueres noted "the irony is not lost on the president." The concept of irony succinctly captures the political significance of issue bundling; biodiversity conservation and air pollution are so closely associated that it appears absurd, or ironic, to devote such attention and resources to the one area without following suit in the other.

Transnational Dynamics of Cultural Change

How can we account for the rise of environmental policy cultures in Costa Rica and Bolivia? One potential explanation is that environmentalism is merely an ideological component of European and North American power and influence in Latin America. The "cultural imperialism" explanation could assume one of two forms. Either environmentalism was imposed outright by foreign powers, through a collection of sanctions and rewards designed to guarantee sustained access to natural resources beyond their borders; or the idea inadvertently spread as a companion to expanding market and military influence—analogous to the exotic species transported to the New World in the ballast water of foreign commercial vessels.

The projection of international power, however, does not provide a satisfactory explanation for the rise of environmental policy cultures because it cannot account for the three central sources of variation in the phenomenon to be explained: (1) the change that took place in Costa Rica from the 1960s (a time of scant environmental concern) to the 1970s, when an environmental policy culture first arose; (2) the difference between Costa Rica and Bolivia during the 1970s, a period in which Bolivia experienced no equivalent popular concern for environmental issues; and (3) the subsequent change within Bolivia, which saw the rise of an environmental policy culture in the mid- to late-1980s. There is no corresponding tempospatial variation in the power or strategies wielded by foreign hegemons with respect to the two countries that might account for these results.

Meyer and colleagues' (1997) study of the origins of global environmental concern cannot explain the variation observed here because they are silent on the question (indeed, the possibility) of national variation in the adoption of these global ideas. Yet the evidence presented in the previous sections demonstrates that the mere existence of a groundswell of international environmental concern, and associated discourses, resources, and organizational venues, does not preordain the timing or extent of environmental commitments in a given society (see also Buttel 2000). Something must be occurring at the national level to mediate the relation between global environmental concerns and national politics and institutions.

A third plausible hypothesis, one that more readily accommodates the possibility of cross-national variation, is that social concern intensified as domestic environmental conditions worsened. The severity of environmental problems certainly bears some relation to social responses to those problems. But changing physical conditions cannot adequately account for the observed changes in social awareness because the latter occurred simultaneously with respect to a broad number of environmental problems—from soil erosion to air pollution to the exploitation of indigenous peoples—while the objective conditions underlying these problems have varied in their intensity, duration, and trends.

A fourth candidate explanation is Inglehart's (1990) postmaterial thesis. Inglehart argues that the rise of environmental concerns is facilitated by the emergence of new generations of individuals raised in conditions of relative security and prosperity, who place a higher premium on quality of life issues. However, widespread interest in environmentalism in Bolivia arose in one of the poorest countries in the Western Hemisphere, soon after a period of extreme political instability during the coups and countercoups of 1978–1982. Moreover, the changes observed here are too rapid to be accounted for by generational turnover.

To understand the spread of environmentalism in Bolivia and Costa Rica requires a different explanation, one that extends Rochon's insights on rapid cultural change into the realm of transnational relations. Rochon highlights the role of critical communities: small groups of intellectuals who devote a great deal of energy to critiquing orthodoxy and to introducing new concepts into society. In the United States rapid changes in predominant social understandings of issues like racial integration, sexual harassment, and environmental concern have resulted from social movements adopting novel ideas first developed by critical communities.

Bilateral activists have played a similar role, introducing new environmental ideas into their societies. Bilateral activists are distinguished, however, by their participation in a transnational social movement. Unlike critical communities, their role in cultural innovation consists in brokering and reshaping ideas first developed overseas. Specifically, in what follows I argue that environmental policy cultures in Costa Rica and Bolivia are the result of the *transmission* and *translation* of international environmental ideas. Transmission has occurred as bilateral activists, who routinely engage novel concepts and innovations from abroad, have expended a great deal of energy introducing environmental perspectives into their societies. As these ideas are adopted by nascent environmental movements and become a topic of concern to a broad range of social actors, they undergo translation. They are modified to fit domestic agendas, and as a result they resemble less a carbon copy of foreign political debates, and more an adaptation—by accident or design—of international concerns.

Transmission of International Environmental Ideas

It is widely recognized in Bolivia and Costa Rica that the environmental ideas so popular in these societies today have their origins in concepts first applied in Europe and the United States.[17] Although the popularity of environmentalism stems partly from its resonance with preexisting domestic issues and understandings, it is a new idea, borrowed from abroad, that has reshaped and redefined the old concerns—giving them a new vocabulary and rationale, a new political context, and bundling them in new ways. This in no way renders these environmental movements less genuine or meaningful. Just as tomato sauce is no less Italian for the South American origins of the tomato, Bolivian environmentalism is no less Bolivian for drawing on ideas that came to fruition in the United States and Europe. The point is, rather, an empirical one: to understand the rise of environmental policy culture in these countries requires an exploration of the cross-national movement of policy ideas.

How Transmission Works

As discussed in chapter 1, the international sphere of influence offers domestic policy reformers a rich array of ideas and lessons from other countries. Foreign ideas are especially accessible in the environmental arena because foreign environmentalists, construing their cause in global terms, are eager to spread the word to other societies. The domestic demand for these policy ideas is apparent in figure 6.15. These data, from the Gallup International Institute's *Health of the Planet* survey, show that citizens of

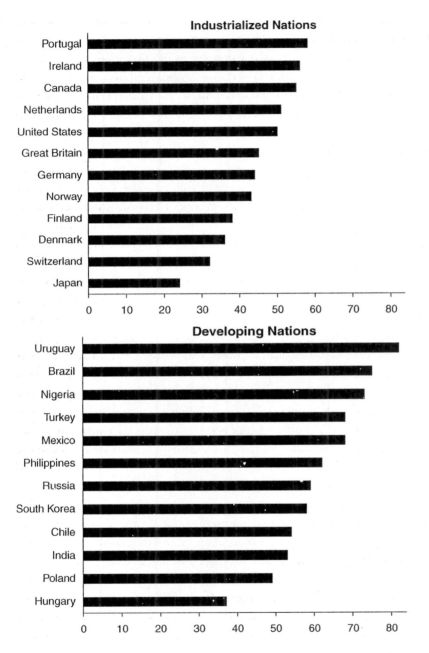

Figure 6.15
Support for providing model environmental laws to developing countries. Percent who say "strongly favor" providing model environmental laws restricting business and industry in developing countries. Source. Dunlap et al. 1993, figure 13c.

developing countries are even more interested in borrowing environmental policy models from abroad than Northerners are interested in sharing them. To explain the cross-border movement of environmentalism, however, it does not suffice to demonstrate the existence of a supply of, and demand for, foreign environmental ideas; this leaves unspecified the mechanism by which this exchange takes place. To use an analogy from institutional economics, even with willing buyers and sellers, a market does not exist unless there is a means to facilitate the exchange of goods.

I will provide two additional pieces of evidence before making the formal argument that bilateral activists were responsible for the cross-border transmission of environmentalism. First, we must consider in more precise terms the geographic origins of the environmental ideas discussed in Costa Rica and Bolivia today. Figures 6.16 and 6.17 map the country of origin for the foreign environmental information appearing in national news media. These are news stories covering actors and events in other countries, or domestic events in which foreign actors figure prominently. These maps may be interpreted as displaying the two countries' environmental policy peer groups. In both cases, neighboring countries are important sources of information relevant to environmental policy. Costa Rica is particularly attuned to events and perspectives of its Central American neighbors, while Bolivia follows environmental developments throughout South America. It is also noteworthy that beyond Latin America, environmental affairs in the rest of the developing world receive little attention. European environmentalism is followed closely in both cases, while the United States is far and away the most important foreign source of environmental information.[18]

The influence of the United States revealed in these figures reflects more than U.S. political and economic hegemony in the region. A study by Buckman (1990) documenting the origin of news and magazine stories covering the arts in fourteen Latin American countries found Europe to be much more influential than the United States in this area.[19] Therefore the pattern of influence observed in figures 6.16 and 6.17 cannot be "read off" relations of economic dependence, because the foreign influence differs by issue area, with the United States particularly influential in the environmental arena.

This leads to the second piece of evidence undergirding the mechanism of transmission outlined below: nearly all of the two or three dozen most

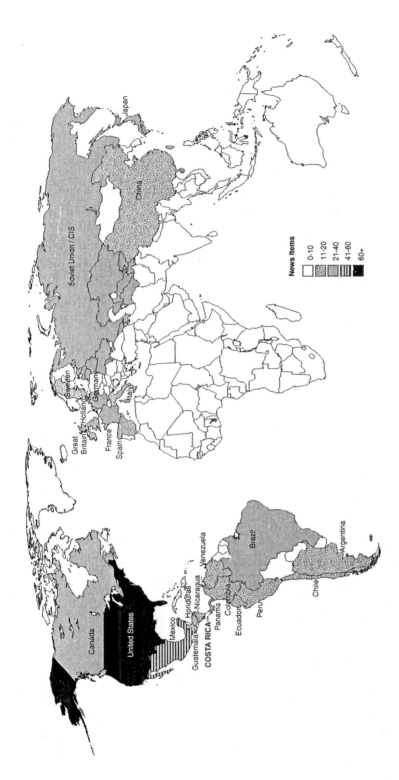

Figure 6.16
Sources of foreign environmental information in Costa Rica, 1960–1995. Note. Mexico = 47, USA = 204. Source. La Nación.

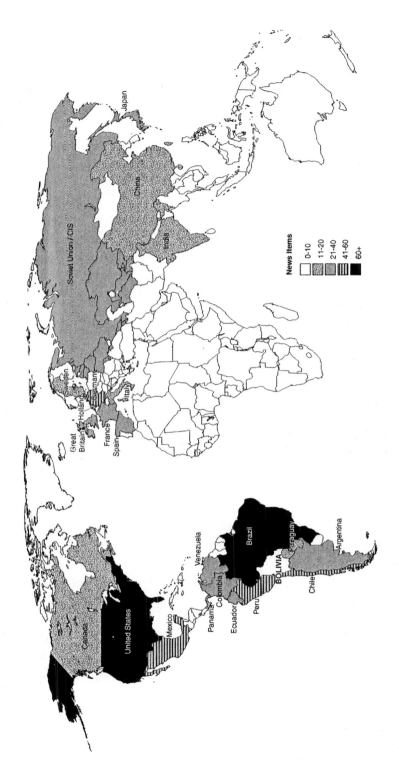

Figure 6.17
Sources of foreign environmental information in Bolivia, 1960–1995. Note. Brazil = 93, USA = 107. Source. Presencia.

influential environmentalists in Bolivia and Costa Rica have spent extended periods of time in the United States, where they were exposed to the U.S. environmental movement and often studied conservation-related topics in American universities.

Having identified more precisely the major foreign influence on environmental policy culture in these societies, we can now place in proper historical and institutional context the question as to why an environmental policy culture arose in Bolivia ten years after its genesis in Costa Rica. In an era of global environmental concern, significant exposure to international ideas—particularly through immersion in dialogue with like-minded individuals overseas—appears to be a prerequisite for the development of a consciously articulated environmental ideology among the earliest environmental activists in a given society. It is certainly not the case that all Costa Ricans and Bolivians with significant exposure to foreign ideas became environmentalists; it is true, however, that all of the early environmental advocates had significant exposure to foreign ideas.

This process was facilitated by a unique category of organizations that we might term *coupling institutions.* From the 1940s through the early 1970s, a series of organizations were created in Costa Rica that served as meeting places for foreign and domestic actors, fostering the birth of a community of bilateral activists. The Organization for Tropical Studies, the Tropical Science Center, and the Inter-American Institute for Agricultural Sciences (shown in figure 6.18) provided a long-term, in-country base for foreign conservationists, allowing them to spend enough time in the country to acquire the domestic political resources described in the previous chapter. These same institutions exposed a group of Costa Ricans to the resources of the international sphere, including foreign environmental ideas and international scientific and donor networks. This enabled Costa Ricans to make personal contacts that often led to scholarships for the study of ecology and other conservation-related subjects in the United States. Over the years these organizations served as common reference points and meeting places for this new breed of environmental advocate with a hand in both the international and domestic spheres of influence. As recounted in chapter 3, soon after the rise of environmental movements in the United States and Europe, this group—and only this group—launched a series of campaigns designed to raise awareness of environ-

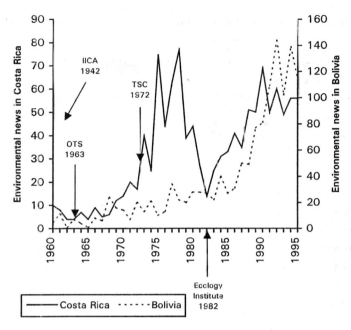

Figure 6.18
Coupling institutions and attention accorded environmental issues. Note. The founding of Costa Rican institutions is noted with arrows pointing downward, that of Bolivian institutions with arrows pointing upward. IICA = Inter-American Institute of Agricultural Sciences, OTS = Organization for Tropical Studies, TSC = Tropical Science Center.

mental problems among the Costa Rican public and to make biodiversity conservation a matter of state policy.

In Bolivia, a similar organization—the Ecology Institute—was proposed in 1974 and was to be funded by the University of Göttingham. The proposal was shelved, however, in response to protests by German students who objected to the idea of providing aid to the Bánzer dictatorship. When democracy was restored to Bolivia in 1982, the proposal moved ahead and the Ecology Institute was founded in La Paz. The Ecology Institute subsequently served the same coupling function as its equivalents in Costa Rica, giving rise to a community of bilateral activists. Most of these were Bolivians who, through contacts made at the Ecology Institute, had the opportunity to study conservation-related sciences in American universities. As documented in chapter 4, these were the pioneers who worked to spread environmental awareness throughout Bolivian society in the 1980s.

To state the causal argument more formally, the conclusion that bilateral activists were responsible for catalyzing the transmission of environmental norms to Costa Rica and Bolivia is based on the evidence summarized in figure 6.19.

Environmental policymaking could have turned out to be a low-profile affair, if bilateral activists had chosen to restrict their activities to behind-the-scenes lobbying of powerful officials. From the start, however, they employed the same strategy as their Northern counterparts, emphasizing consciousness-raising in the broader public. As part of this strategy, bilateral activists helped to create numerous environmental groups, which have played an increasingly important role in environmental debates, as shown in figures 6.20 and 6.21. In addition to diligently ensuring that environmental issues remain part of the public discourse, these groups provide education within their ranks, transforming vaguely interested recruits into committed activists. Many activists relate how they joined an environmental group out of a vague sense of curiosity and concern, and found their personal commitment greatly strengthened once they became immersed in the group's literature and activities and were exposed to the commitment and expectations of peers within the organization. Bilateral activists also led the charge to create government agencies that sponsor a variety of environmental events and

Figure 6.19 (opposite)
Bilateral activism and the diffusion of environmental ideas. Note. There were a handful of Costa Ricans in the post-war era with both exposure to international conservation ideas and a domestic political presence. However, prior to the 1960s, international interest in the environment was minimal. There was little foreign scientific and financial support available, and no foreign environmental movements to be inspired by. Without international resources, these individuals could not be said to engage in bilateral activism during this period. Similarly, there were a few such individuals in Bolivia during the 1960s and 1970s, but absent the appropriate in-country institutions, their contact with foreign environmental organizations—and with one other—was sporadic. They undertook no coordinated activities to raise public environmental awareness, and did not constitute a community of activists.

Temporal Correlation Between Presence/Absence of Bilateral Activists and Presence/Absence of Public Awareness in Costa Rica

1. Prior to the 1960s, there were no bilateral activists in Costa Rica and there was no widespread discussion of environmental issues in that country.

2. In the 1960s, a group of bilateral activists arose in Costa Rica. Beginning in the late 1960s and early 1970s, one of their top priorities was to spread environmental awareness throughout Costa Rican society. They held seminars around the country, created university programs, wrote letters to news media, and established nature education activities in national parks, among other activities.

3. These bilateral activists were the only actors in Costa Rica undertaking this sort of environmental education activity at the time.

4. Soon thereafter (from the mid-1970s onward), environmental themes were discussed widely in Costa Rica, according to both the news analysis and oral histories.

Spatial Correlation Between Presence/Absence of Bilateral Activists and Presence/Absence of Public Awareness in Costa Rica and Bolivia

5. There was no corresponding community of bilateral activists in Bolivia during the 1960s and 1970s. Whereas the environment was a topic of public interest in Costa Rica in the mid-1970s, it was absent from discussions in Bolivia during this time.

Temporal Correlation in Bolivia

6. From the early 1980s onward, a community of bilateral activists developed in Bolivia. One of their top priorities was to spread environmental awareness throughout Bolivian society. They created environmental NGOs, organized ecology conferences around the country, established university programs, and provided environmental training seminars for teachers, among other activities.

7. These bilateral activists were the only ones in Bolivia devoting energy to raising environmental awareness among the general public during this period.

8. Soon thereafter (the mid- to late-1980s), Bolivians began widely discussing environmental themes.

Causal Inference

9. The above evidence strongly suggests that communities of bilateral activists played a catalytic role in the transmission of environmentalism to these societies.

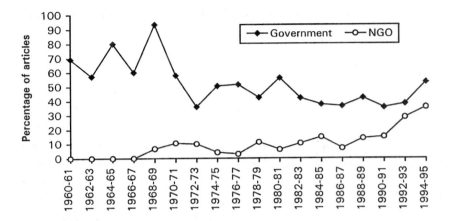

Figure 6.20
Costa Rica: who is primarily responsible for the action/content of the article?
Note. NGO = environmental nongovernmental organization. Responses included
government, NGO, neither, or both. Data are drawn from Costa Rican domestic
news sources only.

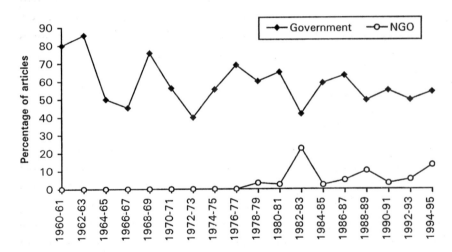

Figure 6.21
Bolivia: who is primarily responsible for the action/content of the article? Note.
See notes accompanying figure 6.20. Data are drawn from Bolivian domestic news
sources only.

public education campaigns, helping to maintain the public profile of environmental ideas.[20]

Translation of International Environmental Ideas

New ideas are more likely to spread rapidly throughout a society when their core concepts are well defined and accompanied by a readily identifiable vocabulary (Rochon 1998). To spread transnationally, however, ideas must fit with the predominant understandings and conceptual precedents of the diverse societies into which they are introduced (Goldstein 1993). Consequently, bilateral activists transmitting concepts and innovations from other cultures must subject these well-established ideas to some form of modification, or *translation*. The process is only partly a deliberate one. Bilateral activists, by virtue of their international exposure and orientation, are responsible for the initial introduction of foreign environmental ideas into their societies, and they willfully translate these ideas to increase their domestic salience. But if and when these new concepts catch on among the broader public—as numerous social groups relate the new environmental thinking to their old concerns—the original international idea is shaped and stretched in ways not entirely foreseeable or controllable by its most ardent proponents.

How Translation Works
Research on the domestic impact of international ideas commonly emphasizes the importance of conceptual compatibility—of the inherent fit between a given idea of foreign origin and the cultural and political orientations of a particular society (Cortell and Davis 2000; Goldstein 1993; Gamson and Modigliani 1989: 5). A shortcoming of the concept of "fit" is that it suggests a static phenomenon, for which one might predict the degree of fit based on a knowledge of the characteristics of the idea in question and those of the society into which it is introduced. But this is a dynamic political process (see Yee 1996; Sikkink 1991; Goldstein 1993: 255–256), more accurately described by the verb form, "fitting." Proponents of environmental policies go to great lengths to argue that environmentalism is consistent with national needs and aspirations, while

opponents of these policies argue that environmentalism is an alien idea, a bizarre foreign transplant that does not fit domestic realities.

The politics of fitting are evident in attempts by both environmentalists and their adversaries to couch their arguments in nationalist terms and to portray the opposition as unpatriotic. Economic sectors affected by environmental regulations have portrayed environmentalists as *comunistas reciclados* (recycled communists) intent on destroying the national economy.[21] Environmentalists have used a similar tactic, painting the timber lobby as unpatriotic in its hurried attempt to clear the country's remaining forests at the expense of national planning.

In societies eager to escape a legacy of foreign domination, the first instance of translation has been the link forged between conservation and national sovereignty. Defending natural resources from foreign control has been the central political aspiration of the G-77 and Nonaligned Movement for the past half century (Mortimer, 1984). Sovereignty concerns are an enduring feature of political discourse in the South—a common conceptual thread running from independence to import-substitution industrialization, OPEC, the New International Economic Order, and contemporary debates over plant genetic resources and intellectual property rights. Not surprisingly, national sovereignty is frequently evoked in efforts for and against environmental protection.

According to former President Jaime Paz Zamora, in the 1930s "in Bolivia we didn't speak of ecology, but rather of the defense of natural resources against the voraciousness of foreign monopolists and imperialists" (quoted in Libermann and Godínez, 1992: 17). Today the two causes are often intertwined, as in the oft-heard phrase "defending our national patrimony"—*patrimonio* denoting both natural heritage and *patria*. Nationalist arguments were used by proponents of Costa Rica's Manuel Antonio National Park (created on lands formerly controlled by a foreign developer), and by opponents of biodiversity prospecting agreements with foreign pharmaceutical firms. In Bolivia national sovereignty has figured prominently in arguments for the protection of the Chimanes Forest, in opposition to Amboró National Park, in support of Noel Kempff National Park, and in opposition to debt-for-nature swaps.

Translation has also resulted from the deliberate association of environmentalism with a political goal so sacred and widely shared that it has been called one of the defining characteristics of developing countries: the commitment to economic development [Heady 1991]. Antonio Andaluz, a Peruvian environmental attorney working in Bolivia, recalled the stigma of environmentalism that prevailed in South America in the 1960s and 1970s. "In our countries, discussion of environmental issues was seen as something for gringos. . . . it was basically a concern for hippies" (Andaluz 1997). To erase this image and establish ecology as a mainstream concern, environmentalists have gone to great lengths to portray conservation as commonsense, long-term development planning. Engaging in what social movement scholars refer to as strategic framing (Snow and Benford 1988), reformers have pitched their arguments in terms that resonate with predominant development ideologies.

Popularization of the term "sustainable development" was a major achievement in this regard. Sustainable development became part of the vocabulary of international environmental diplomacy following the publication of *Our Common Future* by the Brundtland Commission in 1987. But this concept—defined by the commission as development that meets present needs without sacrificing the ability of future generations to meet their own needs—has its origins in development-environment links established many years earlier by activists and intellectuals in the South. In 1973 Bolivian environmentalist Wagner Terrazas (1973: 103) wrote:

. . . the concept of social and economic development requires a clear and concrete definition. This definition should embrace the concept of "sustained development," that is, maintaining an acceptable lifestyle that can not only be improved, but must also be enduring. It follows from this view that the exploitation of renewable natural resources has a human limit—that of avoiding the destruction of the environment and of the resources that feed the population. To do otherwise is to threaten human life itself.

Bearing in mind the influence of the U.S. environmental movement in these countries, it is noteworthy that in one quick blow, sustainable development resolved the major philosophical divide of the American environmental movement—that of protecting the environment for its own sake versus protecting it as a means to improving the human condition.[22] As is commonly the case in developing countries, these societies have translated environmentalism into an idea in which *Homo sapiens* figures front and center. Even the most ardent nature lovers, field biologists who spend weeks at a time with minimal human contact, are quick to clarify "*No soy preservacionista*" (I'm no preservationist), preferring instead the term "conservationist," with its more anthropocentric emphasis on sustained resource use.

The foregoing examples of translation resulted from deliberate attempts by bilateral activists to move the environmental cause from the margins to the center of public attention. But to answer the question Who translates? we must also look beyond the efforts of the environmental community and examine how environmental ideas affect—and are in turn shaped by—diverse social groups and their ideologies. As environmentalism has become increasingly popular in Costa Rica and Bolivia, numerous organizations and popular movements have folded ecology in with their traditional concerns. Translation occurs as these diverse groups mobilize their distinct organizational and ideological resources on behalf of the environment (see Dalton 1994; McCarthy and Zald 1977). Many of the groups now mobilizing for ecology are led by activists whose formative political experience was in earlier left-inspired movements emphasizing social and economic justice; it is no coincidence when these activists tie environmental arguments to radical critiques of neoliberal economics. Likewise, when women's organizations like Bolivia's Casa de la Mujer create environmental programs, this represents not only the greening of the women's movement, but the entry of feminist discourse into the demands of the environmental movement. The result is that the bundle of issues placed under the environmental rubric has not been neatly under the control of the bilateral activists who first introduced the idea (see also Rochon 1998: 195).

The connections forged between ecology and broader social concerns have intensified as environmentalism has gained in popularity, conferring legitimacy on anyone who can credibly claim to further its ends.[23] Thus the Catholic Church in Bolivia links its pro-life philosophy to pro-nature arguments, while crusaders against drugs highlight the ecological damage wreaked by the coca industry, and partisans of administrative reform argue that decentralization is indispensable for sustainable development (López 1996). Human rights advocates try to imbue environmentalism with a concern for social justice, as when Nobel Peace Prize winner Rigoberta Menchú argues:

Poverty and environmental degradation will continue until we abandon the absurdity of the current form of producing and distributing wealth. . . . Sustainable development must be built on historical and cultural diversity, on the equality of opportunities between men and women and on the unrestricted participation of the citizenry in the exercise of democracy. (Menchú 1996: 12)

Just as these causes derive legitimacy from their connection with ecology,[24] the latter increases its standing by association with other popular causes. While environmental activists may chuckle about the lack of scientific training among these new recruits, no politically astute Latin American environmentalist will refuse the participation of organizations like the Catholic Church in the environmental movement.

Translation in Action: The Indigenous Rights-Environment Connection

A poignant example of the translation of international environmental ideas is found in the association forged between conservation and the struggle for the rights of indigenous peoples. The argument runs as follows: as long-term residents of natural areas, engaged in low-impact activities and possessing an intimate knowledge of the land, indigenous peoples are in a unique position to provide environmental stewardship— provided they are given the land title and legal guarantees needed to ensure both cultural survival and ecological well-being. Prior to the 1980s, this was not a struggle that environmentalists viewed as their own. Likewise, indigenous organizations, whatever their specific philosophies on conservation, did not emphasize environmental issues when pressing their demands before government. In an article entitled "The Indigenous American Race in Its Relation to the Soil," Peruvian delegates to the 1948 Inter-American Conference on Conservation of Renewable Natural Resources described this relationship in markedly different terms from those used today:

This group, then, because of its lack of culture, its low standard of living, its malnutrition, and the ignorance and oblivion in which it lives, represents what we could perhaps call a true parasite of the soil. It represents a parasite whose essential activity determines the loss of millions of hectares of arable land per year . . . incited by the primitive agricultural practices and by the superabundance of human and animal populations which exercise such strong biological pressure on the poor environment in which circumstances oblige these people to live. (Llosa, De Armero, and González 1948: 271)

When not portrayed as perpetrators of environmental destruction, indigenous peoples were cast as its victims. In a report to the Costa Rican Legislative Assembly in 1968, Arturo Trejos protested that under the existing laws "one can authorize contracts for the extraction of timber within ancient indigenous reserves. This has accentuated deforestation and has destroyed the natural environment protecting our aboriginal peoples. . . ."

Whereas earlier in the century indigenous peoples were depicted as perpetrators or victims of ecological destruction, by the late 1980s the image had changed to that of defenders of the environment. Two developments facilitated this change: the rise of environmentalism as a legitimizing discourse and a surge in political mobilization by indigenous groups on a scale unprecedented in the twentieth century (see Yashar 1996; Brysk 2000). In Bolivia, supporters of the indigenous March for Territory and Dignity drew on the rhetoric and popularity of Bolivia's environmental movement, arguing that "indigenous peoples plus land equals conservation," as Guillermo Rioja (1997a, 1997b) succinctly expressed the equation. A similar argument was used by advocates of indigenous rights throughout the South.

It did not take environmentalists long to appreciate the strategic importance of allying themselves with the indigenous cause—both from a political standpoint and as a means to conservation—and the combination of movements has been a formidable one. Indigenous rights figure prominently in Bolivia's General Environmental Law, and the Bolivian government has handed over management responsibility for several national parks to indigenous organizations. When the World Bank and Inter-American Development Bank sponsored the construction of a gas pipeline through one such park, private developers were required to not only produce an environmental impact report but an analysis of likely impacts on local indigenous communities, accompanied by a multimillion dollar fund for indigenous park administration.

Most remarkable is the way that international environmental ideas, transmitted across borders and translated by indigenous rights movements, have in turn fed back into the international sphere of influence in their modified form. Recall that from a Costa Rican perspective, Bolivia is part of the international sphere–the wealth of ideational and institutional resources whose productive dynamic resides beyond Costa Rican borders. Interestingly, the indigenous rights-environment connection forged in countries like Bolivia has entered the environmental discourse of self-consciously westernized Costa Rica, which lacks a well-organized indigenous rights movement. This is reflected in figure 6.22, which shows an

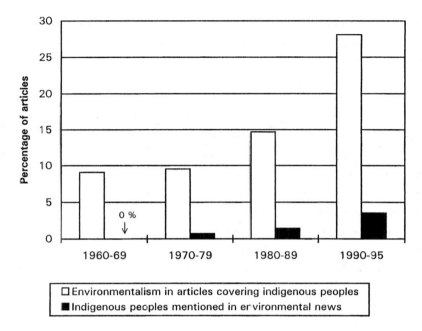

Figure 6.22
The indigenous rights-environment connection in Costa Rica.

increasing proportion of the country's environmental news articles discussing indigenous themes, and the growing prominence of ecology within articles on indigenous peoples.[25]

Environmental Protection: Lost in the Translation?
There are many potential sources of domestic translation in addition to the ones detailed here. The core philosophy of a government agency given responsibility for environmental protection will affect its interpretation of the environmental mandate (Steinberg 1998b)—a point not lost on environmentalists, who have fought to wrest environmental regulatory authority from agriculture and tourist ministries, preferring to invest it in new agencies created specifically for this purpose. Translation also occurs when environmentalists are forced to incorporate the concerns of their adversaries during the give-and-take of political bargaining over environmental statutes. Perhaps the greatest translator of all is history. Different nations address the same issue area during different time periods, which affects the way these issues are defined and addressed.[26] Moreover, the mix of domestic influences to which international environmental ideas are

subjected is itself mediated by domestic institutions, which determine the opportunities for expression and mobilization by various sectors of society (see Yee 1996).

Given the many forces shaping and stretching international environmental ideas to fit domestic agendas, we might ask whether at the end of the day there is anything left of the original idea, or whether it is completely lost in the translation. After all, if environmental rhetoric serves merely as a new medium for old concerns, the true impact of environmental ideas must be called into question. For example, from an environmental standpoint, there are risks accompanying the rewards of association with causes like economic development and indigenous rights. If environmental protection is merely a means to promoting long-term national development, presumably it can be dispensed with if and when other approaches more effectively promote that goal—such as a rapid liquidation of standing natural assets to finance the defense of national territory. Likewise the relationship between indigenous control of land and conservation is not nearly as formulaic as some popular accounts would have it (see Redford and Stearman 1993; Simonian 1995: 9–27).

It is noteworthy, however, just how intact international environmental discourses remain in Costa Rica and Bolivia. The core concepts, concerns, and vocabulary of environmental protection have shown considerable resilience across borders, despite the force and requirement of translation (see also Peritore 1999). Bilateral activists have likely had a hand in this. Sensitive to the needs of their own societies, they may be more likely than foreign environmentalists to make sure that at least some translation occurs; but with their continued exposure to the ideas and expectations of the international environmental community, they have a stake in ensuring that environmentalism does not lose its meaning altogether. Their power and legitimacy to mediate this process stems from both their issue expertise and their positions as leaders of their nations' most important environmental organizations, both inside and outside of government.

Conclusions

The connection between cultural change and political reform lies in the fact that political preferences, in Wildavsky's words (1987: 3), "come from the most ubiquitous human activity: living with other people." As studies of culture have increasingly captured the attention of political scientists, the question is no longer whether ideas matter for policy, but what sorts of ideas and under what conditions (see Winch 1996). Studies of policy culture can help situate these questions in the context of transnational relations. Policy culture is an analytically tractable, politically relevant, and—most importantly—readily measurable social variable. It demonstrates considerable variation across countries and over time, and it is therefore well suited to research on the means by which public ideas move across cultures.

This chapter has documented the rise of environmental policy cultures in Costa Rica and Bolivia, and the mechanisms by which international environmental ideas have been transmitted and translated across borders. As we fold these results back into the larger question of determinants of policy change, we must bear in mind that the development of a culture of concern surrounding an issue area provides no guarantee of institutional reform or improved policy outcomes. The idea of poverty alleviation, for example, enjoys public support and is a focus of official rhetoric throughout the developing world, with widely varying results. Policy reform involves both changing minds and moving stones. It is in combination with institutional resources—particularly the blend of technical, financial, and political resources described in the previous chapter—that bilateral activists have been able to transform novel ideas into effective institutions.

7

Comparative Perspectives on Global Problems

It is fruitless to debate whether domestic politics really determine international relations, or the reverse. The answer to that question is clearly "Both, sometimes." The more interesting questions are "When?" and "How?"
—Robert Putnam, 1988[1]

To motivate the subject of this book I began by making three interrelated claims: First, national policy in developing countries is and will continue to be an important determinant of global environmental quality. Second, policy outcomes vary across countries and over time, as documented in chapters 3 and 4. Third, the sources of this variation are worthy of explanation. The explanation I provide highlights the importance of bilateral activism. In a context of global concern and national political authority, policy entrepreneurs with simultaneous access to domestic and international spheres of influence have been responsible for policy innovation and institutional strengthening over a period of decades. Combining international scientific and financial resources with domestic political resources, they have enabled Costa Rica and Bolivia to create a series of environmental institutions that work reasonably well despite the great odds facing policy reformers in poor countries. With the benefit of both extensive international exposure and a long-term, in-country presence, they have introduced environmental policy ideas from abroad and fostered the growth of constituencies of concern at home.

Taking domestic politics seriously and viewing international influences from the inside out, the spheres of influence framework offers a new lens for exploring three questions of central concern to students and practitioners of international environmental policy: (1) What explains state behavior with respect to global environmental problems? (2) What is the nature and extent of international influences on domestic policy? (3) How might we enhance the ability of international institutions to contribute to global environmental management? Let us consider each of these questions in turn.

Understanding Domestic Responses to Global Problems

Over the course of the next few decades, the state of the planet will be strongly shaped by policy decisions in developing countries on issues ranging from energy production to land use, agricultural policy, transportation infrastructure, coastal planning, and protected areas management. Yet research on the social forces affecting global environmental quality has paid meager attention to the dynamics of policymaking and institutional reform in the South. One of the greatest benefits of a comparative-historical approach to the study of international environmental policy is that it allows us to understand in more precise terms the causal mechanisms driving national responses to global ecological concerns. To reveal these processes requires cumulative, cross-national explorations into the process of institution building, the evolution of public preferences and their relation to state behavior, and the role of domestic-international linkages in catalyzing these processes.

We have a long way to go to reach this level of understanding. Recent attempts to explain cross-national differences in environmental policy commitments have had to make due with poor quality data sets and arm's-length measures of causes and effects. Thus in arguing that domestic environmental advocacy is an important predictor of state behavior, Lowry (1998) uses levels of urbanization as a proxy for the existence of environmental advocacy coalitions. But to the extent that levels of urbanization and social activism are correlated, this affects activism of every stripe, on issues ranging from labor rights to religious expression to community development; there is no reason why this should tilt the balance of national power toward environmental ends in particular. Moreover, with urbanization levels typically surpassing 70 percent throughout the Americas, such a measure is too roughly hewn to distinguish among the nations of the Western Hemisphere.

In another study, Meyer and colleagues (1997) make the plausible assertion that state environmental commitments are the result of international influences as mediated by domestic "receptor sites." But they use the presence of domestic environmental groups as the measure of receptiveness to international ideas, and membership in international environmental organizations as a proxy for national commitments. This begs the question of the origin of each and of the direction of causation. The approach also obscures differences among environmental groups in their precise historical roles as transnational mediators or domestic consumers of international ideas. Finally, the model does not allow for countries to be receptive to some environmental ideas and resistant to others.

Comparative policy research can offer greater analytic resolution, more reliable variable construction, and higher quality data with which to explore these questions. To take full advantage of the rich detail offered by in-depth field research, we must first overcome two hurdles. To start, we need to revisit the assumption, common in the comparative literature, that national governments in developing countries are both unwilling and unable to play a constructive role in natural resources management. The political ecology school (see Blaikie 1985; Peluso 1992; Gadgil and Guha 1995) and studies of environmental policy failures (see Asher 1999; Gibson 1999) provide a wealth of insights into the hurdles facing proponents of sustainability and social justice in developing countries. But this literature has little to say about the probability and causes of improvements in government performance. Without denying the importance or prevalence of the government pathologies revealed by these works, the findings reported in this book suggest that they present us with an incomplete picture. It is also necessary to ask why government sometimes plays a constructive role, why things sometimes go right, and how we might promote more of the same. Viewing state behavior as a variable opens up new lines of inquiry for the analyst and suggests new possibilities for the practitioner.

Comparative policy research must also be approached in such a way as to facilitate the accumulation of insights across countries and cases. There is certainly no lack of material for such an enterprise. In Mexico, advocates recently convinced the government to halt expansion of a large salt factory in the Baja peninsula that would threaten gray whale calving grounds. In Hong Kong, environmental policy entrepreneurs pressing for the protection of Victoria Harbor are navigating planning department politics, shifts in executive-legislative relations, and the transition to Chinese rule. In Zimbabwe, government officials have crafted innovative institutional approaches that give local communities a greater stake in wildlife conservation. In the past few years some highly informative accounts describing these diverse activities have begun to emerge (see, for example, Lee and So 1999; Dedina 2000; Hochstetler 1997; Child 1996). What we lack are explanatory frameworks that can help us understand the implications of one study's findings for those of another. We need descriptive categories that can facilitate meaningful cross-national comparisons in conditions, processes, and outcomes as well as causal theories that are testable in diverse national settings. For scholars, theory is what allows research to amount to more than the sum of its parts. For practitioners, the value of these models comes in facilitating conversations between experts from Senegal and Suriname, providing a focal point for dialogue and for lesson-learning across borders.

Modeling Global Environmental Politics

The spheres of influence framework is designed to provide a transparent and testable model to help explain the policy responses of sovereign developing nations to global environmental problems. In approaching this complex topic, given the choice between using coarse statistical measures of 100 countries and a careful analysis of a very few, I have chosen the latter route. If the perennial challenge of large-N studies is the construct validity of the arm's-length measures they employ, generalizability is the mirror challenge for studies choosing empirical depth over geographic breadth. The strategy I have used is to present the results from Costa Rica and Bolivia in generalizable terms so that they might be of use to those with expertise in other parts of the world.

There is good reason to believe that bilateral activism will be found to constitute a significant force in environmental policymaking in many developing countries. Where intense global concern exists alongside jealously guarded national sovereignty; where the major centers of science and finance relevant to conservation are located outside of a country's borders; and where institutional success depends on the application of political expertise specific to that country and off-limits to foreigners, bilateral activism is likely to play an important role. Nevertheless, while this study strives for broad applicability, it does not assume it. Therefore to be as clear as possible as to the advantages and limitations of the spheres of influence framework, let me briefly sketch an efficient methodology for researchers interested in testing its applicability in the countries they know best.

The essence of the method is to assess international influences from the inside out. First, one should identify the dozen or so most important environmental policy accomplishments in the country of interest over the past two or more decades. Next, inquire as to who have been the key players most consistently responsible for the success of these institutions. To do this, in the course of interviews make a point of revealing sources of inertia (as described in chapter 1) and understanding how these were overcome. Ask where the idea for a new institution came from, and look for instances of trial and error, and for learning over time and across policy arenas. Discern the most important sources of funding and technical support, and explore whether political resources of the type described in chapter 5 were as important as I claim. Once the most influential actors have been identified, along with the resources and strategies they have used to promote policy change, explore the characteristics of the actors themselves to see whether they may fairly be described as bilateral activists.

For a theoretical framework to be useful, it must not only be potentially applicable to a wide range of cases, but easily refutable with empirical evidence. So let me further suggest the easiest way to disprove the central causal tenets of the spheres of influence framework. Evidence that would most strongly suggest that the framework does not apply, and that some other conceptual approach may be needed, includes the following: (1) There is little distinction between the resources of the international and domestic spheres of influence, because (a) most of the science and finance required for conservation have been generated domestically, with little dependence on foreign resources; or (b) foreign actors have equal access to domestic political resources, such that these are not properly described as "domestic"; or (c) international finance has been used to directly purchase domestic political access by foreign actors themselves. In the latter case, we would expect international environmental funds to go to politically influential nationals who, unlike bilateral activists, may care little for environmental protection, analogous to foreign firms paying hired guns to push for tax exemptions and preferential contracts.[2] Given this, we would expect these hired guns to often switch sides, lobbying for foreign environmentalists or foreign timber companies, whoever can pay the highest premium. (2) The coupling of international and domestic resources does not occur within individuals as I have asserted. Rather, this coupling is more characteristically accomplished through a series of collaborations between foreigners with little domestic expertise and various nationals with minimal international exposure. This might be the case if enduring domestic environmental institutions maintain relationships with the same foreign institutions over time, such that the actors frequently change while the nature of the relationship persists. More generally, the model's emphasis on activism and entrepreneurship might reflect an unrealistic assumption about the causal importance of human agency. The easiest way to refute this assumption is to demonstrate that the major catalysts for policy change are not long-term participants. Opportunities arise that inspire one or another policy reformer to rise to the occasion provided by a fortuitous confluence of conditions, but there is little consistency in the major players over time.

It would be difficult to disprove the notion that political resources are important for policy change, because the term "political resources" is simply a heuristic label designed to draw attention to a category of institutional assets often overlooked. That is, we cannot test the statement "political resources are important for policy change," because as soon as a resource has proven its worth in the political arena we might properly call it a political resource, making this assertion impossible to refute. A more productive approach is to test the relevance of the specific types of political resources described in this book, such as familial contacts[3] and process expertise. Expanding the menu of political resources beyond the examples elaborated here is likely to be one of the most immediate benefits of testing the spheres of influence framework in different national settings.

Leadership and Constraints

One advantage of the spheres of influence framework is that it captures elements of both structure and agency—of relatively immovable constraints on social action, and of the significant degree of creativity and entrepreneurship that individuals exercise within these constraints. The relevance of national structures for the study of global environmental politics is apparent if we contrast conservation policymaking in Kenya before and after independence. Under colonial rule, transnational advocacy by British conservationists was subject to few of the political constraints of the contemporary era. When the Society for the Preservation of the Fauna of the Empire wanted to push for game parks in British East Africa, they lobbied their home government (Adams and McShane 1992). To achieve political gains in the region required connections, presence, and expertise in London, with the effect that British advocates possessed a monopoly over both economic and political resources. Independence brought both political sovereignty and continued economic impoverishment, such that today the centers of conservation science and finance remain in places like London, while the decision-making power and political skill sets bearing on those decisions are concentrated in Nairobi. These structural constraints exercise an important influence on the roles, strategies, and impacts of participants in North-South environmental relations.

One difference between the Latin American cases reviewed here and developing countries as a whole is that in Africa and Asia the recent influence of colonial conservation policy is still keenly felt, leaving a residue of local distrust and often a legacy of authoritarianism in state resource agencies. Everywhere in the developing world, however, attempts to craft enlightened state responses to environmental problems face formidable political challenges. The environmental management agencies that have proliferated across the South over the past three decades almost invariably carry less political weight than powerful ministries devoted to resource extraction and economic growth, which command vast resources and answer to well-endowed constituencies well-represented in the upper echelons of power. Achieving gains in environmental management objectives against these odds requires advocates who make strategic use of political resources of their own. Effective national responses to global biodiversity loss require both adequate budgets and ample political connections; well-maintained park trails and regularly renewed commitments from multiple political parties; knowledge of the habitat requirements of large carnivores and of the political preferences of potentially troublesome agency leaders.

Political resources fit the category of phenomena described by Stephen Jay Gould (1996: 15–16) as "an unconventional mode of interpretation that seems obvious once stated, but rarely enters our mental framework. . . ." If at this point in the book the importance of domestic policy reformers strikes the reader as obvious, I would count that as a success. To date, research on transnational environmental relations has largely overlooked these actors, focusing instead on the activities of highly visible multinational environmental groups, with headquarters in industrialized countries, as the empirical basis for conclusions regarding the nature of global environmental politics. More generally, the information on tropical conservation reaching Northern audiences, primarily through news media and international environmental groups, almost invariably stars advocates from Europe and the United States: with cameras rolling, the foreign scientist wades through the marshes of exotic lands with a sense of purpose and adventure, whispering bits of ecological expertise to a breathless television audience. How many times have nature documentaries covered the story of the domestic political expertise responsible for the park in which the foreign scientist advances? (A story which, I readily confess, is less visually arresting.)

There are many reasons for this bias, among them the relative ease with which journalists can interview their compatriots overseas, and the fact that foreign financial and scientific contributions are easier to document than are domestic political resources. My purpose here is not to pass an ethical judgment, but an analytical one. The inordinate amount of attention given Northern scientists and donors obscures the essential role played by domestic environmentalists in developing countries, and draws our attention away from an entirely different category of resources in need of further study. The precise nature of domestic political resources will vary from one developing country to the next. But regardless of the specific configuration of political skills best suited to a given country, domestic political resources comprise an indispensable analytic category for those who seek to understand the policy responses of sovereign developing nations to global environmental problems.

The Origins of National Concern

National responses to global environmental problems are not merely a function of the capacity for action but of the willingness to devote this capacity to environmental goals (see Haas, Keohane, and Levy 1993). Throughout this book I have argued that to understand state behavior with respect to the environment we must study the origins of political preferences and the mechanisms by which policy ideas diffuse across borders and become institutionalized in the mandates, resource allocations, and day-to-day decisions of national bureaucracies. As noted in chapter 2, we must employ measures of environmental concern that are separate from measures of environmental outcomes, if we hope to gauge the effect of the former on the latter. If only the Gallup International Institute had conducted its revealing 1992 survey of environmental views in developing countries ten years earlier, we would have a wealth of information for tracing the dynamics of mass preference formation in developing countries (see Dunlap, Gallup, and Gallup 1993). In the absence of longitudinal public opinion data, content analysis of mass media and public hearings, together with qualitative interviews and historical research, can provide insights into the origins of national environmental concern. These rougher measures provide the equivalent of a black-and-white moving picture to complement the color snapshot provided by recent surveys. This long-term view is needed to document changes in public belief systems and in public policies and to understand the relation between the two. Contemporary cross-national comparisons can provide some suggestive correlations, but we must document the timing, extent, and nature of changes in national concern for environmental issues if we are to pinpoint the driving forces behind one of the most remarkable empirical facts of our time: the widespread expression of support for environmental protection by citizens of rich and poor nations alike.

The results presented in this book support the conclusion that environmental policy ideas initially are transmitted across borders by means of small group interactions. These interactions bring foreigners together with nationals who are cosmopolitan both in their travel routines and in their attitudinal predisposition to entertain foreign ideas. The exchanges typically take place in one of two physical venues: national organizations that routinely attract large numbers of foreign visitors interested in a specific issue area, or immersion of nationals in foreign settings where such issues are already being discussed. In the course of face-to-face dialogue, these cosmopolitans are exposed to ethical arguments and technical information bearing on the issue, and to powerful demonstration effects as they witness the enthusiasm of the idea's proponents and the feasibility of their proposals. Often this idea diffusion is facilitated by the shared intellectual orientation of individuals within a scientific research community (see Haas 1992), although my findings suggest that the process also includes individuals from a fairly wide range of professions and disciplinary backgrounds. Recalling the discussion of tipping models in chapter 6, small group interactions are how we can understand the endurance of isolated pockets of environmental concern in societies that have yet to embrace these ideas on a larger scale.

The second stage of diffusion occurs if and when the ideas of these small groups of cosmopolitans are adopted by state authorities and social movements (see Rochon 1998). The impact of international environmental ideas on government institutions in Costa Rica and Bolivia has been the direct result of bilateral activism, with cosmopolitans using their domestic political clout to insert these ideas into forestry legislation, park agency mandates, congressional committee structures, party platforms, foreign affairs ministries, and even national constitutions. The early pioneers have also fomented changes in social preferences by creating new university programs; providing training sessions to teachers, journalists, and professional associations; and most importantly, by forming numerous civic environmental organizations with the help of funding from their overseas contacts.

Ecology offers a vast ideological umbrella that can accommodate all manner of social goals—from economic efficiency and improved business strategy to civic engagement, spiritual enlightenment, and social justice. The precise content of environmentalism evolves as it diffuses among nations with diverse histories and cultural orientations. The political necessity of this conceptual translation, and its power to shape the content of environmental ideas, are captured by the Bolivian writer Teresa Flores, who in 1991 reiterated the humanistic brand of environmentalism preferred in Latin America: "We conservationists are no longer the marginal group that in the eyes of many appeared more interested in nature than in its own people. It has become clear that the conservation of nature is inextricably linked to the welfare of our people, and that it is neither a caprice, nor a luxury, nor a form of snobbery coming from the North."[4]

The flexibility of environmental ideology has undoubtedly contributed to the widespread popularity of environmentalism around the globe, but it also raises a troubling question: What exactly is it that is enjoying such popularity? If environmentalism undergoes so much cultural translation from one society to the next that the idea shares little in common across borders, then we are observing not national responses to global concerns, but a conveniently global discourse applied to diverse, and perhaps diverging, national concerns. Although linkages with domestic discourses emphasizing humanism, social justice, sovereignty, and development have indeed affected approaches to conservation in Costa Rica and Bolivia, the environmental ideas that have filtered into Latin America from the United States and Western Europe retain much of their original content. Bilateral activists mediate this tension between the need for conceptual translation and the possibility of losing the original international idea altogether. As noted in chapter 6, when environmental ideas manage to attract the attention of thousands of citizens, and diverse constituencies begin to link environmental arguments to their causes, the process of translation is no longer firmly under the control of the tight-knit circles of bilateral activists who first introduced these ideas. Nonetheless, as the recognized spokespeople for the environmental cause, bilateral activists and those working under their tutelage in government agencies, universities, and social movement organizations play an important role in ensuring the integrity of the core idea, as they decide in negotiation with other social actors whether a given issue is an appropriate focus for environmental advocacy.

My findings suggest that issue bundling—the process of tying together previously distinct, well-developed discourses—is the primary mechanism by which environmentalism is translated from one society to the next. Issue bundling affects the transnational diffusion of ideas in diverse issue areas, but it is especially relevant to environmental concerns because ecology is a concept emphasizing connectedness—between physical media, between humans and nature, and between distant causes and effects. Researchers analyzing the content of environmental ideas in developing countries typically search for broad differences in environmentalism as practiced in the North and South (Guha and Martínez-Alier 1998; see also Brechin 1999; Christen et al. 1998; Hsiao et al. 1999). Indeed I have taken the liberty of asserting some of these differences in this book. But these broad generalizations obscure important variants of environmental concern within and among developing nations—to say nothing of diversity within and among industrialized countries (see Dalton 1994; Brickman et al. 1985). Assessments of issue bundling permit the finer-grained analysis needed to understand variation and congruence in the content of environmental concern across borders, which in turn shapes both the composition of demands by social movements and the resource allocations of state authorities.

Assessing the Impact of International Actors and Institutions

In the absence of world government, national policy reform is central to the success of international environmental agreements and is eagerly sought by the transnational coalitions pressing for their adoption. To date, assessments of the impacts of these international actors and institutions have focused largely on industrialized nations, reflecting the fact that historically the great majority of environmental treaties have been concluded among Northern states. But with the emergence of global-scale concerns such as climate change, tropical deforestation, and international trade in hazardous wastes, the South is now in a stronger position to influence the content and effectiveness of international environmental agreements—a fact that has not gone unnoticed by developing country negotiators. A comparative perspective on global environmental politics brings new evidence to bear on the question of whether these international actors and institutions are having a significant causal effect, by allowing us to situate their impact relative to the larger constellation of forces bearing on environmental policy outcomes in developing countries.

My findings concerning the impact of international resources differ markedly from those of Haas, Keohane, and Levy (1993), whose analysis of international environmental institutions revealed a very modest influence on national policy in developing countries. The discrepancy is a methodological one, for I construe international influences more broadly. These authors focused on specific multilateral institutions, whereas in the present analysis international influences include everything from a Swiss technical assistance agency to the pocket change of a foreign nature tourist. Viewed in isolation, the causal impact of an international initiative is rarely cause for celebration among institutionalists. Viewed from the inside out and in the aggregate, however, international resources have exercised a pervasive influence on nearly every policy initiative undertaken in Costa Rica and Bolivia over the past four decades. Evaluations of the impact and effectiveness of specific environmental regimes will remain a vital part of the research agenda (see Victor, Raustiala, and Skolnikoff 1998; Weiss and Jacobson 1998; Young 1999). My results suggest that these evaluations may nonetheless be underestimating the potential for international resources to affect national outcomes.

The findings in this book present a more serious challenge to the published literature on transnational environmental advocacy. As noted above, research in this area has focused an inordinate amount of attention on large environmental NGOs operating out of the United States and Europe. When a Greenpeace vessel docks in a poor developing country like Costa Rica for a few days, it may have an important short-term impact, but such activity does not represent the central tendency of transnational environmental relations. The limitations of this Northern empirical focus quickly become apparent when one attempts to assess the overseas impact of these Northern actors. Princen and colleagues observe that Northern NGOs often avoid entanglement in national politics overseas, working instead in diplomatic venues or with local organizations. On this basis they conclude that the nation-state is irrelevant to the resolution of global environmental problems (Princen, Finger, and Manno 1994: 223–224; see also Fisher 1993: 10). As documented in the preceding chapters, foreign groups' avoidance of national politics has more to do with the fact that such direct involvement is often illegal and almost always considered inappropriate by nationals. Domestic environmental groups, by contrast, devote considerable attention to reforming government policies and institutions, which they recognize as indispensable for improving environmental outcomes.

The conclusions of this book also bear little resemblance to the mechanisms of influence highlighted in Keck and Sikkink's (1998) analysis of transnational citizens' campaigns to slow tropical deforestation and reform World Bank environmental policy. The reason for the discrepancy is that these high-profile international campaigns are of minor causal importance for the pattern of institutional accomplishments described in this book and for environmental policymaking in developing countries generally. The effort to reform World Bank policy is a rare instance in which environmentalists in industrialized countries have a near monopoly on political resources affecting a policy outcome in the South, by virtue of wealthy countries' voting power in the bank and its physical location in Washington, D.C. This fact is no doubt related to Northern environmentalists' enthusiasm for the approach.

The point I wish to emphasize is that in attempting to understand the nature of transnational environmentalism, if we take our cues from the agendas of multinational environmental NGOs, we are left with a small and unrepresentative subset of cross-border environmental activity. In contrast, the political dynamic at the heart of this book is one of bureaucratic maneuvering by domestic policy reformers in developing countries, who engage in lesson-learning and experimentation, behind-the-scenes mobilization of personal contacts, and persistent policy entrepreneurship over a period of decades. They seek out a broad range of foreign allies—from scientific institutions to private philanthropists, religious organizations, universities, overseas development agencies, and a wealth of environmental NGOs large and small—and combine these foreign resources with the domestic political expertise needed to see through major policy innovations. The transnational dynamic is of lower profile, higher complexity, and longer duration.

New Approaches for International Institutions

Whereas the design and execution of a research project is typically undertaken by one or a few individuals, I believe that policy prescriptions are best developed in the course of conversation among many, including those most affected by proposed policies and institutions. In this spirit, let me suggest three major implications of this book that may serve as a useful launching point for wider discussions on the practice of international environmental policy.

The first implication stems from the subject of chapter 2, which lays out a logical and empirical critique of the notion that developing countries are too poor to care about environmental protection absent foreign financial inducements. Rejecting this assumption creates space for more nuanced conceptions of environmental politics in developing countries and for more creative roles on the part of international institutions. On matters relating to developing countries, the central thrust of international environmental policy has been to purchase support for environmental protection via institutions like the Global Environment Facility, operating within the legal framework established by treaties on stratospheric ozone, climate change, and biodiversity. Given the fallacy of environmental privilege, this strategy should be complemented by an approach that assesses the potential contributions of international institutions from the inside out—first identifying existing sources of public concern and policy change in developing countries, and then asking how international institutions might support these ongoing domestic processes.

We must now ask: Why have environmental movements arisen throughout the South—what are their strengths, shortcomings, and expressed needs? What are the sources of environmental leadership in developing countries, and how might the relevant institutions or processes be supported? What domestic policy innovations have been tried and what is their record of success? And importantly, why do high levels of environmental concern often exist alongside poor environmental performance? Only by dispensing with the mythology of environmental privilege can international actors contribute to the domestic capacity to translate these concerns into workable institutions.

It is almost axiomatic in environmental policy circles to say that the support of local communities is a necessary condition for the success of conservation initiatives in developing countries. Less commonly acknowledged is the importance of enlisting support from committed policy entrepreneurs at the national level, and this omission comprises the subject of my second point. Research on common-pool resource management has revealed that a supportive national policy environment is a necessary condition for the success of local institutions (Ostrom 1990). With due respect to the old summons to think globally and act locally, we must not lose sight of the fact that the political authority to act on global environmental problems—through price policies, industry regulation, support for scientific research, wealth redistribution, maternal and child health programs, education initiatives, tax incentives, import-export controls, and the like—is generally concentrated at the level of national government.

To create a supportive policy environment requires a cadre of skilled policy entrepreneurs capable of garnering political support within the relevant bureaucracies, who are willing and able to spearhead fundamental reforms of state institutions when the need and opportunity arise. The most effective environmental policy communities will include participants from diverse political parties, regions, and constituencies to ensure a measure of continuity across changes in political leadership. Fostering a supportive policy environment also requires individuals who are involved over long enough periods to test alternative management approaches, to engage in trouble shooting as programs reach maturity, and to take advantage of rare windows of opportunity for institutional strengthening. Long-term involvement by domestic policy entrepreneurs helps to transform isolated donor-supported projects into a more continuous process of capacity building for environmental management.

This brings us to the third major policy implication of the present study. Policy entrepreneurs with simultaneous access to resources of domestic and international origin have been central to the success of biodiversity policy initiatives in Costa Rica and Bolivia. Therefore it may be worth increasing international support for coupling institutions, of the sort described in chapter 6, that have given rise to communities of these bilateral activists. Three principles should guide any such effort.

First, these institutions should be located in the developing countries of interest. In-country organizations have been important sites for informal networking among advocates, providing resources and employment opportunities that allow domestic actors to stay with the cause over a period of decades. These organizations should have the ability to attract the participation of large and diverse groups of nationals. This suggests that the "centers of excellence" model—the approach favored by international donors supporting agricultural research in developing countries—would be inappropriate, given these centers' emphasis on cultivating elite groups of foreign researchers with few national ties. Second, these institutions should be nonpartisan; the capture of institutions by political parties more interested in patronage than policy has been the bane of conservation efforts in both countries. Third, these organizations should have the ability to routinely attract prominent foreign actors, thereby providing nationals with links to international scientific resources, policy ideas, and fundraising networks. The experience of Costa Rica's Organization for Tropical Studies and Bolivia's Ecology Institute could inform efforts along these lines.[5]

The Measure of Success

If the literature on environmental politics in developing countries may be faulted for a narrow attraction to policy failures, I realize that by honing in on the success stories, I may be committing a different variety of the same sin. Though I have insisted on the difficulties of conservation policy in Costa Rica and Bolivia, and the hurdles that reformers have faced at every turn, this book may nonetheless convey an overly optimistic tone. At times I have the image of a broad landscape subjected to all kinds of natural slaughter, and in the midst of the many failures, the reader's attention has been directed to those areas receiving effective protection and conferring community benefits. Does this not amount to applauding the saving of a chair while the house burns down? I take solace in three observations on this point. First, the accomplishments described in this book are by no means trivial. They have afforded protection to tens of thousands of species and have inspired the participation of an equal number of citizens.

Second, the successful protection of even relatively small proportions of national territory can have significant consequences for the conservation of biological diversity, because species diversity is often highly concentrated in a few spots.[6] Finally, if what is needed are more sweeping sorts of reforms—radical democratization, expansive environmental taxes and subsidies, or some as yet undiscovered measure—the processes, institutions, actors, and resources described in this book will likely be essential to bringing such ideas to fruition.

Methodological Appendix

Article Collection

Choice of Newspapers

In Costa Rica, articles were collected from *La Nación,* the larger of the country's two major daily newspapers. *La Nación*'s editorial orientation is right-center, corresponding roughly to that of the country's Social Christian Party. (The powerful news organization is not, however, controlled by the party; some would argue the reverse is true.) In Bolivia, articles were collected from *Presencia,* one of several major daily national papers. *Presencia* is owned and operated by the Bolivian Catholic Church, and has a populist, left-center editorial orientation. Very little of *Presencia*'s news information or editorials relate to religion or the Catholic Church; its content resembles that of high quality secular news organizations, and it is akin to the *Christian Science Monitor* in the United States. Choosing a left-leaning newspaper in Bolivia and a right-leaning paper in Costa Rica carries a methodological advantage: Environmentalism is more commonly associated with the political left than with the right. Therefore the increase in environmental stories in *La Nación* a full decade before the same occurred in *Presencia* is all the more convincing as evidence that Costa Rican society paid attention to environmental issues earlier.

Two pieces of evidence support the conclusion that these news outlets are representative of broader media coverage of environmental issues in their respective countries. First, a perusal of other major newspapers in the 1990s readily confirms the finding that environmental issues have received a great deal of coverage in both countries in recent years; the local news daily *El Deber* in Bolivia typically carried two to three environmental news stories per day in the latter half of 1997. Second, the timing of the increases in environmental stories corresponds closely to the accounts provided in qualitative interviews.

There exist no reliable subject indices for these newspapers, so research assistants reviewed hard copy issues, page by page, photocopying all environmental news stories (following collection criteria detailed below). In Costa Rica, four assistants, all upper-division undergraduates at the University of Costa Rica, reviewed a weekly sample of *La Nación* (Wednesday of each week) for the period 1960 to 1995. I decided to begin as far back as 1960 to provide an adequate baseline for comparison to subsequent changes in the 1970s and beyond. Beginning in 1975, the weekly agriculture and livestock supplement "Agropecuaria" appeared in *La Nación*. Research assistants reported that not only did the new supplement carry many environmental articles, but this was accompanied by a decrease in their appearance in the rest of the newspaper (i.e., editors were apparently moving most environmental news to the new section). Therefore I decided to include the weekly supplement, which appeared regularly from 1975 onward, in the sample of papers searched for environmental news. This may have exaggerated the sudden increase in environmental news stories observed in Costa Rica beginning in 1975. However, four observations suggest this influence was minimal.

First, the supplement did not significantly increase the overall quantity of news stories searched (see newspaper size analysis below). Second, the existence of the weekly supplement cannot provide a sufficient explanation for the increase in environmental news stories, because the number of stories dropped in the early 1980s and increased thereafter, without any corresponding changes in the frequency or size of the weekly supplement. Third, the news supplement was never a necessary precondition for environmental news; nothing prohibited the routine publishing of environmental news before its advent. Fourth, and most importantly, the mid-1970s saw a corresponding increase in editorials and letters to the editor on environmental topics, appearing primarily in the main news section.

In Bolivia, a team of three upper-division undergraduates from various universities in Santa Cruz de la Sierra searched *Presencia* issues covering the same 1960 to 1995 period. Because *Presencia* is a smaller newspaper, assistants searched three issues per week (Monday through Wednesday) in the 1960s, when issues were particularly small, and two per week (Tuesday and Wednesday) from 1970 to 1995. Oversampling in the 1960s brought the total number of pages closer to that of subsequent decades. It also creates an upward bias in the number of news articles found in the 1960s, because the 1960s sample includes a larger number of days in which environmental events might occur. As with all such decisions, I purposely chose the option that would make it more difficult to prove my case. That is, despite the upward bias, the number of news stories in the 1960s was still small compared to subsequent decades, bolstering the credibility of the conclusion that environmental awareness arose later. Occasionally *Presencia* issues were missing from the university archive in Santa Cruz de la Sierra, in which case research assistants searched adjacent weekdays. In cases where entire weeks were missing from the archive, the relevant issues were obtained from *Presencia* offices in La Paz and offices of the national archives in Sucre.

Newspaper Size

This book argues that the increase in environmental news stories over time reflects a growing level of environmental awareness and activity in Costa Rican and Bolivian societies. Such increases, however, could easily be a simple function of increasing newspaper size. Therefore research assistants took sample measurements of the size of the newspapers over time. This has the added benefit of facilitating a comparison with the attention given other (nonenvironmental) issues. Specifically, if environmental news stories increase over time, and if this increase cannot be explained by a larger overall amount of news coverage, then environmental coverage has increased in both absolute and relative terms. I decided not to simply count the number of pages, because changes in the proportion of advertisements over time would render the results difficult to interpret. Instead, research assistants measured the amount of text (rounded to the nearest quarter page) on each page in the sections searched. A sample of eight issues per year were measured in Costa Rica, and twenty-seven issues per year (on average) were measured in Bolivia. Figures A.1 and A.2 show trends in the amount of newspaper text over time. In neither case can changing newspaper size account for the observed changes in environmental news.

Selection Criteria

Determining which articles qualified as "environmental" news presented a methodological dilemma. One of the major goals of the content analysis

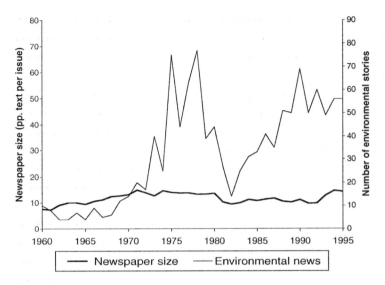

Figure A.1
Newspaper size in Costa Rica. Note. The typical length of news articles does not change substantially over time.

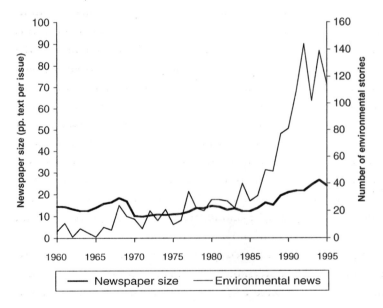

Figure A.2
Newspaper size in Bolivia. Note. The typical length of news articles does not change substantially over time. This figure does not reflect the fact that the 1960s were oversampled by 33 percent (see text for explanation). That is, the relative quantity of news searched in the 1960s was one-third higher than what is shown.

was to document the types of issues figuring prominently in environmental discourses in these societies; the risk was that the collection criteria could bias the conclusion by imposing from the outset my view of what constitutes an environmental issue. This problem was addressed through a two-stage selection procedure. First, the collection teams were provided with very broad criteria, to err on the side of inclusion. Next, during the content analysis, each article had to pass a specific test (detailed in the next section) to be included in the analysis.

In the first stage, collection teams were instructed to gather articles on a wide variety of topics, including those frequently addressed in the publications of environmental agencies and NGOs in these countries, as well as issues commonly considered part of the environmental cause by international environmental organizations such as the United Nations Environment Programme. An identical list was used for both countries, with the exception that environmental impacts of mining were added as a separate topic in Bolivia, and slightly different protected area designations were used, corresponding to the different regulatory regimes of the two countries. The full list of topics is shown in the attached coding sheets.

In recent years, efforts have been made to expand the menu of environmental issues in developing countries to include not just those problems arising from industrial development (which are most common in industrialized countries), but those resulting from inadequate development, such as a lack of access to drinking water. Therefore drinking water access was included in the initial selection criteria. Cigarette smoking is one topic that was not included, but which in retrospect is plausibly considered part of the environmental problematique in Bolivia, where it is mentioned in the General Environmental Law. Articles covering energy shortages were not included. It is also important to note that collectors did not gather all articles dealing with natural resources (e.g., "Bumper Crop Affects Cocoa Prices"); only those covering identified environmental problems (e.g., "Soil Erosion Continues in Tarija") were included in the sample.

Research assistants only collected articles for which environmental issues were the principal and overriding theme. For example, an article on a public demonstration for three major causes—women's rights, community development, and environmental protection—would not be included in the data set unless the latter figured most prominently. Assistants were instructed to decide whether or not to include an article on the basis of the headline alone. In cases where headlines were ambiguous, assistants had the option of reading the first sentence or two to make a clearer determination. Paid advertisements were not included in the analysis.

In addition to collecting environmental articles, all articles on forestry were collected from the issues searched in both countries, to facilitate a special analysis of the forestry sector; in Costa Rica, all articles covering indigenous peoples were collected as well for a separate analysis.

Collection teams were provided with several pages of instructions, and collection criteria were discussed extensively before they began work. These discussions included practice exams with lists of fictitious environmental headlines, to make sure there was agreement on collection criteria. Collectors recorded any questions or observations in notebooks, and these were discussed in weekly group meetings lasting two to four hours. As a rule, if a collector was in doubt as to whether or not to collect an article, she or he was to collect it; its appropriateness for inclusion in the data set was then scrutinized in the subsequent content analysis.

Rather than assign different years to different research assistants, each assistant searched a few assigned months of every year. This prevented any remaining discrepancies in selection criteria among the assistants from biasing interyear comparisons. The results of different collectors were also plotted to ensure that observed patterns in the combined data set were not the result of any one collector's months.

The research assistants were instructed to collect articles in chronological order from 1960 to 1995. I strongly suspect that this gave the earlier years a "better chance" of producing environmental articles: After receiving extensive instructions, the assistants were eager to find environmental articles at the beginning of their work and carefully searched the old issues (in vain) for environmental news. By the time collectors reached the later years, in which hundreds of environmental news stories appeared, they were no doubt accustomed to visually scanning the newspapers more rapidly. Once again this created a higher hurdle for the posited longitudinal changes to clear.

Content Analysis

After the articles were collected according to the criteria described above, they were analyzed using the attached coding sheet. In Costa Rica, the content analysis was conducted by a separate team of three students, all pursuing advanced degrees in forestry management. In Bolivia, the analysis team consisted of two of the undergraduates who undertook the collection and one recent college graduate.

Final Selection Criteria

The collection procedure in Bolivia unexpectedly produced a sample of nearly 2,500 articles, which were too numerous to analyze. Therefore a random number generator was used to exclude one of every three dates searched, which reduced the number of articles to 1,784. The 1960s were excluded from the reduction procedure because the sample from that period was already quite small, and I wanted to maintain enough articles from the 1960s to make meaningful longitudinal comparisons of article content. This had the effect of further oversampling the 1960s, again increasing the credibility of the conclusion that environmental awareness arose in later decades, which produced many more environmental articles despite this sampling bias.

All of the collected articles were then subjected to a second round of elimination. To be included in the final analysis, the articles had to pass one of two tests. They had to contain one or more strongly environmentalist keywords (Spanish-language equivalents of environment, ecology, sustainable development, biodiversity, extinction, conservation, pollution, or protection); or they had to reflect the following perspective, in the judgment of the coders: "Our natural resources (or environment) are threatened. Something must be done to protect them." Many more nuanced definitions of environmentalism could have been used, incorporating perspectives on progress, technology and development, a holistic view of problem interconnectedness, and so on. A simpler definition was chosen to facilitate easy and consistent coding judgments. As Earl Babbie (1990) points out, manifest content (such as keywords) are more reliable but less valid than latent content (such as deciding on the presence of an environmentalist perspective). For this reason both were included. The presence of one of these keywords is a strong indicator of an environmentalist discourse, providing a solid rationale for inclusion of an article in the data set, while the absence of such words does not necessarily mean an article should be excluded. The same is true of the more subjective criterion; many articles that failed the environmental perspective test were picked up by the keyword test.

The articles weeded out by this process were given one last chance for inclusion, using a "limits to growth" criterion: Any article that discussed both population growth and hunger/famine was kept in the final sample.

The final sample of environmental articles likely contains a disproportionate amount of articles on forestry issues in both countries and on indigenous issues in Costa Rica. Articles on these two topics were collected for a special analysis (drawn from the same issues searched for general environmental news), and were subsequently added to the environmental article database if they passed the selection criteria described above. These selection criteria "passed" an article if an environmental keyword or perspective appeared anywhere in that article, whereas the larger set of environmental articles were chosen on the basis of the title alone. That is, many forestry articles that would not have been collected on the basis of the title alone were included in the final data set.

Two other important inclusion decisions were made, one of these concerning population articles in Bolivia. I have argued that the number and content of environmental news stories are fair reflections of environmental thinking in these societies. Because *Presencia* is published by the Catholic Church, however, it carries a large number of articles on population issues, exaggerating the importance of this concern in Bolivian environmental discourse. To weed out articles motivated more by the concerns of the publishing organization, the following additional criteria were applied to population articles in Bolivia. First, the articles had to emphasize population growth per se, as opposed to reporting on birth control or abortion. The articles also had to feature population growth as a *problem,* rather than simply report the latest census data. Articles whose primary focus was a reaction against the portrayal of population growth as a problem were also included. This problem also had to be the primary focus of the article, meaning it was mentioned in the title or first paragraph, or comprised one-third or more of the text. Finally, any population articles were excluded that featured the Catholic Church prominently (again using the criteria of title, first paragraph, or one-third of the text) as were any population editorials, since these reflect the view of the news organization. These tests reduced the number of population articles considerably, to an amount and proportion that I believe more accurately represent the role of population issues in Bolivian environmental discourse.

The second special inclusion decision concerned drinking water. As noted earlier, all articles on drinking water provision were collected to capture a potentially broader interpretation of environmentalism in developing countries. This produced an enormous number of articles, covering every instance in which a community clamored for a new water pump. The vast majority of these would also fail the inclusion tests described earlier; as it turns out, access to drinking water is not generally pitched as an environmental issue by affected communities or by environmentalists in these two countries (except when tied to pollution, dams, or deforestation). To avoid having to complete a full analysis of each of these articles (particularly the thorough keyword search), they were first subjected to the following test: Articles concerning the quality of water (e.g., "Community Blames Illness on Water Source") were advanced to the keyword and environmental perspective tests. If they just concerned the quantity of drinking water available, they were not included in the analysis.

Obviously there is an arbitrary component to these decisions, as is the case with many smaller judgment calls on inclusion and coding. As a result, conclusions about the relative importance of different environmental topics should be interpreted with care. Note, however, that most of the conclusions from the content analysis presented in the previous chapters concern temporal changes—in effect controlling for any influence of these decisions on the final results. For example, clearly the rules for drinking water articles (applied consistently over the thirty-six-year span) could not have produced the surge in environmental news observed in later years. Therefore what is most important in devising such rules is consistency in their application to ensure that observed temporal changes are not an artifact of selection and coding criteria. If major environmental topics had been excluded, such as deforestation or water pollution, this could influence observed longitudinal trends, since changes in attention accorded these important issues are responsible for much of the change in attention accorded the environment. I am confident, however, that the data set accurately captures the vast majority of environmental articles. Most judgment calls were of a much smaller scale, such as the decision that the subject category "drought" only applied to water shortages that were chronic and affected an area larger than a city.

The inclusion criteria produced a final set of 1,174 articles in Costa Rica, and 1,326 in Bolivia.

Coding Procedures and Reliability Tests

Coding teams were provided with extensive written and oral instructions on coding criteria. Five additional steps were taken in each country to improve accuracy and consistency among coders. First, two weeks of discussions preceded the commencement of coding to ensure clarity and consensus and to resolve outstanding questions. The coding sheet was revised in response to this initial feedback from the Costa Rican coders. Second, each team analyzed a common set of practice articles together. The coding sheet then was revised a second time in response to remaining ambiguities revealed by this exercise in Costa Rica. Third, for the first two weeks of coding in each country, research assistants began every daily work session by reviewing the printed coding guidelines. Fourth, coders recorded any questions or concerns in notebooks, and these were discussed in weekly meetings typically lasting three to four hours.

Fifth, two intercoder reliability analyses were conducted in each country to document and improve consistency. The first reliability analysis was conducted toward the beginning of the work period and resulted in a third redesign of the coding sheets in Costa Rica. (All three coding sheet revisions occurred in response to feedback from the Costa Rican team because the content analysis was first conducted in Costa Rica.) Final intercoder reliability scores were calculated during roughly the fourth week of coding in each country. (In each country, article collection took approximately two and one-half months with three research assistants working twenty hours per week; coding required about the same amount of time.) Scores were calculated only for questions of a subjective nature, such as whether an article reflected an environmentalist perspective, or whether biodiversity was its primary subject. The analysis excluded purely objective questions about the presence of a keyword or a photograph. Their inclusion would have biased the intercoder reliability scores upward. The final intercoder reliability score for the Costa Rican team, based on an analysis of twenty-two articles, was 95.6 percent. The score for the Bolivian team, based on twenty-five articles, was 93.7 percent.

As with the collection procedures, each coder analyzed a certain number of months of every year, so that any remaining discrepancies in the criteria used by different coders would not affect interyear comparisons. For the same reason, direct comparisons between Costa Rican and Bolivian news stories with respect to their content and frequency must be interpreted cautiously. Even if one were to control for the different size of the two countries' newspapers, I would hesitate to directly compare the absolute number of environmental articles in each country in a specific year. If the Costa Rican figure were twice that of Bolivia, this could be due to Costa Rican collectors and coders applying selection criteria in a more forgiving fashion. For cross-national comparisons it is more meaningful to compare the timing of changes in the two countries, which removes this potential bias. Therefore the reported results focus on such temporal comparisons. As an extra precaution, however, I judged it worthwhile to measure consistency in the criteria used by coders in the two countries. Therefore a between-country intercoder reliability score was calculated. Twenty-two Costa Rican environmental news stories were brought to Bolivia for analysis by the Bolivian team. The "consensus answer" from Costa Rica (meaning the yes/no response chosen either unanimously or by two of the three Costa Rican coders) was the consensus answer in Bolivia 97.2 percent of the time.

The original coding sheets are reproduced here, followed by an English translation. Instruction sheets providing coders with additional details and criteria concerning specific questions are available from the author upon request.

ANALISIS DE PRENSA

1. ID de artículo:	

2. Titular (bien escrito)	

Sí	No	3. ¿Primera plana?

Nac	**Int**	4. Fuente de noticias

Internacional: ACAN, AFP, ALA, AP, Earthscan, EFE, IPS, LATIN, Reuters, SBI,

SICA, UP, UPI, USIS, o periódico extranjero: (nombre, país):_____

Sí	No	5. ¿Con foto/dibujo?

Sí	No	6. ¿Opinión? a) editorial b) carta/columnista

7. Número de párrafos (sin titular):_____ Titular, párrafos equivalentes:_____

8. Describa en una frase (15 palabras max.) de qué se trata este artículo:

9. Tipo de evento. (¿Quién es directamente responsable por el evento?)

Sí	No	• ¿Se trata PRINCIPALMENTE de una acción (reunión, ley, decisión, etc.) de gobierno?
		Extranjero o/y Boliviano: local o/y federal: Legislativa, Judicial, Ejecutiva
Sí	No	• ¿Se trata PRINCIPALMENTE de una acción de una ONG AMBIENTAL?
Sí	No	• ¿Se trata PRINCIPALMENTE de evento extranjero/internacional?

Si es extranj/int'l, escoja UNA de las siguientes opciones:
____ No menciona Bolivia
____ Bolivia está mencionada pero Bolivia no fue la causa del evento
____ El evento no existiría sin involucro de Bolivia
Si es extranj/int'l, indique país(es):_____ o sin lugar específico

Sí	No	10. ¿Representa el artículo una perspectiva ambientalista?

Sí	No	11. ¿El enfoque principal consiste en una crítica al gobierno boliviano?

Sí*	No	12. ¿Es el artículo patentemente anti-ambientalista?

			13. Temas principales y secundarios del artículo. Ponga un círculo alrededor de la opción apropriada.
1	2	No	Abastecimiento de agua potable
1	2	No	provisión de acueductos/alcantarillados/cañería/pozos
1	2	No	represas
1	2	No	Capa de ozono estratosférico
1	2	No	Conferencia de Naciones Unidas Sobre el Medio Humano (Estocolmo, 1972)
1	2	No	Contaminación
1	2	No	contam. del agua dulce (de ríos, de pozos, etc.)
1	2	No	contam. del aire (humo de buses, etc. NO capa de ozono/NO efect invern.)
1	2	No	contam. marina
1	2	No	contam. por desechos biológicos humanos (por bacterias, aguas negras, etc.)
1	2	No	contam. por radiación
1	2	No	contam por pesticidas/plaguicidas (DDT, DBCP, etc.)
1	2	No	contam. por otros químicos tóxicos (derrame, explosión, petróleo, etc.)
1	2	No	contam. o saneamiento de alimentos humanos
1	2	No	Convenio Internacional Sobre Diversidad Biológica (1992)
1	2	No	Crecimiento demográfico humano
1	2	No	Cumbre de la Tierra/Confer. Sobre Ambiente y Desarrollo (Río, 1992)
1	2	No	Daños militares al ambiente (efectos ambientales de bombas, guerras, etc.)
1	2	No	Desechos sólidos generales (basura, rellenos sanitarios, reciclaje)
1	2	No	Deforestación provocada por causas humanas
1	2	No	Desertificación
1	2	No	Efecto invernadero (recalentamiento de atmosfera)
1*	2*	No	Especies amenazadas o en peligro de extinción. (Incluye protección o amenaza a cualquiera especie o población - más de un animal individual).
1	2	No	Asuntos Forestales/bosques fuera de áreas protegidas (viveros, etc. NO deforest.)
1	2	No	Ganadería provocando problemas ambientales
1	2	No	Hambruna u otra falta de alimentación humana severa y general
1	2	No	Indígenas: Derechos/reclamaciones de pueblos indígenas
1	2	No	Invierno nuclear
1	2	No	Letrinización
1	2	No	Minería provocando problemas ambientales
1*	2	No	Parque nacional/reserva biológica/estación biológica/reserva de biosfera
1	2	No	Otro área protegida (reserva forestal, etc.)
1	2	No	Pobreza humana
1	2	No	Sequía
1	2	No	Suelos (erosión, manejo, productividad, etc.)
1	2	No	Vida silvestre NO amenazada/NO dañada/NO solo árboles/NO en peligro de extin.
1	2	No	General (Solo cuando no hay tema principal claro; RECUERD. TEMAS SECUNDAR'S)

		14. Palabras ambientalistas. ¿Contiene el artículo una forma de las palabras siguientes?
Sí	No	BIODIVERSIDAD (o diversidad biológica. Solo estas dos formas.)
Sí	No	CONTAMINACION (contaminar, contaminado, etc.) o POLUCION
Sí	No	CONSERVACION (conservar, conservacionista, etc.) o PRESERVACION (preservar, etc.) o PROTECCION (protejer, etc.)
Sí	No	DESARROLLO SOSTENIBLE (sostenible, sostenibilidad, etc. No "desarrollo" solo.)
Sí	No	ECOLOGIA (ecologista, ecológico, etc.)
Sí	No	EXTINCION
Sí	No	MEDIO AMBIENTE (ambiental, ambientalista, medio, medio humano, etc.)

Sí	No	15. Análisis verificado por segunda vez.

16. Personas u organizaciones citadas o mencionadas en el artículo.
(Si no hay ninguna, escriba la palabra "no" aquí:_____.)

NOMBRE	ORGANIZACION
NACION: Ex/Bol/Esp	NACION: Ex/Bol
CITADO: sí/no GOB: sí/no: Ex/Bol: loc/fed: Legisl/Judic/Ejec ONG: sí/no: ambio/otro CIENTIFICO: sí/no DESTRUCT: sí/no	

NOMBRE	ORGANIZACION
NACION: Ex/Bol/Esp	NACION: Ex/Bol
CITADO: sí/no GOB: sí/no: Ex/Bol: loc/fed: Legisl/Judic/Ejec ONG: sí/no: ambio/otro CIENTIFICO: sí/no DESTRUCT: sí/no	

NOMBRE	ORGANIZACION
NACION: Ex/Bol/Esp	NACION: Ex/Bol
CITADO: sí/no GOB: sí/no: Ex/Bol: loc/fed: Legisl/Judic/Ejec ONG: sí/no: ambio/otro CIENTIFICO: sí/no DESTRUCT: sí/no	

NOMBRE	ORGANIZACION
NACION: Ex/Bol/Esp	NACION: Ex/Bol
CITADO: sí/no GOB: sí/no: Ex/Bol: loc/fed: Legisl/Judic/Ejec ONG: sí/no: ambio/otro CIENTIFICO: sí/no DESTRUCT: sí/no	

NOMBRE	ORGANIZACION
NACION: Ex/Bol/Esp	NACION: Ex/Bol
CITADO: sí/no GOB: sí/no: Ex/Bol: loc/fed: Legisl/Judic/Ejec ONG: sí/no: ambio/otro CIENTIFICO: sí/no DESTRUCT: sí/no	

NOMBRE	ORGANIZACION
NACION: Ex/Bol/Esp	NACION: Ex/Bol
CITADO: sí/no GOB: sí/no: Ex/Bol: loc/fed: Legisl/Judic/Ejec ONG: sí/no: ambio/otro CIENTIFICO: sí/no DESTRUCT: sí/no	

PRESS ANALYSIS

		1. Article ID:

		2. Title (carefully written)

Yes	No	3. First page?

Nat'l	Int'l	4. News source
		International: ACAN, AFP, ALA, AP, Earthscan, EFE, IPS, LATIN, Reuters, SBI,
		SICA, UP, UPI, USIS, or foreign newspaper: (name, country):_____

Yes	No	5. Photo?

Yes	No	6. Opinion article? a) editorial b) letter, column

		7. Number of paragraphs (absent title):_____ Title (paragraph equivalents):_____

		8. Describe in one sentence (15 words maximum) the subject of the article:

		9. Type of event. (Who is directly responsible for the event?)
Yes	No	• Is this principally an action (meeting, law, decision, etc.) of the government?
		Foreign and/or Bolivian: local and/or federal: legislative judicial executive
Yes	No	• Is this principally an action of an environmental NGO?
Yes	No	• Is this principally a foreign/international event?
		If so, choose one of the following options: ___ It does not mention Bolivia ___ Bolivia is mentioned but is not the cause of the event ___ The event would not have taken place without Bolivian involvement If it is foreign/int'l, indicate countries:_____ or no specific location

Yes	No	10. Does this article reflect an environmentalist perspective?

Yes	No	11. Is the primary focus a criticism directed toward the Bolivian government?

Yes*	No	12. Is the article patently anti-environmentalist?

13. Primary and secondary themes of the article. Circle the appropriate option.

1	2	No	Provision of drinking water
1	2	No	provision of aqueducts/water pipe infrastructure/wells
1	2	No	dams
1	2	No	Stratospheric ozone
1	2	No	UN Conference on the Human Environment (Stockholm, '72)
1	2	No	Pollution
1	2	No	freshwater pollution (of rivers, wells, etc.)
1	2	No	air pollution (from buses, etc. NOT ozone layer or global warming)
1	2	No	marine pollution
1	2	No	pollution from human biological waste (by bacteria, infected water, etc.)
1	2	No	radiation pollution
1	2	No	pesticide pollution (DDT, DBCP, etc.)
1	2	No	pollution from other toxics (a spill, explosion, oil, etc.)
1	2	No	food contamination and hygiene
1	2	No	Convention on Biological Diversity (1992)
1	2	No	Human population growth
1	2	No	Earth Summit/UN Conference on Environment and Development (Rio, '92)
1	2	No	Military environmental impacts (effects of bombs, wars, etc.)
1	2	No	Solid waste (trash, landfills, recycling)
1	2	No	Deforestation caused by humans
1	2	No	Desertification
1	2	No	Greenhouse effect (global warming)
1*	2*	No	Threatened or endangered species. (Include protection or threat to any
			species or population - more than an individual animal.)
1	2	No	Forestry issues outside of protected areas (nurseries, etc. NOT deforestation)
1	2	No	Ranching that causes environmental problems
1	2	No	Famine or other severe and generalized food shortage
1	2	No	Indigenous peoples' rights and demands
1	2	No	Nuclear winter
1	2	No	Latrines
1	2	No	Environmental impacts of mining
1*	2	No	National parks/biological reserves/biological stations/biosphere reserves
1	2	No	Other protected area (forest reserve, etc.)
1	2	No	Human poverty
1	2	No	Drought
1	2	No	Soils (erosion, management, productivity, etc.)
1	2	No	Wildlife NOT threatened/NOT harmed/NOT simply trees/NOT endangered
1	2	No	General (Only when no clear primary themes. REMEMBER SECONDARY THEMES)

		14. Environmentalist keywords. Does the article contain a form of the following words?
Yes	No	*BIODIVERSIDAD* (Or *diversidad biológica*. Only these two forms.)
Yes	No	*CONTAMINACION* (*contaminar*, *contaminado*, etc.) or *POLUCION*
Yes	No	*CONSERVACION* (*conservar*, *conservacionista*, etc.) or *PRESERVACION* (*preservar*, etc.) or *PROTECCION* (*protejer*, etc.)
Yes	No	*DESARROLLO SOSTENIBLE* (*sostenible*, *sostenibilidad*, etc. Not "*desarrollo*" alone.)
Yes	No	*ECOLOGIA* (*ecologista*, *ecológico*, etc.)
Yes	No	*EXTINCION*
Yes	No	*MEDIO AMBIENTE* (*ambiental*, *ambientalista*, *medio*, *medio humano*, etc.)

Yes	No	15. Analysis double checked.

16. People or organizations cited or mentioned in the article.
   (If there are none, write "no" here:_____.)

NAME	ORGANIZATION
NATIONALITY: Foreign/Bolivian/Span[1]	NATIONALITY: Foreign/Bolivian
CITED: yes/no GOV'T: yes/no: Foreign/Bol: loc/fed: Legisl/Judic/Exec NGO: yes/no: environmental/other SCIENTIST: yes/no DESTROYER[2]: yes/no	

NAME	ORGANIZATION
NATIONALITY: Foreign/Bolivian/Span	NATIONALITY: Foreign/Bolivian
CITED: yes/no GOV'T: yes/no: Foreign/Bol: loc/fed: Legisl/Judic/Exec NGO: yes/no: environmental/other SCIENTIST: yes/no DESTROYER: yes/no	

NAME	ORGANIZATION
NATIONALITY: Foreign/Bolivian/Span	NATIONALITY: Foreign/Bolivian
CITED: yes/no GOV'T: yes/no: Foreign/Bol: loc/fed: Legisl/Judic/Exec NGO: yes/no: environmental/other SCIENTIST: yes/no DESTROYER: yes/no	

NAME	ORGANIZATION
NATIONALITY: Foreign/Bolivian/Span	NATIONALITY: Foreign/Bolivian
CITED: yes/no GOV'T: yes/no: Foreign/Bol: loc/fed: Legisl/Judic/Exec NGO: yes/no: environmental/other SCIENTIST: yes/no DESTROYER: yes/no	

NAME	ORGANIZATION
NATIONALITY: Foreign/Bolivian/Span	NATIONALITY: Foreign/Bolivian
CITED: yes/no GOV'T: yes/no: Foreign/Bol: loc/fed: Legisl/Judic/Exec NGO: yes/no: environmental/other SCIENTIST: yes/no DESTROYER: yes/no	

[1]If uncertain of nationality, coders indicate whether the name is of Spanish origin

[2]An actor clearly represented in the article as a perpetrator of environmental harm

Notes

Chapter 1

1. Biological diversity (or biodiversity) refers to the total variety of life forms inhabiting a given area, with an emphasis on diversity at the level of genes, species, and ecosystems (see Wilson 1992; Steinberg 1998a). Biodiversity prospecting is the systematic search for new chemical compounds of economic importance, such as therapeutic drugs, that are synthesized by diverse wild organisms.

2. Debt-for-nature swaps are financial transactions in which an environmental organization purchases part of a nation's external debt and cancels it in exchange for domestic investments in nature conservation.

3. The literature on international cooperation draws on international relations scholars' long-standing interest in the sources of cooperation and conflict among sovereign nations (see Young 1994, 1998; Roseneau and Czempiel 1992). Particular emphasis has been placed on international treaties, including analyses of negotiation (Parson 1992; Susskind and Ozawa 1992; Sebenius 1984), compliance (Mitchell 1994; Chayes and Chayes 1995), and effectiveness (Haas, Keohane, and Levy 1993; Bernauer 1995; Victor, Raustiala, and Skolnikoff 1998; Young 1992, 1999).

4. Over the past decade, research on common-pool resource regimes has significantly advanced our understanding of natural resource management at the local level (see Ostrom 1990; Gibson, McKean, and Ostrom 2000). Combining game theory and case study approaches, this literature analyzes the manner in which community governance structures pattern the incentives facing individual resource users in a context of shared ownership. Political ecology represents a second and distinct literature on local environmental management. Rooted philosophically in Marxist political economy, and drawing methodological inspiration from on-farm systems research, political ecology relates local resource conflicts to larger historical and economic patterns of exploitation (see Blaikie 1985; Peluso 1992; Gadgil and Guha 1995).

5. The mechanisms of influence described in Keck and Sikkink's (1998) rich account of transnational citizens' campaigns bear little relation to the conclusions of this book because these high-profile campaigns are so rare that they are of minor

causal importance in environmental policy reform efforts in developing countries. Thus it is important to distinguish between transnational advocates' activities (their priorities, strategies, and aspirations) and their causal impact. To do so requires a comprehensive study of the many forces affecting the outcome that is the object of their attention. On the need for further research into the causal mechanisms through which transnational expert communities influence policy, see Hirschman (1989).

6. This observation is consistent with the literature on innovation in government, which finds that the actions of policy entrepreneurs cannot be understood without reference to their personal belief in the righteousness of reform (Bardach 1998; Grindle and Thomas 1991).

7. The presence of a community of bilateral activists in a developing country is probably necessary, but not sufficient, to produce a significant pattern of accomplishments in conservation policy. Policy outcomes depend not only on the existence of a skilled cadre of reformers capable of navigating institutional challenges but on the intensity of the challenges themselves. In countries with high levels of each, the model presented here predicts fewer accomplishments than in countries with less intense challenges, but it also predicts that the rare institutional successes in such countries are typically the result of bilateral activism.

8. In recent years a consensus has emerged among research ecologists that a significant portion of the earth's natural variety will be lost within the coming decades if the current rate of habitat destruction is not slowed. Reid and Miller (1989) estimate that between 1990 and 2020, 5 to 15 percent of the world's species will occupy habitats so reduced in size that these species will go extinct during this period or shortly thereafter. Raven (1987, 1988) examines forested areas likely to be destroyed or severely degraded in the near future and, assuming the extinction of half the species in these areas, he predicts the loss of 25 percent of the world's species between the mid-1980s and 2015. Simberloff (1986) estimates that by the year 2000 tropical deforestation in the Americas will result in the eventual loss of 12 percent of the region's tropical plant species and 15 percent of Amazonian bird species. Lovejoy (1981) estimates that 15 to 20 percent of all species will be destroyed between 1980 and 2000.

Wilson (1992) notes that by 1989 the planet's tropical rainforests were reduced to just under half their prehistoric cover. At a destruction rate of 1.8 percent per year, half the remaining tropical forests will disappear in a thirty year period, leading to an estimated extinction of between 10 and 22 percent of the world's species. Koopowitz, Thornhill, and Andersen (1994) estimate that 5 percent of all tropical plants in the Western Hemisphere went extinct between 1950 and 1992, and another 1 to 2 percent will be lost every decade thereafter. Absent human influences, natural processes typically lead to the extinction of only one to ten species (out of a total of roughly ten million) per year (Reid and Miller 1989). Current human actions are precipitating an extinction event of a scale experienced only five times in the last 600 million years, the most recent being the Mesozoic extinction of 66 million years ago, in which dinosaurs and numerous other species disappeared. Of course, natural recovery from previous episodes of mass extinction occurred absent human dominance of the landscape.

9. The international sphere of influence is not synonymous with the North; it refers to the orbit of influence beyond an individual developing country's borders. With financial flows the pattern generally follows a North to South gradient. When discussing the flow of policy ideas, other developing countries and South-South relations will figure more prominently in discussions of the international sphere of influence.

10. Ecologists have found that natural systems defy easily transferable management prescriptions (Doak and Mills 1994). Closely related species often exhibit different demographic characteristics and susceptibilities. When considering the fate of complex and interacting assemblages of species in distinct physical environments, this uncertainty is compounded.

11. It is noteworthy that those with the least "imperial" power are most vulnerable to accusations of imperialism; the International Monetary Fund can take these accusations in stride, such is its power over its accusers, whereas for an environmental group, a similar charge may be followed by the revocation of visas.

12. For a more detailed categorization see Yee (1996).

13. This has been observed of Asia's first environmental advocates (Lee and So 1999). On the role of interpersonal interaction in social movement recruitment, see Rochon (1998: 112–121).

14. In recent years qualitative and small-N research strategies have been the subject of intense and fruitful debate. (See Bennett 1999; Mahoney 2000; King, Keohane, and Verba 1994; Collier and Mahoney 1996; Mitchell and Bernauer 1998.)

Chapter 2

1. Nash (1967: 343).

2. Wallace (1992: 75).

3. Thus my argument should be distinguished from the more deterministic claims of authors who posit a genetically based psychological affinity with nature (Wilson 1984), or who argue that certain public ideas inevitably accompany economic development (Rostow 1960).

4. The term is from Martínez-Alier (1995).

5. Castro spearheaded efforts to improve urban air quality despite the economic costs imposed on the capital's politically vocal transportation sector. Historically, Costa Ricans have often foregone revenues from oil pipeline development to protect undeveloped areas.

6. Cook 1994; McMenamin 1996; Anon. (1992) "Ecology and the New Colonialism," *New Scientist* 133 (1806): 55–56; Anon. (1992) "Environmental Imperialism: GATT and Greenery," *The Economist* 322 (7746): 78; Anon. (1993) "Environmental Protection or Imperialism," *Nature* 363 (6431): 657–658.

7. Levels of urbanization in Latin America and the Caribbean (75%) are roughly equal to that of the United States (77%), and surpass those of Switzerland (68%), Finland (67%), Austria (65%), and Ireland (59%). (World Bank 2000.)

8. For a discussion of this category of inference problem see King (1997).

9. See the critique provided by McConnell (1997).

10. The exception is Ireland, where respondents were aware of the environmental focus of the survey.

11. See articles by Kidd and Lee; Brechin and Kempton; Pierce; Lee and Kidd; and Abramson, in *Social Science Quarterly,* vol. 78 (1), 1997.

12. Bohrt and colleagues (1987) explore socioeconomic correlates of environmental support in Bolivia, but they do not include personal income in their study.

13. According to Press (1998), there are approximately 650 nongovernmental environmental groups in California, which has a population of 33 million. Costa Rica has approximately 245 organizations and a population of 3.5 million. The Costa Rican figure is from FECON (1994) and data collected in 1997 at the Costa Rican Public Registry, Department of Associations. This figure only includes organizations for which environmental protection is the primary activity. It also excludes production-oriented groups (such as "Conservationist Growers of Sixaola") and university programs. The national registry lists many organizations that may have since folded without notifying the authorities, thereby inflating the estimated number of active organizations. This is offset by the fact that many additional environmental groups never travel to the Costa Rican capital to register.

Chapter 3

1. Castro (1949/1940: 159).

2. For an insightful analysis of deforestation from the perspective of a rural community, see Nygren (1995).

3. For an overview of Costa Rican politics, see Booth (1998). For an introduction to the biodiversity of Costa Rica, see Janzen (1983).

4. Anon. (1950) "Primera Semana Nacional de la Conservación de los Recursos Naturales," *Suelo Tico* 4 (21–22): 175–176, quote p. 175.

5. Anon. (1944) "La Agricultura," *Surco—Publicación Mensual del Centro para el Estudio de Problemas Nacionales* 347: 30–36.

6. With one of the fastest population growth rates in Latin America, Costa Rica's numbers grew from 656,000 in 1940 to 1.8 million in 1973. (Rojas 1988: 78, as cited in Nygren 1995.)

7. Resolution by the Colegio de Biólogos, attached to Sáenz 1969.

8. Anon., "Poder Ejecutivo Reitera Apoyo a Contrato de ALCOA," *La Nación,* 22 April 1970.

9. Anon., "No Me Daría Verguenza Defender de Nuevo los Recursos Nacionales," *Periódico Universidad,* 19 April 1985.

10. The early history of the park system described in this section draws primarily from Wallace (1992). See also Evans (1999).

11. Anon., "Viceministro de Agricultura Visitó Ayer Parque Santa Rosa," *La Nación*, 10 March 1971.

12. Anon., "Costa Rica Is the 'Leading Country in Conservation,'" *The Tico Times*, 7 February 1975.

13. The prestige and popularity of the growing park system was sufficient to arouse a jealous interest on the part of other government agencies. Culture Minister Carmen Naranjo made an unsuccessful bid in 1974 to transfer the Park Service out of the agriculture ministry and under her care, arguing that the goals of the Park Service were closer to those of her ministry (Anon., "Ministerio de Cultura Pide los Parques," *La Nación*, 4 September 1974).

14. In the first half of the twentieth century Costa Rica experienced a rapid expansion in community and labor organizing, professional associations, school groups, and mutual aid societies. Today Costa Ricans have levels of civic engagement roughly comparable to that found in the United States and Western Europe. In 1973 Costa Rican heads of household reported an average of 1.5 civic organizational memberships each; two-thirds of these reported having held office in a group (Booth 1989).

15. Anon., "Latins Study U.S. Conservation," *The Tico Times*, 21 July 1978.

16. Anon., "Regional Society for Conservation," *The Tico Times*, 5 January 1979.

17. Albeit with financial support from the U.S. Agency for International Development and the Swiss Overseas Development Agency.

18. Anon., "'Friends of Nature' Fight to Give Endangered Species a Chance," *The Tico Times*, 1 November 1974.

19. In 1971 an estimated 135,000 ocelot skins and 68,000 jaguar skins were imported into the United States, many of these from Costa Rica (Monestel 1972).

20. Anon., "Wildlife Chief Makes Every Penny Count to Protect Endangered Animals . . .," *The Tico Times*, 23 January 1976.

21. Anon., "More Ecology Prizes for President Oduber," *The Tico Times*, 18 November 1977.

22. Anon., "C.R. Es Modelo, Dijo Reagan al Dar Premio a Costarricenses," *La República*, 26 July 1983.

23. In 1997, Costa Rica had roughly 245 citizens' environmental groups (see chapter 2 notes).

24. Anon., "Protesta," *La Nación*, 8 June 1988; Anon., "Solicitarán Investigar Contaminación de Mina," *La Nación*, 24 February 1988; Olga Marta Cokyeen, "ACIDE Promoverá Campaña Ecologista," *La Nación*, 16 May 1990; Alejandra Zuñiga, "Alerta Verde por el Planeta," *La Nación*, 29 August 1990.

25. Lucy Delgadillo, "Ondas Educológicas," *La Nación*, 5 May 1993; Alejandra Zuñiga, "Programa Ecológico," *La Nación*, 26 August 1992; Alejandra Zuñiga, "Programa 'Verde,'" *La Nación*, 5 August 1993; Anon., "Programación Ecológica," *La Nación*, 21 April 1993.

26. Anon., "Voluntarios para Educación Ambiental," *La Nación,* 15 April 1992; Carlos Arguedas, "Se Inicia Formación de Partido Ecologista," *La Nación,* 3 June 1992.

27. Anon., "Abren Fideicomiso para Conservación en Osa," *La República,* 29 April 1992; Johnson and Scheid (1994).

28. During the Stone Container protests, three environmental activists were killed in a residential fire of suspicious origins, another disappeared and was found dead, and others complained of death threats. (Anon., "Environmental Activists Complain of Death Threats," *The Tico Times,* 14 February 1997.) Similarly, Swedish park advocate Olof Wessberg was murdered in 1975 while pressing for the protection of rainforests in the Osa Peninsula.

Chapter 4

1. Quoted in Libermann and Godínez (1992: 78).

2. Eudoro Galindo and Enrique Quintela, letter read before the Senate, *Sesión Ordinaria 32 del Honrado Senado Nacional,* 9 October 1991, Senate archives, La Paz.

3. The Ulla Ulla reserve is now part of the Apolobamba Natural Integrated Management Area.

4. Although most conservationists during this period were trained in the natural sciences, not all scientists devoted their energies to conservation. The country's most famous biologist, Martín Cárdenas, did lead the Bolivian delegation to the 1948 Inter-American Conference on the Conservation of Renewable Natural Resources. But while he was possessed of a love for Bolivia's astounding floral diversity—he once complained that to know it all, "I would need ten times the number of years I have and at least 50 assistant botanists"—he devoted his time to writing, research, and science education; conservation themes play little part in his personal memoirs. (See Cárdenas 1973. Quote is from Anon., "Técnico Instó a Salvaguardar la Riqueza Piscícola Evitando Explotación Irracional," *Presencia,* 6 November 1968.)

5. Anon., "Protección de la Fauna," *El Diario,* 29 October 1964.

6. Anon., "IV Jornadas de la Fauna y la Flora Amazónica," *Nueva Epoca,* 17 October 1971.

7. Anon., "Con Expectativa y Exito Realízanse Jornadas de Fauna y Flora Amazónica," *Nueva Epoca,* 16 October 1971.

8. Anon., "Protección de la Flora y de la Fauna," *El Deber,* 24 October 1971.

9. Anon., "Refugio Silvestre se Inaugura en Noviembre 18," *El Deber,* 26 October 1971.

10. In contrast, Costa Rica's status as a stable, pro-Western democracy was one of the primary rationales cited by the U.S.-based Organization for Tropical Studies in its decision to locate in Costa Rica.

11. Klein (1992) notes that in the suite of military regimes that governed from 1969–1982, "Government policies depended completely on the personalities and ideas of the individual officers who seized power," at a time when most South American military regimes had a more corporate personality and more consistent policy direction.

12. Anon., "Organizaron Ayer un Comité Para Defender los Recursos Naturales," *Presencia,* 13 February 1968.

13. Terrazas (1973: 129) also notes the connection between the two discourses.

14. This cause was especially popular in the 1930s, as Latin American nations experimented with import-substitution industrialization to lessen economic dependence on foreign powers.

15. At the initiative of early conservation advocates like Percy Baptista and Manuel Posnansky, who occupied posts within the Department of Agriculture, in the 1960s and 1970s the government occasionally declared parks and issued decrees pertaining to forest management and wildlife conservation. Few of these proclamations were ever implemented.

16. Anon., "Pro Santa Cruz Clama Jusiticia por Asesinato de Ecologista," *El Deber,* 7 September 1986.

17. For a description of the constellation of campesino syndicates and other organizations in Amboró, see Soto et al. (1995); and Catholic Relief Services-USCC Bolivia Program (1994).

18. For an overview, see Moscoso (1995).

19. Jakobeit (1996) underestimates the importance of the first debt-for-nature swap for Bolivian conservation but provides a highly useful overview and analysis of the mechanism's use worldwide.

20. The history of the Chimanes forest is based on Campos-Dudley (1992); Miranda (1997); Quiroga and Salinas (1996); Rioja (1997); and de Marconi and de Baixeras (1995).

21. Anon., "Indígenas Desafían la Montaña para Llegar a Pie hasta La Paz," *Presencia,* 13 September 1990.

22. Marthadina Mendizábal de Finot, "Desarrollo y Medio Ambiente: El Caso de las Etnias," *Presencia,* 18 September 1990.

23. Teresa Flores, "Por los Caminos de la Dignidad," *Presencia,* 18 September 1990.

24. As with other instances of Bolivia's environmental leadership, FONAMA was not problem-free. After a few years of successful operation, the fund ran into serious management problems by 1997, prompting Quintela to return to FONAMA to overhaul its management structure and to repair its credibility among international donors.

25. The USAID-funded Project on Sustainable Forest Management.

26. The Forest Superintendency did in fact survive the transition into the Bánzer administration, as did the biodiversity conservation agency, despite the latter's

close association with the Sánchez de Lozada administration. The agency was re-named the Biodiversity General Directorate and placed under the leadership of Mario Baudoin. The park system also continued to grow. It was granted semiau-tonomous status in late 1998 and renamed the National Protected Areas Service.

Chapter 5

1. Gómez (1988: 128).

2. Boza (1993: 240–241).

3. As noted in chapter 4, vicuña populations in Bolivia rebounded from roughly 1,000 individuals in the late 1960s to 4,493 in 1981, and 33,844 in 1996 (Cardozo 1997; DNCB 1996; U.S. Department of Interior 1999).

4. Although my findings may be relevant to some regional or cross-border envi-ronmental problems, the spheres of influence framework is intended for scenarios in which both industrialized and developing countries are trying to affect environ-mental outcomes in the latter. My findings should, therefore, be applicable to is-sues such as climate change, pesticide use in developing countries, and population policies. They are not intended to apply to problems that affect the South but whose resolution is largely in the hands of Northern countries, as is the case with ozone depletion. My description of the process of environmental policy reform may have some explanatory power for the resolution of local environmental prob-lems in developing countries, but it will be especially pertinent to the extent that these have attracted international attention.

5. The term is from Anzaldúa (1987).

6. In theory, there is nothing preventing individuals who have served as high-ranking elected officials from playing a longer-term role, alternating between non-governmental venues and elected or appointed office. My point pertains to the role of elected officials rather than to the individuals serving in these capacities.

7. The circumstances surrounding this event are described in chapter 3.

8. The ability to inform the present with the past is important for cross-national learning as well. When importing policy models from abroad, reformers com-monly draw on historical experience to decide how these prototypes might be adapted and applied. (See chapter 6 and Rose 1993.)

9. International environmental organizations concerned with domestic conserva-tion in developing countries focus the great majority of their time and resources on local projects rather than national policies. This is apparent in an assessment by the World Wildlife Fund's Latin America and Caribbean Program that concludes "very few field projects were identified where policy issues were explicitly being ad-dressed or tested," and notes "WWF staff capacity to deal with policy issues is lim-ited." It further notes that "WWF policy interventions have been most successful on 'high-profile' issues where the strengths of the WWF network have been utilized (NAFTA, Hidrovia, timber certification)" (Pielemeier 1996: 7, 30).

10. These "external shocks" are commonly identified as an important source of policy change in the U.S. context (see Baumgartner and Jones 1993; Sabatier 1991).

11. The credibility of such criticism depends, in turn, on the social reputation of the accuser.

12. People of considerable power and wealth have the greatest such resources at their disposal. But similar patterns of influence are reproduced at smaller scales, within villages and across government agencies, such that this resource is not used exclusively by political and economic elites.

13. A flavor for this diversity can be gained from Pike and Stritch (1974); Diamond, Linz, and Lipset (1989); Erickson (1977); and Stepan (1985).

14. That said, many of the actors described here can fairly be characterized as members of epistemic communities. For clarity and to avoid the reification of academic constructs, terms like "epistemic" and "bilateral activist" are best interpreted as adjectives rather than nouns. Overlapping descriptions are perhaps the price we pay in the policy sciences for the transition from group theory to the current emphasis on networks. While criticizing theories based on interest group politics, Schattschneider (1960) observed that special interest organizations do have the advantage of being readily identifiable, with self-chosen names, and mutually exclusive.

Chapter 6

1. Budowski (1978).

2. For a review of the literature on mechanisms of social learning, see Parson and Clark (1991).

3. Putnam (1993) attributes variation in policy outcomes in Italy to regional cultural differences stretching back several hundred years. While his analysis is compelling, the prognosis is daunting: proponents of change must first overcome centuries-old cultural constraints. The inability of political culture theory to account for episodes of political change is the subject of an insightful essay by Eckstein (1988).

4. This category of policy idea corresponds to the "core policy beliefs" held by specialized groups of advocates in Sabatier's (1989) formulation. Gamson and Modigliani (1989) use the term "issue culture" in their research on the role of media in shaping public opinion. It is difficult to assess the relation of their findings to the present study absent greater clarity regarding the scope (mass versus elite) of an issue culture and its relation to government policy.

5. The political relevance of mass beliefs, and hence of policy culture, varies across nations. In countries where social mobilization is forbidden or tightly controlled, where critical discourse is disallowed and the citizenry exert little influence on national affairs, policy culture as such may not exist. But even the most oppressive regimes often go out of their way to convince the mass public of the righteousness of a given course of policy. To the extent that broad swaths of society are convinced, and form shared expectations that shape the actions of future rulers in a specific issue area, one may speak of a policy culture, albeit a tightly controlled one.

6. The focus here on national policy culture follows from the fact that environmental policy is generally concentrated at the national level in developing countries. In cases where subnational units of governance have primary responsibility for policy formulation—coupled with persistent regional differences in social expectations surrounding an issue area—it may be appropriate to speak of policy cultures at the subnational level.

7. According to Hellman (1992), one of the defining traits of contemporary social movements in Latin America is their preoccupation with maintaining autonomy from the state. The environmental movements of Costa Rica and Bolivia clearly do not fit the pattern. If this finding holds for green movements throughout the region, further research will be needed to determine whether environmental movements share certain characteristics—in their ideological and organizational makeup or in the opportunities they find available—that make them more apt to work with and through state institutions.

8. There are many other examples. Costa Rica has long used voluntary youth organizations to maintain park trails, while Bolivia's new forestry law contains provisions allowing citizen inspection of private timber management practices. Soon after the Bolivian law entered into force, a new environmental group was formed to take advantage of the opportunity.

9. Environmental policy culture is politically relevant in other ways. In democratic systems, elected officials may see the need to respond directly to voter concerns. Were it not for multipartisan interest in environmental themes in Costa Rica and Bolivia, these countries would never have achieved the political momentum needed for cumulative policy reforms on a long time scale. A culture of environmental concern can also shape the formative beliefs of future political leaders. And where a policy culture is present, government reformers who stand to lose an important but low-profile interagency scuffle can move the debate into the public arena—shedding the light of social opinion on the actions of their adversaries. (On this last point see Grindle and Thomas 1991.)

10. The following results are from a content analysis of over 3,000 environmental articles from the newspapers La Nación in Costa Rica and Presencia in Bolivia from 1960 to 1995. Collection and coding criteria are described in the methodological appendix.

11. The dip in the early 1980s corresponds to a period of severe economic recession in Costa Rica and may be an example of "issue-attention cycles" as described by Downs (1972).

12. The one discrepancy between the content analysis and interviews is that while Costa Rican observers agree that the mid-1970s saw a significant upswing in public discussion of environmental issues, they were surprised that the figures for the 1990s were not even higher. This likely reflects two facts: First, news media may be particularly sensitive measures of new trends in public discourse, given their mandate to actively search out that which is new. Second, by the time the Costa Rican data in this twice-per-week sample reach 60 stories in figure 6.1, the newspaper is publishing roughly 210 environmental stories per year. This may represent a maximum beyond which even greater social concern cannot feasibly trans-

late into more environmental letters and news stories, given newspaper space limitations.

13. Both figures include only groups for which environmental protection is the primary activity, excluding many hundreds of social organizations such as agricultural cooperatives, church groups, and women's organizations that have adopted environmental programs in recent years. The Bolivian figure draws on three sources: (1) The membership roster of Bolivia's national environmental alliance. (2) Groups mentioned in the newspaper content analysis and identified by coders as environmental NGOs of national origin. Some of these may have folded since the time of the news article. Many others were no doubt missed in the sample or not covered by the media. (3) The 1996 National Directory of Bolivian NGOs (Ministerio de Hacienda 1996). Sources for the Costa Rican figure are provided in note 13 of chapter 2.

14. This only includes theses for which the title unambiguously reflects an environmentalist perspective. As in the news content analysis, this determination is made according to the presence of certain strongly environmentalist keywords (Spanish equivalents of ecology, conservation, preservation, pollution, extinction, sustainable development, biodiversity, or environment), or if the title reflects the following sentiment: "Our natural resources (or environment) are threatened. Something must be done to protect them."

15. The observed changes are not the product of an increasing number of recognized environmental problems; of the thirty-four topics included in the analysis, only seven are new environmental topics, and these were the subject of relatively few stories.

16. The precise figures are 55.2 percent for Costa Rican articles and 47.5 percent for Bolivian articles.

17. Environmental ideas in the United States and Europe have, in turn, drawn on concepts developed in other cultures. The American resource conservation movement was inspired by ideas developed in German forestry academies, and Western environmental writings often cite Eastern philosophies emphasizing holism and connectedness. (See also Grove 1992.) I am referring to the *proximate* origins of the environmental ideas adopted by social movements in Costa Rica and Bolivia—which, as identified by the vocabulary, philosophy, and core problems, clearly draw on ideas that took shape during the environmental movements that arose in the United States and Europe in the late 1960s.

18. Brazil's prominence in these data is largely a function of its having served as host for the Earth Summit in 1992.

19. For twenty-five newspapers and magazines in fourteen countries, an average of 22.7 percent of arts-related stories are of European origin, while the United States is responsible for 10.7 percent. (Based on tables 3 and 4 in Buckman [1990].) In contrast, in the data reported in figures 6.16 and 6.17, the number of environmental stories of U.S. origin exceeds the aggregate European figure.

20. There are numerous examples, among them the conservation messages given during tours of national parks; government-sponsored television commercials in Costa Rica with messages such as "Some people worship God inside the church;

we Costa Ricans also find God in Nature"; and the message on municipal garbage cans throughout Santa Cruz de la Sierra, Bolivia, that reads "Nature is life—don't kill it."

21. See, for example, Anon., "Tradición, Familia, Propiedad Advierte a la Opinión Costarricense, Por Detrás de Ciertos Ecologistas Radicales Están los Designios del Socialismo," *La Nación,* 12 August 1992.

22. The lines of this debate were first clearly demarcated in the classic disputes between the homespun naturalist and explorer John Muir, who cofounded the Sierra Club, and Gifford Pinchot, the first director of the U.S. Forest Service.

23. The role of environmentalism as a legitimizing discourse has also been observed in Southeast Asia (Hirsch and Warren 1998: 2, 7) and Eastern Europe (Tickle and Welsh 1998).

24. Rochon (1998) describes the deliberate linkage of previously distinct discourses as "value connection." Hirschman (1981: 150) observes a similar process: "One possible way of gaining access [to policymakers] is to forge a link between the neglected and the privileged problem through the demonstration that the former lies at the root of the latter. For example, the problem of land distribution in Latin America, long a neglected problem in the above sense, gained considerably in access to the policymaker and in persuasiveness when it was connected, by the structuralist theorizers, to the problem of inflation which was eminently a privileged problem."

25. In addition to covering environmental articles, the news content analysis included a weekly sample of articles on indigenous peoples published in *La Nación* from 1960 to 1995. Such articles were not collected for Bolivia because the indigenous population there comprises a majority of the country's citizens, making this sort of analysis infeasible (or moot). Other evidence for the entry of the indigenous-environment connection into Costa Rican environmentalism includes Costa Rica's hosting of an international conference on indigenous peoples and conservation in 1993, and the establishment of a project for the legal defense of indigenous peoples by the prominent environmental group CEDARENA.

26. The national park movements of the United States and Costa Rica pursued very different ends. North American parks established in the late nineteenth century were designed to preserve scenic beauty, while Costa Rican parks, created a century later in the era of ecology, were designed most often to preserve biological diversity.

Chapter 7

1. Putnam (1988: 427).

2. For an analysis of the strategies employed by foreign firms lobbying for policy changes in the United States and Japan, see Katzenstein and Tsujinaka (1995).

3. In an analysis of public sector performance in Africa, Peterson (1997) emphasizes the importance of informal networks based on family, ethnicity, friendship,

and professional identity, and contrasts this with the hierarchical bureaucratic approach common to Western organizational thinking.

4. Teresa Flores, "La Problemática Ambiental en 1990," *Presencia,* 7 January 1991.

5. The Organization for Tropical Studies is run by a consortium of American universities and is unmatched in its ability to attract international actors to Costa Rica; the participation of Costa Ricans has been a secondary consideration. The Ecology Institute has the opposite strengths, focusing first and foremost on the needs of Bolivians, and attracting a steady but comparatively smaller amount of international interest.

6. Over 25 percent of the world's bird species are restricted to 221 sites covering only 5 percent of the earth's land surface (Bibby et al. 1992). According to Myers (1991), 20 percent of all plant species are confined to just 0.5 percent of the earth's land surface.

References

Abramson, Paul R. 1997. "Postmaterialism and Environmentalism: A Comment on an Analysis and a Reappraisal." *Social Science Quarterly* 78 (1): 21–23.

Abramson, Paul R., and Ronald Inglehart. 1995. *Value Change in Global Perspective*. Ann Arbor, MI: The University of Michigan Press.

Acosta, Walter. Letter to Carlos Quesada, 17 September 1974. Quesada personal records. San José.

Adams, Jonathan S., and Thomas O. McShane. 1992. *The Myth of Wild Africa: Conservation Without Illusions*. New York: W. W. Norton & Co.

Allen, William H. 1988. "Biocultural Restoration of a Tropical Forest." *BioScience* 38 (3): 156–161.

Almond, Gabriel A., and G. Bingham Powell. 1978. *Comparative Politics: System, Process, and Policy*. Boston: Little, Brown and Company.

Alvarez, Sonia E., Evelina Dagnino, and Arturo Escobar, eds. 1998. *Cultures of Politics/Politics of Cultures: Re-visioning Latin American Social Movements*. Boulder, CO: Westview Press.

Andaluz, Antonio. BOLFOR. Personal communication, 7 October 1997. Santa Cruz de la Sierra.

Anderson, Charles W. "The Logic of Public Problems: Evaluation in Comparative Policy Research." In Douglas E. Ashford ed. 1978. *Comparing Public Policies: New Concepts and Methods*. Beverly Hills, CA: Sage Publications.

(Anon.) 1944. "La Agricultura." *Surco—Publicación Mensual del Centro para el Estudio de Problemas Nacionales* 347: 30–36.

(Anon.) 1950. "Primera Semana Nacional de la Conservación de los Recursos Naturales." *Suelo Tico* 4 (21–22): 175–176.

(Anon.) "Protección de la Fauna." *El Diario*. 29 October 1964.

(Anon.) "Organizaron Ayer un Comité Para Defender los Recursos Naturales." *Presencia*. 13 February 1968.

(Anon.) "Técnico Instó a Salvaguardar la Riqueza Piscícola Evitando Explotación Irracional." *Presencia*. 6 November 1968.

(Anon.) "Poder Ejecutivo Reitera Apoyo a Contrato de ALCOA." *La Nación.* 22 April 1970.

(Anon.) "Viceministro de Agricultura Visitó Ayer Parque Santa Rosa." *La Nación.* 10 March 1971.

(Anon.) "Con Expectativa y Exito Realízanse Jornadas de Fauna y Flora Amazónica." *Nueva Epoca.* 16 October 1971.

(Anon.) "IV Jornadas de la Fauna y la Flora Amazónica." *Nueva Epoca.* 17 October 1971.

(Anon.) "Protección de la Flora y de la Fauna." *El Deber.* 24 October 1971.

(Anon.) "Refugio Silvestre se Inaugura en Noviembre 18." *El Deber.* 26 October 1971.

(Anon.) "Ministerio de Cultura Pide los Parques." *La Nación.* 4 September 1974.

(Anon.) "'Friends of Nature' Fight to Give Endangered Species a Chance." *The Tico Times.* 1 November 1974.

(Anon.) "Costa Rica Is the 'Leading Country in Conservation.'" *The Tico Times.* 7 February 1975.

(Anon.) "Wildlife Chief Makes Every Penny Count to Protect Endangered Animals . . ." *The Tico Times.* 23 January 1976.

(Anon.) "More Ecology Prizes for President Oduber." *The Tico Times.* 18 November 1977.

(Anon.) "Latins Study U.S. Conservation." *The Tico Times.* 21 July 1978.

(Anon.) "Regional Society for Conservation." *The Tico Times.* 5 January 1979.

(Anon.) "C. R. Es Modelo, Dijo Reagan al Dar Premio a Costarricenses." *La República.* 26 July 1983.

(Anon.) "No Me Daría Verguenza Defender de Nuevo los Recursos Nacionales." *Periódico Universidad.* 19 April 1985.

(Anon.) "Pro Santa Cruz Clama Jusiticia por Asesinato de Ecologista." *El Deber.* 7 September 1986.

(Anon.) "Solicitarán Investigar Contaminación de Mina." *La Nación.* 24 February 1988.

(Anon.) "Protesta." *La Nación,* 8 June 1988.

(Anon.) "Indígenas Desafían la Montaña para Llegar a Pie hasta La Paz." *Presencia.* 13 September 1990.

(Anon.) "Voluntarios para Educación Ambiental." *La Nación.* 15 April 1992.

(Anon.) "Abren Fideicomiso para Conservación en Osa." *La República.* 29 April 1992.

(Anon.) 1992. "Environmental Imperialism: GATT and Greenery." *The Economist* 322 (7746): 78.

(Anon.) 1992. "Ecology and the New Colonialism." *New Scientist* 133 (1806): 55–56.

(Anon.) "Tradición, Familia, Propiedad Advierte a la Opinión Costarricense, Por Detrás de Ciertos Ecologistas Radicales Están los Designios del Socialismo." *La Nación.* 12 August 1992.

(Anon.) "Programación Ecológica. *La Nación.* 21 April 1993.

(Anon.) 1993. "Environmental Protection or Imperialism." *Nature* 363 (6431): 657–658.

(Anon.) "Environmental Activists Complain of Death Threats." *The Tico Times.* 14 February 1997.

Anzaldúa, Gloria. 1987. *Borderlands/La Frontera: The New Mestiza.* San Francisco: Aunt Lute Books.

Araya, Alejandro Alfaro. "Análisis de la Ratificación de Tratados Internacionales con Énfasis en el Tema Ambiental." Graduate thesis, University of Costa Rica Law School, 1995.

Arce, Juan Pablo, FONAMA. Personal communication, 8 July 1997. La Paz.

Arguedas, Carlos. "Se Inicia Formación de Partido Ecologista." *La Nación.* 3 June 1992.

Arrow, Kenneth, et al. 1995. "Economic Growth, Carrying Capacity, and the Environment." *Ecological Economics* 15 (2): 91–95.

Arroyo, Jorge. "El Jardín Sensual del Artista." *Ancora.* 24 November 1996.

Ascher, William. 1999. *Why Governments Waste Natural Resources: Policy Failures in Developing Countries.* Baltimore, MD: The Johns Hopkins University Press.

Ayres, Robert U. 1995. "Economic Growth: Politically Necessary But *Not* Environmentally Friendly." *Ecological Economics* 15 (2): 97–99.

Babbie, Earl. 1990. *Survey Research Methods.* Belmont, CA: Wadsworth.

Barbier, E. B., ed. 1997. *Environment and Development Economics* 2 (4), *Special Issue: The 'Environmental Kuznets Curve.'*

Bardach, Eugene. 1998. *Getting Agencies to Work Together: The Practice and Theory of Managerial Craftsmanship.* Washington, D.C.: Brookings Institution Press.

Barnes, Chaplin B., International Activities, National Audubon Society. Letter to Joanna A. Barnes, 28 June 1974. Archives of the Legislative Assembly, CITES volume. San José.

Barquero, Guillermo, legislative aide, Legislative Assembly. Personal communication, 28 January 1997. San José.

Baudoin, Mario, Ecology Institute. Personal communication, 10 July and 25 August 1997. La Paz.

Baumgartner, Frank, and Bryan D. Jones. 1993. *Agendas and Instability in American Politics.* Chicago: University of Chicago Press.

Bedoya, Eduardo, and Lorien Klein. 1993. "Forty Years of Political Ecology in the Peruvian Upper Forest: The Case of Upper Huallaga." In Susan C. Stonich ed. *I Am*

Destroying the Land! The Political Ecology of Poverty and Environmental Destruction in Honduras. Boulder, CO: Westview Press.

Beinart, William. 1989. "Introduction: The Politics of Colonial Conservation." *Journal of Southern African Studies* 15 (2): 145–162.

Bennett, Andrew, "Causal Inference in Case Studies: From Mill's Methods to Causal Mechanisms." Paper presented at the annual meeting of the American Political Science Association, Atlanta. September 2–5, 1999.

Bennett, Hugh H. 1949. "El Creciente Interés en el Exterior por la Conservación de Suelos." *Suelo Tico* 2 (11): 357–361.

Bermúdez, Fernando. "Evolución del Turismo en las Areas Silvestres, Período 1982–1991." Ministerio de Recursos Naturales, Energía y Minas, Servicio de Parques Nacionales, April 1992.

Bernauer, Thomas. 1995. "The Effect of International Environmental Institutions: How We Might Learn More." *International Organization* 49 (2): 351–77.

Bibby, Colin J. et al. 1992. *Putting Biodiversity on the Map: Priority Areas for Global Conservation.* Cambridge, U.K.: International Council for Bird Preservation.

Binswanger, Hans. 1985. "Brazilian Policies that Encourage Deforestation in the Amazon." *World Development* 19 (7): 821–829.

Blaikie, Piers. 1985. *The Political Economy of Soil Erosion in Developing Countries.* Essex, U.K.: Longman Scientific & Technical (with John Wiley & Sons, Inc., New York).

Blum, Elissa. 1993. "Making Conservation Profitable: A Case Study of the Merck/INBio Agreement." *Environment* 35 (4): 17–20, 38–45.

Bohrt, R., C. Wilde, A. Aliaga, E. Roth, and E. Salinas. 1987. "Actitudes y Patrones de Conducta Hacia el Medio Ambiente." La Paz: Centro Interdisciplinario de Estudios Comunitarios (CIEC).

Booth, John A. 1989. "Costa Rica: The Roots of Democratic Stability." In Larry Diamond, Juan J. Linz, and Seymour Martin Lipset eds. *Democracy in Developing Countries, Vol. 4, Latin America.* Boulder, CO: Lynne Rienner Publishers.

Booth, John A. 1998. *Costa Rica: Quest for Democracy.* Boulder, CO: Westview Press.

Borzutzky, S. 1993. "Social Security and Health Policies in Latin America: The Changing Roles of the State and the Private Sector." *Latin American Research Review* 28 (2): 246–256.

Boza, Mario, Alfonso Mata, and Carlos Quesada. Letter to Rodrigo Suárez, General Manager, Costa Rican Electricity Institute, 20 April 1976. Quesada personal records. San José.

Boza, Mario A. 1993. "Conservation in Action: Past, Present, and Future of the National Park System of Costa Rica." *Conservation Biology* 7 (2): 239–247.

Boza, Mario A., Diane Jukofsky, and Chris Wille 1995. "Costa Rica Is a Laboratory, Not Ecotopia." *Conservation Biology* 9 (3): 684–685.

Boza, Mario, Central American Commission on Environment and Development. Personal communication, 30 April 1997. San José.

Brechin, Steven R. 1999. "Objective Problems, Subjective Values, and Global Environmentalism: Evaluating the Postmaterialist Argument and Challenging a New Explanation." *Social Science Quarterly* 80 (4): 793–809.

Brechin, Steven R., and Willett Kempton. 1994. "Global Environmentalism: A Challenge to the Postmaterialism Thesis?" *Social Science Quarterly* 75 (2): 245–269.

Brechin, Steven R., and Willett Kempton. 1997. "Beyond Postmaterialist Values: National Versus Individual Explanations of Global Environmentalism." *Social Science Quarterly* 78 (1): 16–20.

Brickman, Ronald, Sheila Jasanoff, and Thomas Ilgen. 1985. *Controlling Chemicals: The Politics of Regulation in Europe and the United States.* Ithaca, NY: Cornell University Press.

Broad, Robin, and John Cavanagh. 1993. *Plundering Paradise: The Struggle for the Environment in the Philippines.* Berkeley: University of California Press.

Brockmann, Carlos, PL-480 Program. Personal communication, 28 October 1997. La Paz.

Brysk, Alison. 2000. *From Tribal Village to Global Village: Indian Rights and International Relations in Latin America.* Stanford, CA: Stanford University Press.

Buckman, Robert. 1990. "Cultural Agenda of Latin American Newspapers and Magazines: Is U.S. Domination a Myth?" *Latin American Research Review* 25 (2): 134–155.

Budowski, Gerardo. "La Conservación de la Naturaleza como Alternativa Válida para Promover el Desarrollo Económico y Social: El Papel de Una Entidad Privada Dedicada a la Conservación." In *Proceedings, Primera Reunión Regional de Asociaciones Conservacionistas No Gubernamentales,* Ciudad de Guatemala, 4–7 December 1978. Asociación Guatemalteca de Historia Natural, ASCONA, and CATIE.

Bullock, Stephen H., Harold A. Mooney, and Ernesto Medina eds. 1995. *Seasonally Dry Tropical Forests.* New York: Cambridge University Press.

Buttel, Frederick H. 1987. "New Directions in Environmental Sociology." *Annual Review of Sociology* 13: 465–488.

Buttel, Frederick H. 2000. "World Society, the Nation-State, and Environmental Protection—Comment on Frank, Hironaka, and Schofer." *American Sociological Review* 65: 117–121.

Campos-Dudley, Liliana. 1992. "Beni: Surviving the Crosswinds of Conservation." *Américas* 44 (3): 6–15.

Cárdenas, Martín. 1973. *Por las Selvas, las Montañas y los Llanos de Bolivia—Memorias de un Naturalista.* La Paz: Editorial Don Bosco.

Cardozo, Armando, Bolivian National Academy of Sciences. Personal communication, 27 August 1997. La Paz.

Castro, Gonzalo (1949/orig. 1940). "Canto al Arbol." *Suelo Tico* 2 (9): 159.

Castro, René, Minister of Energy and Environment. Personal communication, 21 May 1997. San José.

Castro, Rolando, CEDARENA. Personal communication, 25 February 1997. San José,

Catholic Relief Services-USCC Bolivia Program. "Diagnóstico Socioeconómico y de Manejo de Recursos Naturales en Comunidades de la Zona de Amortiguamiento del Parque Nacional Amboró." Santa Cruz de la Sierra, Bolivia, August 1994.

Chayes, Abram, and Antonia Handler Chayes. 1995. *The New Sovereignty: Compliance with International Regulatory Agreements.* Cambridge, MA: Harvard University Press.

Child, Brian. 1996. "Zimbabwe." In Ernst Lutz and Julian Caldecott eds. *Decentralization and Biodiversity Conservation.* Washington, D.C.: World Bank.

Christen, Catherine, Selene Herculano, Kathryn Hochstetler, Renae Prell, Marie Price, and J. Timmons Roberts. 1998. "Latin American Environmentalism: Comparative Views." *Studies in Comparative International Development* 33 (2): 58–87.

Clare, Pablo, Swiss Contact. Personal communication, 16 January 1997. San José,

Clarke, R. O. S. "Amboró National Park: Proposal for Immediate Action." Mimeograph, August 1986.

Clarke, Robin Oskar. "Preliminary Proposal for the Practical Development of Amboró National Park." Unpublished report, Bolivia, 1984.

Cokyeen, Olga Marta. "ACIDE Promoverá Campaña Ecologista." *La Nación.* 16 May 1990.

Collier, David, and James Mahoney. 1996. "Insights and Pitfalls: Selection Bias in Qualitative Research." *World Politics* 49 (1): 56–91.

Collinson, Helen ed. 1996. *Green Guerillas: Environmental Conflicts and Initiatives in Latin America and the Caribbean.* London: Latin American Bureau.

Cook, Michael ed. 1994. *The New Imperialism: World Population and the Cairo Conference.* Crows Nest, NSW: Little Hills Press.

Corrales, Javier, and Richard E. Feinberg. 1999. "Regimes of Cooperation in the Western Hemisphere: Power, Interests, and Intellectual Traditions." *International Studies Quarterly* 43 (1): 1–36.

Cortell, Andrew P., and James W. Davis. 2000. "Understanding the Domestic Impact of International Norms: A Research Agenda." *International Studies Review* 2 (1): 65–87.

Cortés, Jorge. In Kitula Libermann and Armando Godínez eds. 1992. *Territorio y Dignidad: Pueblos Indígenas y Medio Ambiente en Bolivia.* Caracas, Venezuela: Editorial Nueva Sociedad.

Coto, Rogelio. ca. 1952. "Declaración Universal de los Derechos de la Naturaleza y de los Deberes del Hombre." *Suelo Tico.* Edición Especial (28): 275–276.

Crane, Diana. 1971. "Transnational Networks in Basic Science." In Robert O. Keohane and Joseph S. Nye eds. *Transnational Relations and World Politics*. Cambridge, MA: Harvard University Press.

Dahl, Robert A. 1961. *Who Governs? Democracy and Power in an American City*. New Haven, CT: Yale University Press.

Dalton, Russell. 1994. *The Green Rainbow: Environmental Groups in Western Europe*. New Haven, CT: Yale University Press.

Dankelman, Irene, and Joan Davidson. 1988. *Women and Environment in the Third World: Alliance for the Future*. London: Earthscan Publications. In association with the International Union for Conservation of Nature and Natural Resources (IUCN).

Darlington, Susan M. 1998. "The Ordination of a Tree: The Buddhist Ecology Movement in Thailand." *Ethnology* 37 (1): 1–15.

Dauvergne, Peter. 1997. *Shadows in the Forest: Japan and the Politics of Timber in Southeast Asia*. Cambridge, MA: The MIT Press.

de Blohm, Cecilia, Sierra Club. In *Proceedings, Primera Reunión Regional de Asociaciones Conservacionistas No Gubernamentales*. Ciudad de Guatemala, 4–7 December 1978. Asociación Guatemalteca de Historia Natural, ASCONA, and CATIE.

de Marconi, María, and Susana Donoso de Baixeras. 1995. "Inhabitants in Protected Areas of Bolivia." In Stephan Amend and Thora Amend eds. *National Parks Without People? The South American Experience*. Quito, Ecuador: IUCN/Parques Nacionales y Conservación Ambiental, no. 5.

de Morales, Cecile, Ecology Institute. Personal communication, 28 October 1997. La Paz.

Dedina, Serge. 2000. *Saving the Gray Whale: People, Politics, and Conservation in Baja California*. Tucson, AZ: University of Arizona Press.

Delgadillo, Lucy. "Ondas Educológicas." *La Nación*. 5 May 1993.

Delgado, Guillermo. 1994. "Indigenous Contestation and Ecological Plundering: Lumber Companies and Ranchers Challenged in Bolivia." *Occasional Papers of the Native American Organized Research Program (NAORP)*, University of California Davis, 1 (May): 1–14.

Della Cava, Ralph. 1989. "The 'People's Church,' the Vatican, and *Abertura*." In Alfred Stepan ed. *Democratizing Brazil: Problems of Transition and Consolidation*. New York: Oxford University Press.

Desai, Uday ed. 1998. *Ecological Policy and Politics in Developing Countries: Economic Growth, Democracy, and Environment*. Albany, NY: State University of New York Press.

Diamond, Larry, Juan J. Linz, and Seymour Martin Lipset eds. 1989. *Democracy in Developing Countries*. Vol. 1–4. Boulder, CO: Lynne Rienner Publishers.

Dias, Ayesha K., and Mary Begg. 1994. "Environmental Policy for Sustainable Development of Natural Resources." *Natural Resource Forum* 18 (4): 275–286.

DNCB (Dirección Nacional de Conservación de la Biodiversidad), Unidad de Vida Silvestre. "Censo Nacional de la Vicuña en Bolivia." La Paz, 1996.

Doak, Daniel F., and L. Scott Mills. 1994. "A Useful Role for Theory in Conservation." *Ecology* 75 (3): 615–626.

Downs, Anthony. 1972. "Up and Down with Ecology—The 'Issue-Attention Cycle.'" *The Public Interest* 28: 38–50.

Dunlap, Riley E., George H. Gallup, and Alex M. Gallup. 1993. *Health of the Planet: Results of a 1992 International Environmental Opinion Survey of Citizens in 24 Nations.* Princeton, NJ: The George H. Gallup International Institute.

Dunlap, Riley E., and Angela G. Mertig. 1995. "Global Concern for the Environment: Is Affluence a Prerequisite?" *Journal of Social Issues* 51 (4): 121–137.

Dwivedi, O. P., and Dhirendra K. Vajpeyi eds. 1995. *Environmental Policies in the Third World: A Comparative Analysis.* Westport, CT: Greenwood Press.

Dwivedi, O. P., and Renu Khator. "India's Environmental Policy, Programs, and Politics." In Dwivedi and Vajpeyi, op. cit.

Echeverría, Jaime, Michael Hanrahan, and Raúl Solórzano. 1995. "Valuation of Non-Priced Amenities Provided by the Biological Resources within the Monteverde Cloud Forest Preserve, Costa Rica." *Ecological Economics* 13: 43–52.

Eckstein, Harry. 1988. "A Culturalist Theory of Political Change." *American Political Science Review* 82 (3): 789–804.

Edwards, Bob, and Michael W. Foley. 1998. "Civil Society and Social Capital Beyond Putnam." *American Behavioral Scientist* 42 (1): 124–139.

Erickson, Kenneth Paul. 1977. "Populism and Political Control of the Working Class in Brazil." In J. Nash, J. E. Corradi, and H. Spalding. *Ideology and Social Change in Latin America.* New York: Gordon and Breach.

Evans, Sterling. 1999. *The Green Republic: A Conservation History of Costa Rica.* Austin, TX: University of Texas Press.

Federación Costarricense para la Conservación del Ambiente (FECON). 1994. *Directorio de Organizaciones, Instituciones y Consultores en el Sector de Recursos Naturales en Costa Rica.* San José.

Fisher, Julie. 1993. *The Road from Rio: Sustainable Development and the Nongovernmental Movement in the Third World.* Westport, CT: Prager.

Flores, Teresa. "Por los Caminos de la Dignidad." *Presencia.* 18 September 1990.

Flores, Teresa. "La Problemática Ambiental en 1990." *Presencia.* 7 January 1991.

Fournier, Luís A. 1991. *Desarrollo y Perspectivas del Movimiento Conservacionista Costarricense.* San José, Costa Rica: Editorial de la Universidad de Costa Rica.

Fournier, Luís, University of Costa Rica. Personal communication, 3 March 1997. San José.

Fox, Stephen. 1981. *The American Conservation Movement: John Muir and His Legacy.* Madison, WI: University of Wisconsin Press.

Freeman, Peter et al. 1980. "Bolivia: State of the Environment and Natural Resources—A Field Study." Washington, D.C.: U.S. Agency for International Development.

Gadgil, Madhav, and Ramachandra Guha. 1995. *Ecology and Equity: The Use and Abuse of Nature in Contemporary India.* New York: Routledge.

Galeano, Eduardo. 1989 (1971). *Las Venas Abiertas de América Latina.* Mexico: Siglo Veintiuno Editores.

Galindo, Eudoro, and Enrique Quintela. Letter read before the Senate, Sesión Ordinaria 32 del Honrado Senado Nacional, 9 October 1991. Senate archives. La Paz.

Gamarra, Eduardo A., and James M. Malloy. 1995. "The Patrimonial Dynamics of Party Politics in Bolivia." In Scott Mainwaring and Timothy R. Scully eds. *Building Democratic Institutions: Party Systems in Latin America.* Stanford, CA: Stanford University Press.

Gámez, Rodrigo et al. 1993. "Costa Rica's Conservation Program and National Biodiversity Institute (INBio)." In Walter Reid et al. *Biodiversity Prospecting: Using Genetic Resources for Sustainable Development.* Washington, D.C.: World Resources Institute.

Gámez, Rodrigo, INBio. Personal communication, 23 May 1997. San José.

Gamson, William A., and Andre Modigliani. 1989. "Media Discourse and Public Opinion on Nuclear Power: A Constructionist Approach." *American Journal of Sociology* 95 (1): 1–37.

Geertz, Clifford. 1995. *After the Fact: Two Countries, Four Decades, One Anthropologist.* Cambridge, MA: Harvard University Press.

Gibson, Clark C. 1999. *Politicians and Poachers: The Political Economy of Wildlife Policy in Africa.* New York: Cambridge University Press.

Gibson, Clark C., Margaret A. McKean, and Elinor Ostrom. 2000. *People and Forests: Communities, Institutions, and Governance.* Cambridge, MA: The MIT Press.

Goldstein, Judith. 1993. *Ideas, Interests, and American Trade Policy.* Ithaca, NY: Cornell University Press.

Gómez, Luis Diego, and Jay M. Savage. 1983. "Searchers on that Rich Coast: Costa Rican Field Biology, 1400–1980." In Daniel H. Janzen ed. *Costa Rican Natural History.* Chicago: The University of Chicago Press.

Gómez, Luis Diego. 1988. "The Conservation of Biological Diversity: The Case of Costa Rica in the Year 2000." In Frank Almeda and Catherine M. Pringle eds. *Tropical Rain Forests: Diversity and Conservation.* San Francisco: California Academy of Sciences, American Association for the Advancement of Science.

Gonzales, León, FECON. Personal communication, 19 March 1997. San José.

Gould, Stephen Jay. 1996. *Full House: The Spread of Excellence from Plato to Darwin.* New York: Three Rivers Press.

Grindle, Merilee S. 2000. *Audacious Reforms: Institutional Invention and Democracy in Latin America*. Baltimore, MD: The Johns Hopkins University Press.

Grindle, Merilee S., and John W. Thomas. 1991. *Public Choices and Policy Change: The Political Economy of Reform in Developing Countries*. Baltimore, MD: The Johns Hopkins University Press.

Grosko, J. Brett, with Justin R. Ward. 1996. "Forest Management in Costa Rica: Developments in National Law and Policy." NRDC discussion paper, Natural Resources Defense Council. Washington, D.C.

Grove, Richard H. 1992. "Origins of Western Environmentalism." *Scientific American* 267 (1): 42–47.

Guha, Ramachandra, and Juan Martínez-Alier. 1998. *Varieties of Environmentalism: Essays North and South*. New York: Oxford University Press.

Gumucio-Dagrón, Alfonso. 1992. "El Rol de los Comunicadores en la Formación de Criterios sobre Asuntos Ambientales." In *Memoria—Seminario Comunicación, Conservación, y Desarrollo Regional: Reserva de la Biósfera La Amistad*. Jardín Botánico Wilson, San Vito de Coto Brus, Costa Rica, 5–7 April, 1991. San José: Iriria Tsochok (Fundación para la Defensa de la Tierra).

Haas, Peter M. 1990. *Saving the Mediterranean: The Politics of International Environmental Cooperation*. New York: Columbia University Press.

Haas, Peter ed. 1992. *International Organization—Special Issue on Epistemic Communities*. Vol. 46.

Haas, Peter M., Robert O. Keohane, and Marc A. Levy eds. 1993. *Institutions for the Earth: Sources of Effective International Environmental Protection*. Cambridge, MA: The MIT Press.

Hall, Peter ed. 1989. *The Political Power of Economic Ideas—Keynesianism Across Nations*. Princeton, NJ: Princeton University Press.

Hamwey, Robert M. 1998. "A Sustainable Framework for Joint Implementation." *International Environmental Affairs* 10 (2): 79–97.

Hannerz, Ulf. 1990. "Cosmopolitans and Locals in World Culture." *Theory, Culture & Society* 7 (2–3): 237–251.

Hansen-Kuhn, Karen. 1993. "Sapping the Economy: Structural Adjustment Policies in Costa Rica." *The Ecologist* 23 (5): 179–184.

Harroy, Jean-Paul. Letter to Noel Kempff, 13 February 1968. Kempff family records. Santa Cruz de la Sierra (hereafter Kempff papers).

Heady, Ferrel. 1991. *Public Administration: A Comparative Perspective*. 4th ed. New York: Marcel Dekker Inc.

Heinrich, Freddy, and Mario Ricardo Eguivar. 1991. *El Medio Ambiente en la Legislación Boliviana: Recopilación de Disposiciones Legales, con una Introducción de las Ordenanzas Dictadas en la Colonia, 1574–1991*. La Paz: Calama.

Heinrich, Freddy, Center on Environmental Law and Policy. Personal communication, 27 October 1997. La Paz.

Hellman, Judith Adler. 1992. "The Study of New Social Movements in Latin America and the Question of Autonomy." In Arturo Escobar and Sonia E. Alvarez eds. *The Making of Social Movements in Latin America: Identity, Strategy, and Democracy.* Boulder, CO: Westview Press.

Hirsch, Philip, and Carol Warren eds. 1998. *The Politics of Environment in Southeast Asia: Resources and Resistance.* New York: Routledge.

Hirschman, Albert O. 1970. *Exit, Voice and Loyalty: Responses to Decline in Firms, Organizations, and States.* Cambridge, MA: Harvard University Press.

Hirschman, Albert O. 1981. *Essays in Trespassing: Economics to Politics and Beyond.* New York: Cambridge University Press.

Hirschman, Albert O. 1989. "How the Keynesian Revolution Was Exported from the United States, and Other Comments." In Peter Hall ed. *The Political Power of Economic Ideas—Keynesianism Across Nations.* Princeton, NJ: Princeton University Press.

Hochstetler, Kathryn. 1997. "The Evolution of the Brazilian Environmental Movement and Its Political Roles." In D. Chalmers et al. eds. *The New Politics of Inequality in Latin America: Rethinking Participation and Representation.* New York: Oxford University Press.

Holl, Karen D., Gretchen C. Daily, and Paul R. Erlich. 1995. "Knowledge and Perceptions in Costa Rica Regarding Environment, Population, and Biodiversity Issues." *Conservation Biology* 9 (6): 1548–1558.

Hsiao, Hsin-Huang Michael, On-Kwok Lai, Hwa-Jen Liu, Francisco A. Magno, Laura Edles, and Alvin Y. So. 1999. "Culture and Asian Styles of Environmental Movements." In Yok-Shiu F. Lee and Alvin Y. So eds. *Asia's Environmental Movements: Comparative Perspectives.* Armonk, NY: M. E. Sharpe.

Hurrero, Guardia. In *Actas de la Asemblea Legislativa, Ley Forestal.* Plenario, acta de la sesión extraordinario número 88, 22 October 1969. Archives of the Legislative Assembly. San José.

Inglehart, Ronald. 1990. *Culture Shift in Advanced Industrial Society.* Princeton, NJ: Princeton University Press.

Jackson, Robert H. 1993. "The Weight of Ideas in Decolonization: Normative Change in International Relations." In Judith Goldstein and Robert O. Keohane eds. *Ideas and Foreign Policy: Beliefs, Institutions, and Political Change.* Ithaca, NY: Cornell University Press.

Jakobeit, Cord. 1996. "Nonstate Actors Leading the Way: Debt-for-Nature Swaps." In Robert O. Keohane and Marc A. Levy eds. *Institutions for Environmental Aid: Pitfalls and Promise.* Cambridge, MA: The MIT Press.

Janzen, Daniel H. ed. 1983. *Costa Rican Natural History.* Chicago: The University of Chicago Press.

Janzen, Daniel. Letter to Mario Boza, 12 February 1991, SINAC archives. San José.

Jasanoff, Sheila. 1990. "American Exceptionalism and the Political Acknowledgement of Risk." *Daedalus* 119 (4): 61–81.

Jeyaratnam, J. 1990. "Acute Pesticide Poisoning: A Major Global Health Problem." *World Health Statistics Quarterly* 43: 139–144.

Johnson, Adriana and Adrean Scheid. 1994. "No Chip Mill in Golfo Dulce." *Mesoamerica* 13 (1): 2.

Jones, James C. 1995. "Environmental Destruction, Ethnic Discrimination, and International Aid in Bolivia." In Michael Painter and William H. Durham eds. *The Social Causes of Environmental Destruction in Latin America*. Ann Arbor, MI: The University of Michigan Press.

Katzenstein, Peter J., and Yutaka Tsujinaka. 1995. "'Bullying,' 'Buying,' and 'Binding': U.S.-Japanese Transnational Relations and Domestic Structures." In Thomas Risse-Kappen ed. *Bringing Transnational Relations Back In: Non-State Actors, Domestic Structures and International Institutions*. New York: Cambridge University Press.

Keck, Margaret E. 1995. "Social Equity and Environmental Politics in Brazil: Lessons from the Rubber Tappers of Acre." *Comparative Politics* 27 (4): 409–424.

Keck, Margaret E., and Kathryn Sikkink. 1998. *Activists Beyond Borders: Advocacy Networks in International Politics*. Ithaca, NY: Cornell University Press.

Kempff, Francisco, Forest Superintendency. Personal communication, 18 November 1997. Santa Cruz de la Sierra.

Kempff, Noel. Letter to Paulo Nogueira-Neto, 8 July 1968. Kempff papers.

Kempff, Noel. Letter to María Buchinger, 15 July 1968. Kempff papers.

Kempff, Noel. Letter to Rolando Kempff, 2 August 1971. Kempff papers.

Kempff, Noel. "Situación Actual de la Fauna en Bolivia." In proceedings, *Memoria del Simposio Ecológico: Impacto del Desarrollo en la Ecología del Trópico Boliviano*. 21–25 April, 1986.

Kempff, Rolando. Letter to Noel Kempff, 14 June 1972. Kempff papers.

Kenning, Wilhelm. Letter to Noel Kempff, 9 June 1970. Kempff papers.

Keohane, Robert O. 1984. *After Hegemony: Cooperation and Discord in the World Political Economy*. Princeton, NJ: Princeton University Press.

Keohane, Robert O. "Analyzing the Effectiveness of International Environmental Institutions." In Keohane and Levy, op. cit.

Keohane, Robert O., and Marc A. Levy eds. 1996. *Institutions for Environmental Aid: Pitfalls and Promise*. Cambridge, MA: The MIT Press.

Kidd, Quentin, and Aie-Rie Lee. 1997. "Postmaterial Values and the Environment: A Critique and Reappraisal." *Social Science Quarterly* 78 (1): 1–15.

King, Gary, Robert O. Keohane, and Sidney Verba. 1994. *Designing Social Inquiry: Scientific Inference in Qualitative Research*. Princeton, NJ: Princeton University Press.

King, Gary. 1997. *A Solution to the Ecological Inference Problem: Reconstructing Individual Behavior from Aggregate Data*. Princeton, NJ: Princeton University Press.

Kingdon, John W. 1984. *Agendas, Alternatives, and Public Policies*. Boston: Little, Brown & Co.

Klein, Herbert S. 1992. *Bolivia: The Evolution of a Multiethnic Society.* New York: Oxford University Press.

Koopowitz, Harold, Alan D. Thornhill, and Mark Andersen. 1994. "A General Stochastic Model for the Prediction of Biodiversity Losses Based on Habitat Conversion." *Conservation Biology* 8 (2): 425–438.

Krasner, Stephen D. 1995. "Power Politics, Institutions, and Transnational Relations." In Thomas Risse-Kappen ed. *Bringing Transnational Relations Back In: Non-state Actors, Domestic Structures and International Institutions.* New York: Cambridge University Press.

Lahmann, Enrique, World Conservation Union (IUCN). Personal communication, 14 January 1997. San José.

Lax, David A., and James K. Sebenius. 1986. *The Manager as Negotiator.* New York: The Free Press.

Leach, Bill. 1992. "Where Is Costa Rica? Costa Rican Environmentalists Reevaluate the Movement." *Mesoamerica* January: 12–14.

Lee, Aie-Rie, and Quentin Kidd. 1997. "More on Postmaterialist Values and the Environment." *Social Science Quarterly* 78 (1): 36–43.

Lee, Yok-Shiu F., and Alvin Y. So eds. 1999. *Asia's Environmental Movements: Comparative Perspectives.* Armonk, NY: M. E. Sharpe.

León, Alvaro, Costa Rican Ecology Association. Personal communication, 29 January 1997. San José.

León, Pedro, University of Costa Rica. Personal communication, 18 February 1997. San José.

Leonard, H. Jeffrey, and David Morell. 1981. "Emergence of Environmental Concern in Developing Countries: A Political Perspective." *Stanford Journal of International Law* 17 (2): 281–313.

Lewis, Thomas A. 1989. "Daniel Janzen's Dry Idea." *International Wildlife* 19 (1): 30–36.

Ley Forestal. 1969. Capítulo 6, "De los Parques Nacionales." Archives of the Legislative Assembly, San José.

Libermann, Kitula, and Armando Godínez eds. 1992. *Territorio y Dignidad: Pueblos Indígenas y Medio Ambiente en Bolivia.* Caracas, Venezuela: Editorial Nueva Sociedad.

Liga de Defensa del Medio Ambiente (LIDEMA). 1995. *Memoria de 10 Años, 1985–1995.* La Paz.

Lipschutz, Ronnie, with Judith Mayer. 1996. *Global Civil Society and Global Environmental Governance: The Politics of Nature from Place to Planet.* Albany, NY: SUNY Press.

Llosa, Carlos, Luis O. De Armero, and Oswaldo González. "The Indigenous American Race in Its Relation to the Soil." In *Proceedings of the Inter-American Conference on Conservation of Renewable Natural Resources.* Denver, CO, September 7–20, 1948. U.S. Department of State, Division of Publications, International Organization and Conference Series II, Publication 3382.

Lorini, José, Ecology Institute. Personal communication, 25 August 1997. La Paz.

López, Horst Grebe. 1996. "La Agenda para la 'Cumbre sobre Desarrollo Sostenible,'" *Habitat* 41.

Lovejoy, Annie, INBio. Personal communication, 5 February 1997. San José.

Lovejoy, Thomas. "A Primer of Conservation Programming." In proceedings, *Primera Reunión Regional de Asociaciones Conservacionistas No Gubernamentales*, Ciudad de Guatemala, 4–7 December 1978. Asociación Guatemalteca de Historia Natural, ASCONA, and CATIE.

Lovejoy, Thomas E. "Aid Debtor Nations' Ecology." *The New York Times*, 4 October 1984.

Lovejoy, Thomas E. 1981. "A Projection of Species Extinctions." In Council on Environmental Quality (CEQ). *The Global 2000 Report to the President*. Vol. 2. CEQ, Washington, D.C.

Loveman, Brian, and Thomas Davies. 1985. *Guerrilla Warfare*. Lincoln, NE: University of Nebraska Press.

Lowry, William R. 1998. "Public Provision of Intergenerational Goods: The Case of Preserved Lands." *American Journal of Political Science* 42 (4): 1082–1107.

Madrigal, Patricia, environmental legal consultant. Personal communication, 15 April 1997. San José.

Mahoney, James. 2000. "Strategies of Causal Inference in Small-N Analysis." *Sociological Methods & Research* 28 (4): 387–424.

Marconi, María ed. 1992. *Conservación de la Diversidad Biológica en Bolivia*. Centro de Datos para la Conservación/Bolivia and U.S. Agency for International Development/Bolivia. La Paz.

Martínez-Alier, J. 1995. "The Environment as a Luxury Good or 'Too Poor to Be Green'?" *Ecological Economics* 13: 1–10.

Marx, Karl, and Friedrich Engels. "Manifesto of the Communist Party." In Robert C. Tucker ed. 1978. *The Marx-Engels Reader*. New York: W. W. Norton & Co.

Mata, Alfonso, and Carlos Quesada. Letter to Edgar Arce, 29 August 1974. Quesada personal records. San José.

Matamoros, Alonso, INBio. Personal communication, 19 February 1997. San José.

May, Robert M. 1992. "How Many Species Inhabit the Earth?" *Scientific American* October: 42–48.

McCarthy, John D. 1997. "The Globalization of Social Movement Theory." In Jackie Smith, Charles Chatfield, and Ron Pagnucco eds. *Transnational Social Movements and Global Politics: Solidarity Beyond the State*. Syracuse, NY: Syracuse University Press.

McCarthy, John D., and Mayer N. Zald. 1977. "Resource Mobilization and Social Movements: A Partial Theory." *American Journal of Sociology* 82 (6): 1212–1241.

McConnell, K. E. 1997. "Income and the Demand for Environmental Quality." In Barbier, op. cit., 383–399.

McMenamin, B. 1996. "Environmental Imperialism," *Forbes* 157 (10): 124+.

McPhaul, John. "Menaced Parks Out of Danger, Says Minister." *The Tico Times,* 4 April 1997.

Meckstroth, Theodore W. 1975. "'Most Different Systems' and 'Most Similar Systems': A Study in the Logic of Comparative Inquiry." *Comparative Political Studies* 8 (2): 132–157.

Mejía, Eduardo et al. Summary Minutes, Section II: Renewable Resources and International Relations. In *Proceedings of the Inter-American Conference on Conservation of Renewable Natural Resources.* Denver, CO, September 7–20, 1948. U.S. Department of State, Division of Publications, International Organization and Conference Series II, Publication 3382.

Melgar, Baldemar. Letter to Noel Kempff, 18 September 1971. Kempff papers.

Melgar, Baldemar. Letter to Noel Kempff, 28 September 1971. Kempff papers.

Menchú, Rigoberta. "Ganar Batallas por la Vida." *Tierraamérica,* 6 December 1996.

Mendizábal de Finot, Marthadina. "Desarrollo y Medio Ambiente: El Caso de las Etnias." *Presencia,* 18 September 1990.

Meyer, John W., David John Frank, Ann Hironaka, Evan Schofer, and Nancy Brandon Tuma. 1997. "The Structuring of a World Environmental Regime, 1870–1990." *International Organization* 51: 623–651.

Migdal, Joel. 1987. *Strong Societies and Weak States: State-Society Relations and State Capabilities in the Third World.* Princeton, NJ: Princeton University Press.

Miller, Marian A. L. 1995. *The Third World in Global Environmental Politics.* Boulder, CO: Lynne Rienner Publishers.

Ministerio de Ambiente y Energía (MINAE) et al. 1996. *Memoria del Taller de Legislación Forestal.* San José: CEDARENA.

Ministerio de Hacienda. 1996. *Directorio Nacional de ONG's en Bolivia 1996.* Publ. La Paz: Centro de Información para el Desarrollo CID/Plural Editores.

Ministry of Environment and Energy, National System of Conservation Areas. "Current Situation of Protected Wilderness Areas in Costa Rica." San José. 1997.

Miranda, Carmen, Beni Biological Station. Personal communication, 28 August 1997. La Paz.

Mitchell, Ronald B. 1994. *Intentional Oil Pollution at Sea: Environmental Policy and Treaty Compliance.* Cambridge, MA: The MIT Press.

Mitchell, Ronald, and Thomas Bernauer. 1998. "Empirical Research on International Environmental Policy: Desiging Qualitative Case Studies." *Journal of Environment & Development* 7 (1): 4–31.

Mohai, P. 1985. "Public Concern and Elite Involvement in Environmental Conservation Issues." *Social Science Quarterly* 66: 820–838.

Monestel, Yehudi. "Young American Fights to Save Wildlife Here." *The Tico Times*, 23 June 1972.

Montilla, Ricardo, Venezuelan Minister of Agriculture, (through the official interpreter). Opening Plenary Session. *Proceedings of the Inter-American Conference on Conservation of Renewable Natural Resources*. Denver, CO, September 7–20, 1948. U.S. Department of State, Division of Publications, International Organization and Conference Series II, Publication 3382.

Montoya, Felipe, Committee for the Defense of the Hills of Escazú. Personal communication, 19 May 1997. San José.

Moore, Monica, Pesticide Action Network—North America. Personal communication, 20 May 1998. San Francisco.

Moreno, Abelardo, and Ramona Fernández. "Contribution to the Protection of Fauna in Latin America." In *Proceedings of the Inter-American Conference on Conservation of Renewable Natural Resources*. Denver, CO, September 7–20, 1948. U.S. Department of State, Division of Publications, International Organization and Conference Series II, Publication 3382.

Mortimer, Robert A. 1984. *The Third World Coalition in International Politics*. Boulder, CO: Westview Press.

Moscoso, Arturo. 1995. "Amboró National Park and Settlement Pressures." In Stephan Amend and Thora Amend eds. *National Parks Without People? The South American Experience*. IUCN/Parques Nacionales y Conservación Ambiental. No. 5. Quito, Ecuador.

Moscoso, Arturo, Dutch Embassy. Personal communication, 9 July and 26 August 1997. La Paz.

Myers, Norman. 1991. "Safeguarding the Plant Kingdom," *Bioscience* 41 (2): 109.

Nash, Roderick. 1967. *Wilderness and the American Mind*. 3rd ed. New Haven, CT: Yale University Press.

National Biodiversity Institute (INBio). 1995. *Memoria Anual*.

National Research Council. 1989. *Alternative Agriculture*. Washington, D.C.: National Academy Press.

Neustadt, Richard E., and Ernest R. May. 1986. *Thinking in Time: The Uses of History for Decision-Makers*. New York: Free Press.

Newmark, William D. 1987. "A Land-Bridge Island Perspective on Mammalian Extinctions in Western North American Parks." *Nature* 325 (29): 430–432.

Nijar, Gurdial Singh. 1998. "North Undermining Implementation of Biodiversity Convention." Third World Network (TWN). http://www.southbound.com.my/souths/twn/title/nij-cn.htm.

Nittler, John, BOLFOR. Personal communication, 22 July, 1997. Santa Cruz de la Sierra.

Nogueira-Neto, Paulo. Letter to Noel Kempff, 8 June 1970. Kempff papers.

Nygren, Anja. 1995. *Forest, Power and Development: Costa Rican Peasants in the Changing Environment*. Helsinki: The Finnish Anthropological Society.

Obando, Vilma, INBio. Personal communication, 5 February 1997. San José.

Olson, Mancur. 1965. *The Logic of Collective Action: Public Goods and the Theory of Groups*. Cambridge, MA: Harvard University Press.

Ortiz, María Teresa. 1989. "The Road to El Porvenir." *Orion Nature Quarterly* 8 (3): 18–29.

Ortiz de Macaya, Margarita. Testimony in *Actas de la Asemblea Legislativa, Ley Forestal*. Vol. 1, 1969. Archives of the Legislative Assembly, San José.

Ostrom, Elinor. 1990. *Governing the Commons: The Evolution of Institutions for Collective Action*. New York: Cambridge University Press.

Painter, Michael, CABI. Personal communication, 18 November 1997. Santa Cruz de la Sierra.

Parker, Theodore A. III, et al. *The Lowland Dry Forests of Santa Cruz, Bolivia: A Global Conservation Priority*. RAP Working Papers no. 4. Conservation International and Fundación Amigos de la Naturaleza, July 1993.

Parson, Edward A., and William C. Clark. *Learning to Manage Global Environmental Change: A Review of Relevant Theory*. Unpublished manuscript. John F. Kennedy School of Government. December 1991.

Parson, Edward A. 1992. *Protecting the Ozone Layer: The Evolution and Impact of International Institutions*. Center for Science and International Affairs, John F. Kennedy School of Government, Harvard University.

Pavez, Iciar, and Alan Bojanic. 1998. *El proceso social de formulación de la ley forestal de Bolivia de 1996*. Bosques y Sociedad, no. 1. La Paz, Bolivia: Center for International Forestry Research, El Centro de Estudios para el Desarrollo Laboral y Agrario, La Fundación TIERRA and El Programa Manejo de Bosques de la Amazonia Boliviana.

Peluso, Nancy Lee. 1992. *Rich Forests, Poor People: Resource Control and Resistance in Java*. Berkeley, CA: University of California Press.

Peritore, N. Patrick. 1999. *Third World Environmentalism: Case Studies from the Global South*. Gainesville, FL: University Press of Florida.

Petricone, Stephen, advisor to René Castro. Personal communication, 8 December 1996. San José.

Pielemeier, John. World Wildlife Fund. *Latin America and Caribbean Program Assessment*. June 1996.

Pierce, John C. 1997. "The Hidden Layer of Political Culture: A Comment on 'Postmaterialist Values and the Environment: A Critique and Reappraisal.'" *Social Science Quarterly* 78 (1): 30–35.

Pike, Fredrick B., and Thomas Stritch eds. 1974. *The New Corporatism: Social-Political Structures in the Iberian World*. Notre Dame, IN: University of Notre Dame Press.

Piva, Alfio, INBio. Personal communication, 19 February 1997. San José.

Portes, Alejandro. 1998. "Social Capital: Its Origins and Applications in Modern Sociology." *Annual Review of Sociology* 24: 1–24.

Press, Daniel. 1998. "Local Environmental Policy Capacity: A Framework for Research." *Natural Resources Journal* 38: 29–52.

Pressman, Jeffrey L., and Aaron Wildavsky. 1973. *Implementation,* 2nd ed. Berkeley, CA: University of California Press.

Princen, Thomas, and Matthias Finger. 1994. *Environmental NGOs in World Politics: Linking the Local and the Global.* New York: Routledge.

Princen, Thomas, Matthias Finger, and Jack P. Manno. "Transnational Linkages." In Princen and Finger 1994.

Przeworski, Adam, and Henry Teune. 1970. *The Logic of Comparative Social Inquiry.* New York: John Wiley & Sons. 1970.

Putnam, Robert D. 1988. "Diplomacy and Domestic Politics: The Logic of Two-Level Games." *International Organization* 42 (3): 427–460.

Putnam, Robert D. 1993. *Making Democracy Work: Civic Traditions in Modern Italy.* Princeton, NJ: Princeton University Press.

Quesada, Carlos, and Vivienne Solís eds. 1990. *Memoria 1er Congreso, Estrategia de Conservación para el Desarrollo Sostenible de Costa Rica (ECODES), 1988.* San José, Costa Rica: Servicios Litográficos Ltda.

Quesada, Carlos, Center for Sustainable Development Research. Personal communication, 7 February 1997. San José.

Quintela, Enrique. Personal communication, 18 October 1997. Santa Cruz de la Sierra.

Quiroga, María Soledad, and Elvira Salinas. 1996. *Minerales y Madera: Temas para el Debate Ambiental.* La Paz: Grupo de Reflexión y Acción sobre el Medio Ambiente (GRAMA).

Rajan, S. Ravi. 1998. "Imperial Environmentalism or Environmental Imperialism?—European Forestry, Colonial Foresters and the Agendas of Forest Management in British India, 1800–1900." In Richard Grove et al. eds. *Nature and the Orient.* New York: Oxford University Press.

Ramírez, Marcela, Ambio Foundation. Personal communication, 7 January 1997. San José.

Raven, Peter H. 1987. "Biological Resources and Global Stability." In Shoichi Kawano, Joseph H. Connell, and Toshitaka Hidaka eds. *Evolution and Coadaptation in Biotic Communities.* Tokyo: University of Tokyo Press.

Raven, Peter H. 1988. "Our Diminishing Tropical Forests." In Edward O. Wilson and Francis M. Peter eds. *Biodiversity.* Washington, D.C.: National Academy Press.

Redford, Kent H., and Allyn Maclean Stearman. 1993. "Forest-Dwelling Native Amazonians and the Conservation of Biodiversity: Interests in Common or in Collision?" *Conservation Biology* 7 (2): 248–255.

Reid, Walter V., and Kenton R. Miller. October 1989. *Keeping Options Alive: The Scientific Basis for Conserving Biodiversity.* Washington, D.C.: World Resources Institute.

Repetto, Robert, and Malcolm Gillis eds. 1988. *Public Policies and the Misuse of Forest Resources*. New York: Cambridge University Press.

Riker, James V. "Linking Development from Below to the International Environmental Movement: Sustainable Development and State-NGO Relations in Indonesia." Paper presented at the annual meeting of the Northwest Regional Consortium for Southeast Asian Studies on "Development, Environment, Community and the Role of the State," 16–18 October 1992. University of British Columbia, Vancouver. As cited in Princen and Finger 1994.

Rioja, Guillermo. 1997a. Conservation International. Personal communication, 8 July 1997. La Paz.

Rioja, Guillermo. 1997b. "Deuda por Naturaleza: Reserva de la Biósfera, Pueblos Indígenas, Mercado y Ecoturismo." *Crisálida* 2: 13–20.

Rivera, Lizbeth. "INBIO Es Ejemplo para el Mundo." *La Prensa Libre*, 20 May 1995.

Rochon, Thomas. 1998. *Culture Moves: Ideas, Activism, and Changing Values*. Princeton, NJ: Princeton University Press.

Rodrigo, Luis Alberto, Environmental Defense League. Personal communication, 27 August 1997. La Paz.

Rodríguez, Carlos Manuel, National System of Conservation Areas (SINAC). Personal communication, 21 January, 28 January and 7 March 1997. San José.

Rodríguez, José María, Organization for Tropical Studies. Personal communication, 3 March 1997. San José.

Rojas, Jorge Luís coord. 1988. *Costa Rica: Su Historia, Tierra y Gentes*. Vol. 1. Barcelona: Ediciones Océano-Exito. As cited in Nygren 1995.

Rose, Richard. 1993. *Lesson-Drawing in Public Policy*. Chatham, NJ: Chatham House Publishers.

Roseneau, James N., and Ernst-Otto Czempiel eds. 1992. *Governance without Government—Change and Order in World Politics*. New York: Cambridge University Press.

Rostow, Walt W. 1960. *The Stages of Economic Growth: A Non-Communist Manifesto*. New York: Cambridge University Press.

Rothman, D. S., and S. M. de Bruyn eds. 1998. *Special Issue—The Environmental Kuznets Curve, Ecological Economics* 25 (2).

Sabatier, Paul. 1989. "An Advocacy Coalition Framework of Policy Change and the Role of Policy-Oriented Learning Therein." *Policy Sciences* 21: 129–168.

Sabatier, Paul. 1991. "Toward Better Theories of the Policy Process." *PS: Political Science & Politics*, June: 147–156.

Sáenz, José A., President, Colegio de Biólogos de Costa Rica. Letter to José Molina, President of the Legislative Assembly. 13 June 1969. Archives of the Legislative Assembly, San José.

Sánchez, Aquileo. "Patrimonio Nacional Cae en Manos Privadas." *La República*, 6 April 1992.

Sánchez de Lozada, Alexandra, National Biodiversity Conservation Directorate. Personal communication, 25 August 1997. La Paz.

Schattschneider, E. E. 1960. *The Semisovereign People: A Realist's View of Democracy in America*. New York: Holt, Rinehart and Winston.

Schnell, Charles, Organization for Tropical Studies. Personal communication, 3 February 1997. San José.

Schreurs, Miranda A., and Elizabeth C. Economy eds. 1997. *The Internationalization of Environmental Protection*. New York: Cambridge University Press.

Scott, James C. 1976. *The Moral Economy of the Peasant: Rebellion and Subsistence in Southeast Asia*. New Haven, CT: Yale University Press.

Scott, James C. 1998. *Seeing Like a State: How Certain Schemes to Improve the Human Condition Have Failed*. New Haven, CT: Yale University Press.

Sebenius, James K. 1984. *Negotiating the Law of the Sea*. Cambridge, MA: Harvard University Press.

Sigmund, Paul E. 1994. "Christian Democracy, Liberation Theology, and Political Culture in Latin America." In Larry Diamond ed. *Political Culture and Democracy in Developing Countries*. Boulder, CO: Lynne Rienner Publishers.

Sikkink, Kathryn. 1991. *Ideas and Institutions: Developmentalism in Brazil and Argentina*. Ithaca, NY: Cornell University Press.

Simberloff, Daniel. 1986. "Are We on the Verge of a Mass Extinction in Tropical Rain Forests?" In David K. Elliott ed. *Dynamics of Extinction*. New York: John Wiley & Sons.

Simonian, Lane. 1995. *Defending the Land of the Jaguar: A History of Conservation in Mexico*. Austin, TX: University of Austin Press.

Sloan, John W. 1984. *Public Policy in Latin America: A Comparative Survey*. Pittsburgh, PA: University of Pittsburgh Press.

Snow, David, and Robert Benford. 1988. "Ideology, Frame Resonance, and Participant Mobilization." *International Social Movements Research* 1: 197–217.

Soto, Adriana et al. *Diagnóstico de las Instituciones del Parque Nacional Amboró*. Dirección de Programas de Investigación de la Universidad Núr y Colectivo de Estudios Aplicados y Desarrollo Social. Santa Cruz de la Sierra, Bolivia, September 1995.

Sponsel, Leslie E., Robert C. Bailey, and Thomas N. Headland. 1996. "Anthropological Perspectives on the Causes, Consequences, and Solutions of Deforestation." In Leslie E. Sponsel, Thomas N. Headland, and Robert C. Bailey eds. *Tropical Deforestation: The Human Dimension*. New York: Columbia University Press.

Steinberg, Paul F. 1998a. "Defining the Global Biodiversity Mandate: Implications for International Policy." *International Environmental Affairs* 10 (2): 113–130.

Steinberg, Paul F. 1998b. "Consensus by Design, Policy by Default: Implementing the Convention on Biological Diversity." *Society and Natural Resources* 11 (4): 375–385.

Stepan, Alfred. 1985. "State Power and the Strength of Civil Society in the Southern Cone of Latin America." In Peter B. Evens, Dietrich Rueschemeyer, and Theda Skocpol eds. *Bringing the State Back In.* New York: Cambridge University Press.

Strang, Harold Edgard. Letter to Noel Kempff, 10 October 1967. Kempff papers.

Ströbele-Gregor, Juliana. 1994. "From *Indio* to Mestizo . . . to *Indio:* New Indianist Movements in Bolivia." *Latin American Perspectives* 21 (2): 106–123.

Susskind, Lawrence, and Connie Ozawa. 1992. "Negotiating More Effective International Agreements." In Andrew Hurrell and Benedict Kingsbury eds. *The International Politics of the Environment: Actors, Interests, and Institutions.* New York: Oxford University Press.

Szwagrzak, Andrés, Cruz Verde de Bolivia. Personal communication, 29 October 1997. La Paz.

Terrazas, Wagner. 1973. *Bolivia: País Saqueado.* La Paz: Ediciones Camarlinghi.

Tickle, Andrew, and Ian Welsh eds. 1998. *Environment and Society in Eastern Europe.* New York: Addison Wesley Longman.

Tolba, Mostafa, et al. eds. 1992. *The World Environment 1972–1992: Two Decades of Challenge.* London: Chapman and Hall. As cited in Princen and Finger 1994.

Trejos, Arturo. Report to the Legislative Assembly, August 28, 1968. In *Actas de la Asemblea Legislativa, Ley Forestal.* Vol. 1, 1969. Archives of the Legislative Assembly, San José.

Trejos, Arturo. Testimony in *Actas de la Asemblea Legislativa, Ley Forestal.* Acta 5, 1969. Archives of the Legislative Assembly, San José.

Ugalde, Alvaro. 1997a. United Nations Development Programme. Personal communication, 11 February 1997. San José.

Ugalde, Alvaro. 1997b. Letter to President José María Figueres, 15 January 1997.

Ugalde, Rafael. "Al Tío Caimán le Majaron la Colita." *Periódico Universidad.* 19 April 1985.

United Nations Environment Programme. *Convention on Biological Diversity.* June 1992.

U.S. Department of Commerce, Bureau of the Census. 1975. *Historical Statistics of the United States: Colonial Times to 1970, Part 1.* Washington, D.C.: U.S. Government Printing Office.

U.S. Department of Interior, Fish and Wildlife Service. "Endangered and Threatened Wildlife and Plants; Proposed Reclassification of Certain Vicuña Populations from Endangered to Threatened and a Proposed Specific Rule." *Federal Register* 50 CFR part 17. 23 August 1999.

Valle, Carlos Luís. 1949. "¡Alerta!" *Suelo Tico* 3 (17): 432–438.

Vargas, Gastón, legislative aide, Legislative Assembly. Personal communication, 19 March 1997. San José.

Vaughan, C., and L. Flormoe. 1995. "Costa Rica's National System of Conservation Areas: Linking Local Human Community Sustainability with Neotropical

Biodiversity Conservation." In D. Saunders et al. eds. *Nature Conservation: The Role of Networks.* Sydney, Australia: Surrey Press.

Victor, David G., Kal Raustiala, and Eugene B. Skolnikoff eds. 1998. *The Implementation and Effectiveness of International Environmental Commitments: Theory and Practice.* Cambridge, MA: The MIT Press.

Villalobos, Luís. 1943. "La Deforestación: Un Problema que Debemos Solucionar." *Surco—Publicación Mensual del Centro para el Estudio de Problemas Nacionales* 36: 8–9.

Vogt, William. 1946. *The Population of Costa Rica and Its Natural Resources.* Washington, D.C.: Pan American Union.

Wallace, David R. 1992. *The Quetzal and the Macaw: The Story of Costa Rica's National Parks.* San Francisco: Sierra Club Books.

Wapner, Paul. 1996. *Environmental Activism and Civic World Politics.* Albany: SUNY Press, 1996.

Watson, Alexander F., and Hermes Justiniano. Letter to President Gonzalo Sánchez de Lozada, 30 August 1996. Archives of the Fundación Amigos de la Naturaleza. Santa Cruz de la Sierra.

Weiss, Edith Brown, and Harold K. Jacobson eds. 1998. *Engaging Countries: Strengthening Compliance with International Environmental Accords.* Cambridge, MA: The MIT Press.

Wells, Michael P. 1994. "The Global Environment Facility and Prospects for Biodiversity Conservation." *International Environmental Affairs* 6 (1): 69–97.

Wildavsky, Aaron. 1987. "Choosing Preferences by Constructing Institutions: A Cultural Theory of Preference Formation." *American Political Science Review* 81 (1): 3–21.

Wilson, Edward O. 1984. *Biophilia.* Cambridge, MA: Harvard University Press.

Wilson, Edward O. 1992. *The Diversity of Life.* Cambridge, MA: Harvard University Press.

Winch, Donald. 1990. "Economic Knowledge and Government in Britain: Some Historical and Comparative Reflections." In Mary O. Furner and Barry Supple eds. *The State and Economic Knowledge: The American and British Experience.* New York: Cambridge University Press. As cited in Ira Katznelson 1996. "Knowledge About What? Policy Intellectuals and the New Liberalism." In Dietrich Rueschemeyer and Theda Skocpol eds. *States, Social Knowledge, and the Origins of Modern Social Policies.* Princeton, NJ: Princeton University Press.

Wo Ching, Eugenia, CEDARENA. Personal communication, 9 January 1997. San José.

Working Group. Letter to Alfonso Garro, President of the Legislative Assembly, 8 October 1974. Archives of the Legislative Assembly, CITES volume. San José.

World Bank. 1992a. *Global Environment Facility: The Pilot Phase.* Washington, D.C.: World Bank.

World Bank. 1992b. *Global Environment Facility: Beyond the Pilot Phase.* Washington, D.C.: World Bank.

World Bank, 1997. *World Development Report 1997.* New York: Oxford University Press.

World Bank. 2000. *World Development Report 2000/2001.* New York: Oxford University Press.

World Commission on Environment and Development. 1987. *Our Common Future.* New York: Oxford University Press.

World Resources Institute. *World Resources 1992–93.* As cited in Princen and Finger 1994.

Yashar, Deborah J. "Indigenous Politics and Democracy: Contesting Citizenship in Latin America." Paper delivered at the annual meeting of the American Political Science Association, San Francisco, August 29–September 1, 1996.

Yee, Albert S. 1996. "The Causal Effects of Ideas on Policies." *International Organization* 50 (1): 69–108.

Young, Oran R. 1992. "The Effectiveness of International Institutions: Hard Cases and Critical Variables." In Rosenau and Czempiel 1992.

Young, Oran R. 1994. *International Governance: Protecting the Environment in a Stateless Society.* Ithaca, NY: Cornell University Press.

Young, Oran R. ed. 1998. *Global Governance: Drawing Insights from the Environmental Experience.* Cambridge, MA: The MIT Press.

Young, Oran R. ed. 1999. *The Effectiveness of International Environmental Regimes: Causal Connections and Behavioral Mechanisms.* Cambridge, MA: The MIT Press.

Zuñiga, Alejandra. "Alerta Verde por el Planeta." *La Nación,* 29 August 1990.

Zuñiga, Alejandra. "Conferencia." *La Nación,* 16 October 1991.

Zuñiga, Alejandra. "Programa Ecológico." *La Nación,* 26 August 1992.

Zuñiga, Alejandra. "Programa 'Verde.'" *La Nación,* 5 August 1993.

Index